MODERN
ELEMENTARY
STATISTICS

PRENTICE-HALL MATHEMATICS SERIES

Albert A. Bennett, Editor

MODERN
ELEMENTARY
STATISTICS

BY   ## JOHN E. FREUND, Ph.D.

Professor of Statistics,
Virginia Polytechnic Institute

PRENTICE-HALL, INC.
Englewood Cliffs, N. J.

L. C. Cat. Card No.: 52–11149

First Printing ....*August, 1952*
Second Printing ....*March, 1953*
Third Printing ....*September, 1953*
Fourth Printing ....*June, 1954*
Fifth Printing ....*May, 1955*
Sixth Printing ....*June, 1956*

59346

PREFACE

This book has been written for a general introductory course in statistics. A preliminary draft in mimeographed form was used for several years in a course designed to acquaint beginning students in the social, as well as the natural, sciences with the fundamentals of modern statistical methods.

The order and the emphasis of the material covered follows the modern trend in the teaching of statistics—to include *informally* topics that in the past have often been taught only on an advanced level. Although a large part of this book deals with the concepts and problems of inductive statistics, the standard techniques of descriptive statistics are amply covered in Part I and in Chapters 18 and 19.

Mathematical proofs and derivations have been keyed to the lowest level at which modern statistics can effectively be taught. Since the mathematical training assumed of the reader is a knowledge of arithmetic and, perhaps, some high school or college algebra, many theorems, for example, those relating to sampling distributions, are stated in the text without proof.

To acquaint the reader as early as possible with the idea of a theoretical or expected distribution, Chapter 3 contains a more or less intuitive introduction to the binomial and normal distributions. Problems relating to these distributions are actually not taken up until these distributions are discussed later in more detail in Chapters 6 and 7. This early introduction of theoretical distributions has made it desirable to treat them as percentage rather than as probability distributions, because the concepts of probability and chance are not discussed in Part I of this book.

The exercises which are given at the end of the various sections and chapters were distributed as impartially as possible among the various natural and social sciences. The reader should, therefore, not find it difficult to locate a sufficient number of examples and problems pertaining to his particular field of interest. To facilitate the reader's task of distinguishing between those formulas which are used for practical applications and those which are given primarily as definitions or as part of derivations, the first are marked with a large asterisk.

The author would like to express his appreciation to his many colleagues and students whose helpful suggestions, criticisms, and comments contributed considerably to the writing of this book. The author is greatly indebted to Professor M. Bernstein for his careful reading of the manuscript and proofs, to the editorial staff of Prentice-Hall, Inc. for courteous cooperation in the production of the book, and above all to his wife for her continuous assistance and encouragement.

Finally, the author expresses his appreciation to Professor R. A. Fisher and Messrs. Oliver and Boyd Ltd., Edinburgh, for permission to reprint Tables III and IV from their book *Statistical Methods for Research Workers;* to Professor E. S. Pearson and the Biometrika Office for permission to reproduce Tables III and VI; to Dr. C. E. Eisenhart for permission to use the material which is given in Tables Va and Vb; to Henry Holt and Company, Inc. for permission to reprint Table I; and to The Macmillan Company for permission to reprint Table VIII.

JOHN E. FREUND

CONTENTS

PART ONE: DESCRIPTIVE STATISTICS

1. INTRODUCTION AND MATHEMATICAL FUNDAMENTALS . . 3
1.1 Introduction. 1.2 Descriptive and Inductive Statistics. 1.3 The Use of Summations.

2. FREQUENCY DISTRIBUTIONS I. THE GROUPING OF NUMERICAL DATA 10
2.1 Frequency Tables. 2.2 Graphical Presentations.

3. FREQUENCY DISTRIBUTIONS II. THEORETICAL DISTRIBUTIONS . 29
3.1 Continuous Distribution Curves. 3.2 Expected and Theoretical Distributions. 3.3 The Binomial Distribution. 3.4 The Normal Curve.

4. DESCRIPTIVE MEASURES I. MEASURES OF CENTRAL TENDENCIES 47
4.1 Introduction. 4.2 Measures of Central Tendencies. 4.3 The Arithmetic Mean, Ungrouped Data. 4.4 The Arithmetic Mean, Grouped Data. 4.5 The Median, Ungrouped Data. 4.6 The Median, Grouped Data. 4.7 The Mode, Ungrouped Data. 4.8 The Mode, Grouped Data. 4.9 The Geometric and Harmonic Means. 4.10 The Weighted Mean. 4.11 Quartiles, Deciles, and Percentiles. 4.12 The Arithmetic of Approximate Measurements. 4.13 Grouping Errors.

5. DESCRIPTIVE MEASURES II. MEASURES OF VARIATION AND SYMMETRY 82
5.1 Introduction. 5.2 The Range. 5.3 The Mean Deviation. 5.4 The Standard Deviation, Ungrouped Data.

5.5 The Standard Deviation, Grouped Data. 5.6 The Quartile Deviation. 5.7 Measures of Relative Variation. 5.8 Measures of Symmetry. 5.9 Measures of Peakedness.

6. DESCRIPTIVE MEASURES III. THEORETICAL DISTRIBUTIONS . . 103

6.1 Introduction. 6.2 The Normal Curve and the Use of Normal Curve Tables. 6.3 Applications of the Normal Curve Areas. 6.4 The Use of Normal Curve Graph Paper. 6.5 The Fitting of a Normal Curve to a Set of Observed Data.

PART TWO: PROBABILITY AND SAMPLING

7. PROBABILITY 123

7.1 Introduction. 7.2 The Meaning of Probability. 7.3 Some Rules of Probability. 7.4 The Binomial Distribution and Applications. 7.5 The Law of Large Numbers.

8. SAMPLING AND SAMPLING DISTRIBUTIONS. 144

8.1 Fundamentals of Sampling. 8.2 The Basic Problems of Inductive Statistics. 8.3 Sampling Distributions.

9. PROBLEMS OF ESTIMATION 159

9.1 Introduction. 9.2 Point Estimates and Confidence Intervals. 9.3 Confidence Intervals for Population Means (Large Samples). 9.4 Confidence Intervals for Population Means (Small Samples). 9.5 Confidence Intervals for Proportions. 9.6 Confidence Intervals for Standard Deviations (Large Samples). 9.7 Confidence Intervals for Standard Deviations (Small Samples). 9.8 Probable Errors. 9.9 Sampling from Finite Populations. 9.10 A Word of Caution.

10. THE TESTING OF HYPOTHESES 189

10.1 Introduction. 10.2 Significance Tests and the Null Hypothesis. 10.3 Testing the Significance of a Deviation from an Assumed Proportion. 10.4 Testing the Significance of the Difference Between Two Proportions.

10.5 Testing the Significance of a Deviation from an Assumed Mean. 10.6 Testing the Significance of the Difference Between Two Means. 10.7 Further Tests of Significance.

11. TESTS OF RANDOMNESS . . . . ○ 220
11.1 Introduction. 11.2 The Importance of the Choice of the Correct Population. 11.3 The Theory of Runs. 11.4 Runs Above and Below the Median.

PART THREE: PREDICTION AND CORRELATION

12. THE NATURE OF SCIENTIFIC PREDICTIONS 235
12.1 Perfect and Imperfect Predictions. 12.2 Functional Relationships.

13. LINEAR RELATIONSHIPS 246
13.1 Introduction. 13.2 The Computation of m and b. 13.3 The Goodness of the Predictions.

14. THE COEFFICIENT OF CORRELATION 258
14.1 Introduction. 14.2 The Computation of r from Ungrouped Data. 14.3 The Computation of r from Grouped Data. 14.4 The Interpretation of r. 14.5 Confidence Limits for a Coefficient of Correlation. 14.6 A Significance Test for r. 14.7 Correlation by Ranks. 14.8 Correlation and Causation.

15. THE CORRELATION OF QUALITATIVE DATA 291
15.1 Introduction. 15.2 The Calculation of the Expected Cell Frequencies. 15.3 Contingency Tables. 15.4 The Chi-Square Criterion. 15.5 The Contingency Coefficient.

16. FURTHER APPLICATIONS OF THE CHI-SQUARE CRITERION . . 306
16.1 The Goodness of the Fit of a Normal Curve. 16.2 The Goodness of the Fit of Other Theoretical Distributions. 16.3 The Multinomial Case.

17. MULTIPLE, PARTIAL, AND NONLINEAR CORRELATION . . . 317
17.1 Multiple Correlation. 17.2 Partial Correlation. 17.3 Nonlinear Correlation. 17.4 The Correlation Ratio.

PART FOUR: SPECIAL TOPICS

18. FURTHER DESCRIPTIONS AND INDEX NUMBERS **333**

18.1 Further Descriptive Measures. 18.2 Graphical Presentations. 18.3 Index Numbers. 18.4 Unweighted Index Numbers. 18.5 Weighted Index Numbers. 18.6 Properties of Index Numbers.

19. TIME SERIES **349**

19.1 Introduction. 19.2 The Behavior of Time Series. 19.3 Long-Term or Secular Trends. 19.4 Seasonal Variations. 19.5 Business Cycles and the Calculation of the Normal. 19.6 The Smoothing of Time Series.

20. STATISTICS AND SCIENCE **373**

20.1 Statistics and Science. 20.2 Statistics and the Scientific Method. 20.3 The Analysis of Variance. 20.4 Experimental Design.

STATISTICAL TABLES **387**

ANSWERS TO EXERCISES **407**

INDEX **413**

PART ONE:

DESCRIPTIVE STATISTICS

1. INTRODUCTION
AND MATHEMATICAL
PRINCIPLES

1.1 Introduction

The beginning student in the natural and social sciences, for whom this book is written, often faces the study of statistics with mixed emotions. He knows, or at least he is told, that on the one hand he cannot proceed to advanced studies in his chosen field without a thorough understanding of statistical methods, while he remembers distinctly, on the other hand, the difficulties which he may have encountered in his previous contacts with mathematics.

There can be no doubt that it is practically impossible to understand the meaning and implications of the work which is being done in the social sciences, and for that matter also in the natural sciences, without having at least a speaking acquaintance with statistical theory. The reason for this is that scientists obtain knowledge from experimentation, measurements, and observations. Consequently, they must know how to squeeze usable information from their data, or at least know how to present their data in a form that lends itself to further study and displays the most important features of their results.

Numerous books have been written on business statistics, statistics for psychologists, educational statistics, and on statistical methods in sociology. It is true, of course, that these diversified fields of scientific inquiry demand somewhat different and specialized techniques in particular problems; yet the fundamental principles which underlie all the various methods are identical regardless of the field of application. This will become evident to the reader once he accepts the idea that *statistical methods in general are nothing but a refinement of everyday thinking.*

The approach which we shall follow in this elementary study of the subject of statistics is keynoted by the above statement, because it is our goal to acquaint the beginning student in the natural and social sciences with the ideas and with the concepts which are fundamental to the understanding of statistical methods.   This in turn—at least this is our hope—will give him a sounder understanding of scientific principles and will enable him to see the scope and limitations of empirical knowledge.

As we have said before, the study of statistics may be directed towards its application in a particular field of scientific inquiry. Furthermore, it may also be presented in varying degrees of mathematical refinement and in almost any balance between theory and application.   Since it is, in our opinion, much more important to understand the *meaning and implications* of a few basic concepts than to be able to recite verbatim a large assortment of impressive sounding formulas, we shall have to sacrifice some of the mathematical detail which is customarily covered in introductory texts in statistics.   This is unfortunate in some respects, but rather than miss seeing the forest because of the trees, we shall compromise by chopping down a few of the trees, i.e., eliminate some of the less essential detail.   With the use of this approach we hope to avoid the dangerous effect which often results from the indiscriminate application of so-called standard statistical procedures without a thorough understanding of the fundamental logical principles which are involved.

1.2 Descriptive and Inductive Statistics

Everything which deals even remotely with the collection, analysis, interpretation, and presentation of numerical data may be classified as belonging to the domain of statistics.   The task of computing the batting average of a ballplayer is delegated to a team statistician; births, marriages, and deaths are recorded as vital statistics; and one of the most advanced branches of atomic physics goes by the name of quantum statistics.

The word *statistics* itself can be used in a variety of interpretations. We may use it, for example, in the plural to denote simply a collection of numerical data.   Such statistics can be found in the *World Almanac,* the U.S. census reports, in the records of county clerks, and wherever numerical data are collected and reported.   The second meaning which we give to the word, also in the plural, is that of the totality of methods which are employed in the collection, study, and analysis of numerical data.   In this sense, statistics is a branch of applied mathematics, and it is this field of mathematics which is the subject matter of this book.   In order to complete this linguistic study of the word *statistics*, we also mention that the word *statistic* in the singular is used to denote a particular measure or formula like an average, an index number, or a coefficient of correlation.

In order to clarify the basic differences between the various types of statistical problems which we shall discuss, let us first differentiate between the ideas of *descriptive* and *inductive* statistical methods. Although the term *descriptive statistics* is often limited to denote merely the tabular or graphical presentation of numerical data, we shall use it in a much wider sense.   By descriptive statistical methods we shall understand any treatment of numerical data which does *not* involve inductive generalizations.   In contrast, we shall speak of inductive statistics the very moment that we make generalizations, predictions, or estimations.

This distinction can easily be explained by means of the following simple illustration.   Let us suppose, for example, that students Smith and Jones take three tests each.   Smith received the grades of 63, 41, and 55, while Jones's scores were 60, 58, and 59, respectively. From this information we can easily find that Smith had an "average" of 53, whereas Jones averaged 59.   The word "average" was advisedly given in quotes because, as we shall see later, its meaning is not without ambiguity.   The computation of an average is an elementary statistical technique which accomplishes the task of putting a large volume of numerical data into a (for certain purposes) more *usable* form.

So far we have merely computed two numbers, the two averages, which are in a sense *descriptive* of the numerical information which we were given at the start.   Consequently this part of our work belongs to what we have defined as descriptive statistics.   Now let us suppose that on the basis of the given information we are asked to decide which is the better student, Smith or Jones.   The very moment that we generalize in this fashion and make a statement of the type that Jones is the better student, we are employing inductive methods, since we are saying *more* than we were given in the original data.   We now find ourselves in the domain of inductive statistics.   This distinction is not difficult to see; as long as we restricted ourselves to the computation of the two averages, we added nothing to the given information, but merely rearranged it in a different and possibly more convenient form. It does not follow by any means that Jones is necessarily the better student. Smith might have had an off day, he might have been ill when he took the test, and it could even have happened that Jones was just plain lucky in finding the correct solutions to the problems. Therefore if we claim that the given evidence implies that Jones is the better student, we are making a generalization which may or may not be correct, and we are consequently taking a gamble. Careful evaluation and analysis of the chances which must be taken whenever we make such inductive generalizations are the main task of inductive statistics.

The terms *descriptive* and *inductive statistics* apply, therefore, to the kind of problem which we want to solve, rather than to the particular formula or statistic which we may choose to employ. We can compute, for instance, an average solely for the purpose of description. On the other hand, we can compute it in order to make generalizations and predictions. This is true for practically all statistical measures which will be discussed in later chapters.

Since the primary objective of science is to discover predictable generalizations concerning observable phenomena, we shall emphasize in this text the types of problems which belong to what we have called inductive statistics. The problem of arriving at general hypotheses, "good" estimates, and "fair" predictions requires the type of careful statistical thinking, which is the cornerstone of science. It is, therefore, our goal to acquaint the reader with the type of thinking which is essential for an understanding of the meaning of scientific statements in particular, and scientific theories in general.

Let us now acknowledge the fact that a limited amount of mathematics is indeed necessary as a prerequisite for any course in statistics on the college level. A thorough study of the theoretical principles which underlie statistics would require a knowledge of mathematical subjects which are commonly described as graduate courses even for a student of mathematics. Since this book is written for students who are not only undergraduates, but also usually nonmathematicians, our aims and therefore also our requirements are considerably more modest.

Actually the mathematical background which is necessary for this study of elementary applied statistics is amply covered in college algebra or any equivalent freshman course in mathematics. Besides having a reasonable skill in the elementary arithmetic of addition, subtraction, multiplication, and division, the reader should be familiar with the most common types of problems which are studied in college algebra, such as solving simple equations, substitutions, and use of the functional notation, logarithms, and tables.

1.3 The Use of Summations

Since many of the formulas which we shall develop in the following chapters must be applicable to different sets of numerical data, we shall have to represent the scores, measurements, or observations with which we shall deal by means of some general symbols such as x, y, and z. Unless we introduce a slight modification, however, this symbolism will lead us to immediate difficulties because, if we were to represent, for example, the age of every inhabitant of New York City by means of a different letter, we would easily use up the English, Greek, Russian, and Hebrew alphabets, without accommodating even as much as $1/500$ of 1 per cent of the population of New York City. This makes it clear why we shall have to adjust our symbolism to fit the treatment of mass data, following the customary practice of using subscripts. The three scores which Jones received in our previous illustration can now be written as x_1, x_2, and x_3, respectively. If we want to discuss any one of these scores in general, we shall call it x_i, where i is, so to speak, a variable subscript, which can in this example take on the values 1, 2, and 3. Instead of the letter i we could, of course, have arbitrarily used any other letter such as k, l, m, . . . , and instead of x we could also have used any arbitrary letter or symbol. Therefore x_{31} and x_{73} might stand for the intelligence scores of the thirty-first and seventy-third individuals, while in a different problem x_{12}, y_{12}, and z_{12} might represent the age, height, and weight of the twelfth guinea pig. It is customary to use different letters for different kinds of measurements and different subscripts if we are speaking about different individuals (items).

In order to simplify the many formulas which will involve great quantities of numerical data, we shall now introduce the symbol Σ (capital Greek sigma), which is what might reasonably be called a *mathematical shorthand notation*. We have by definition

$$\sum_{i=1}^{n} x_i = x_1 + x_2 + x_3 + x_4 + \ldots + x_n \qquad (1.3.1)$$

which is read as: "the summation of x_i, i going from 1 to n." It means that we take the sum of the x's which have the subscripts 1, 2, . . . , n. Similarly we might have, for example

$$\sum_{i=1}^{4} y_i^2 = y_1^2 + y_2^2 + y_3^2 + y_4^2$$

or
$$\sum_{i=1}^{5} x_i f_i = x_1 f_1 + x_2 f_2 + x_3 f_3 + x_4 f_4 + x_5 f_5$$

Since the summation sign will appear in many formulas, it will prove to be very helpful to study some of the fundamental theorems concerning summations. These theorems, a few of which will be given below, are not difficult to understand and prove.

THEOREM A: *The summation of the sum (or difference) of two or more variables or terms is equal to the sum (or difference) of their separate summations.*

Symbolically we can write this theorem in the case of three variables as

$$\sum_{i=1}^{n} (x_i + y_i + z_i) = \sum_{i=1}^{n} x_i + \sum_{i=1}^{n} y_i + \sum_{i=1}^{n} z_i \qquad (1.3.2)$$

If we had wanted to use minus instead of plus signs, we could have done so on both sides of the equation. The proof of this theorem, which consists of showing that the two sides of the equation are identical if they are written in full without the use of summation signs, will be left as an exercise to the reader.

THEOREM B: *The summation of a constant times a variable is equal to the constant times the summation of the variable.*

Symbolically this can be written as

$$\sum_{i=1}^{n} k x_i = k \sum_{i=1}^{n} x_i \qquad (1.3.3)$$

This theorem follows immediately from the following considerations:

$$\sum_{i=1}^{n} k x_i = k x_1 + k x_2 + k x_3 + \ldots + k x_n$$
$$= k(x_1 + x_2 + x_3 + x_4 + \ldots + x_n)$$
$$= k \sum_{i=1}^{n} x_i$$

THEOREM C: *The summation of a constant k, from 1 to n, equals the product of k and n.*

This means that

$$\sum_{i=1}^{n} k = kn \qquad (1.3.4)$$

Since the constant k does not depend on the subscript i, we can immediately write

$$\sum_{i=1}^{n} k = k + k + k + \ldots + k = kn$$

REFERENCES

H. Hotelling, "The Training of Statisticians," *The American Statistician*, Vol. 1, No. 3.

W. A. Shewhart, "The Advancing Statistical Front," *Journal of the American Statistical Association*, Vol. 41, No. 233.

H. M. Walker, "Statistical Literacy in the Social Sciences," *The American Statistician*, Vol. 5, No. 1.

S. S. Wilks, "Undergraduate Statistical Education," *Journal of the American Statistical Association*, Vol. 46, No. 253.

EXERCISES

1. Prove Theorem A for the sum of three variables x, y, and z, letting i go from 1 to 4.

2. Write out the following summations in full.

(a) $\sum_{i=1}^{9} y_i$

(d) $\sum_{i=1}^{n} (x_i - a)$

(b) $\sum_{i=1}^{5} x_i^2$

(e) $\sum_{i=1}^{8} x_i f_i$

(c) $\sum_{i=1}^{3} (x_i + y_i)$

(f) $\sum_{i=1}^{7} b$

3. Write each of the following expressions as summations.

(a) $z_1 + z_2 + z_3 + z_4 + \ldots + z_{21}$

(b) $x_1 y_1 + x_2 y_2 + x_3 y_3 + x_4 y_4 + \ldots + x_9 y_9$

(c) $(x_1 - y_1) + (x_2 - y_2) + \ldots + (x_n - y_n)$

(d) $x_1^3 f_1 + x_2^3 f_2 + x_3^3 f_3 + \ldots + x_8^3 f_8$

4. Is it true that $\sum_{i=1}^{n} (x_i - m) = \sum_{i=1}^{n} x_i - nm$?

5. Is it true that $\left(\sum_{i=1}^{2} x_i \right)^2 = \sum_{i=1}^{2} x_i^2$?

6. Is it true that $\left(\sum_{i=1}^{n} x_i \right) \left(\sum_{i=1}^{n} y_i \right) = \sum_{i=1}^{n} x_i y_i$?

Check whether this equation holds for $n = 2$.

7. Prove that $\sum_{i=1}^{n} (x_i - m)^2 = \sum_{i=1}^{n} x_i^2 - 2m \sum_{i=1}^{n} x_i + nm^2$.

2. FREQUENCY DISTRIBUTIONS
I. THE GROUPING
OF NUMERICAL DATA

2.1 Frequency Tables

Grouping and classifying observations and measurements is the most basic operation which we perform, not only in science but also in everyday life. If we want to discuss anything whatsoever we are immediately forced to group and classify, since the use of words in itself necessitates the grouping of whatever we wish to describe. If we observe a chair, we might say, for instance, "This is a chair, " thus classifying whatever we are seeing as a particular kind of an object. This simple statement is, of course, far from a complete description of what we are really experiencing. It does not tell us among other things whether the chair is brown or black, whether it is upholstered or not, and whether it will support us if we test its strength. On the other hand, this statement may well be a sufficient description if we are interested only in the mere fact that the object is a chair.

Science is often accused of telling only "half the story" in its description of what might reasonably be called reality. It is interesting to note, however, that the same can be said of language in general, because the most that we can ever do with the use of words or symbols is to give a partial description of what we experience. There is no need to feel discouraged about this, therefore, because for most practical purposes partial descriptions are all that we really need. If we know, for instance, that Mr. So-and-so is a moron, we may not wish to associate with him, regardless of whether he has a mustache, whether he eats his meals while standing on his head, or whether he parts his hair in the middle. *How much information is needed in any particular situation is determined primarily by what we intend to do with the information after it has been collected.* The manager of a movie theater who wants to compute his receipts for a particular day does not have to know whether Aunt Lucy took little Joe to the matinee; all he needs to know is how many tickets were sold to adults and how many were sold to children. It would be sufficient, therefore, if he knew that 763 adults and 351 children attended his theater. If, however, he is also interested to find out whether the picture which he is showing attracts more women than men, this kind of information would no longer be sufficient. He would have to ask for a more precise description, telling him how many of his customers were male and how many were female.

Let us start our discussion of the grouping of experiences, measurements, and observations by first distinguishing between *categorical* and *numerical* classifications. A grouping is said to be *categorical* if it sorts the individual items (observations) with respect to some attribute. Examples of categorical groupings can be found almost everywhere; sociologists group people with respect to their nationality or income, grocers sort cans of vegetables with respect to their brands, and baseball umpires classify pitches as balls and strikes. *Numerical* classifications, on the other hand, group measurements by their size, and it follows that numerical groupings can be used only if we are dealing with things which are measurable or countable, i.e., if they lend themselves to quantitative descriptions. To give a simple illustration we might, for example, group the residents of a certain village according to their ages by counting how many are 10 years old or less, how many are over 10 but not over 20, how many are over 20 but not older than 30, etc. Representing this information in a tabular form we might get something like this:

Age group	Number of people
1–10	43
11–20	36
21–30	128
. . . .	. . . .
etc.	etc.

The information which is provided by this table may be sufficient for a merchant who wants to stock the proper supply of merchandise, it may be sufficient for a scientist who wants to predict the percentage of the villagers who will be of voting age 10 years hence, but it would definitely *not* be sufficient if we were interested in knowing whether our old friend George Brown is still living in this community.

Since the grouping of numerical data is one of the most basic statistical operations, it is important to realize that the choice of the groupings is essentially arbitrary, and that it will depend to a large extent on what we intend to do with the data after they have been grouped. Consequently, it is difficult to give specific instructions which should invariably be followed.

The various decisions which we always must make before we can begin to classify *raw data* ("raw" in the sense that the data have not yet been subjected to any kind of statistical treatment) can be summarized as follows: we must decide on the *number of groupings* into which we intend to order the data, and furthermore, we must decide on where we are going to draw the *dividing lines* between the various classifications.

The first of these problems is not easy to answer because, as we have mentioned before, the decision of using 1, 3, 10, or for that matter, any arbitrary number of classifications, depends on what we intend to do with our information after we have grouped our data. It will also depend to a large extent on the nature of our measurements, and above all, on the actual number of items, i.e., scores or measurements, which we have at our disposal. If, for example, we have only 5 measurements, we would accomplish extremely little if we were to group them into 25 classes most of which would be completely empty. If the grouped data are to be used for further calculations, it is often advisable to get an approximate idea of the number of classes which should be used, by means of the following formula:

$$k = 1 + 3.3 \log N \qquad\qquad (2.1.1)\,{}^{*}$$

where N stands for the total number of items, and k is the number of classes which we are advised to use. The logarithm in this formula is an ordinary Briggsian logarithm (base 10) which can be found in any handbook of mathematical tables. This formula, which is usually referred to as *Sturges' rule*, is based on mathematical considerations which are too advanced to be studied at this time.

With the use of formula (2.1.1) we will find, for example, that it is advisable to use 8 classifications if we have about 100 cases, 14 classifications if we have 10,000 cases. In general, we can find the recom-

---

    * Formulas which are marked with an asterisk are actually used for practical computations. This will make it easier for the reader to distinguish between formulas used for calculations and those given primarily for definitions or as part of derivations.

mended value of k by substituting our total number of measurements for N, and then solving the resulting equation for k.

Let us now consider, as an illustration, the following data which represent the weekly salaries (in dollars) which are paid to the 40 employees of the ZYX Manufacturing Co.:

44.65	53.39	65.75	47.65
61.25	57.50	41.33	45.50
37.55	47.23	55.12	58.75
56.75	84.50	45.60	47.25
45.60	52.29	63.44	46.32
40.75	63.50	34.60	72.57
75.25	49.50	53.25	41.13
57.30	45.42	46.50	59.50
45.20	38.75	57.42	65.75
67.12	65.42	78.63	63.79

Sturges' rule tells us that the number of classes which we should use is 6. Next, in order to specify the precise classifications into which we are going to group these data, we must determine the smallest and the largest values among the given salaries. If we do this first, we can avoid the embarrassing situation which might develop if our classifications were such that they would not accommodate all the data. Since in our illustration the smallest salary is \$34.60 while the largest one is \$84.50, the classifications must cover roughly the interval from \$30 to \$90. It is, of course, not necessary that all classes be of equal length, but it is most certainly desirable for various reasons, and *equal class intervals (classes of equal length) should be selected whenever this is possible.* Dividing the interval from \$30 to \$90 into 6 classifications, each individual class covers an interval of \$10. If the lengths of the classes are unequal, we can expect to run into difficulties if the grouped data are to be used for further computations or if they are to be represented in a graphical form.

Now let us suppose that we put all salaries which fall anywhere from \$30 to \$40 into the first classification; those salaries which fall anywhere from \$40 to \$50 into the second, etc. Fortunately, this classification does not lead to unforeseen difficulties, since none of the salaries was precisely \$40, \$50, \$60, \$70, or \$80. If, however, one of the salaries had been exactly \$40, we would have had considerable trouble in deciding where to put this particular value. It could be put into the first classification, but it could just as well be put into the second. To avoid ambiguities of this type it is advisable to follow the general rule that *overlapping class intervals should be avoided whenever we group a set of data.*   By overlapping intervals we understand successive intervals which have one or more values in common.

Keeping this rule in mind, we can now choose our classifications as follows: the first class will contain all salaries from $30.00 to $39.99; the second class all those from $40.00 to $49.99; the third class all those from $50.00 to $59.99, etc.   Since the salaries were originally given to the nearest cent, this grouping will accommodate all data, there are no ambiguities with respect to overlapping class intervals, and the classes are, furthermore, all of equal length.

Using this scheme of classification, we can now represent our data, grouped, in a tabular form which will look like the following *frequency table:*

Salary (dollars)	Tally	No. of employees
30.00–39.99	///	3
40.00–49.99	++++ ++++ ++++	15
50.00–59.99	++++ ++++	10
60.00–69.99	++++ ///	8
70.00–79.99	///	3
80.00–89.99	/	1

This kind of a table is also called a *frequency distribution.*   The tally which is shown in the middle of this table is very helpful in its construction, but it is usually not shown in the final presentation.   By definition, frequency tables show us how the salaries (or other data) are distributed among the various classifications, i.e., they display the frequencies with which the salaries occur in the various groupings. It is for this reason that they are called frequency distributions.

The number of items which fall into any given class is called the corresponding *class frequency.*   In our illustration, for example, the class frequency of the first class is 3, that of the second class is 15, etc.

If we were to plot the classifications which we have chosen on a linear scale (see Fig. 2.a), we would discover small gaps between the successive classes.   There is a gap, for example, between the first two classes, which goes from $39.99 to $40.00.   Similarly there is a gap from $49.99 to $50.00, from $59.99 to $60.00, etc.   Fortunately, this discovery does not present us with any serious problems (at least in the given example) because the salaries are such that they cannot possibly fall into any one of the gaps.   However, if we were dealing with a continuous variable, i.e., if our measurements were such that they could take on values on a continuous scale, this scheme of classification would be highly unsatisfactory.

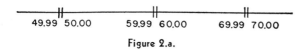

49.99 50.00   59.99 60.00   69.99 70.00

Figure 2.a.

In order to eliminate this difficulty, we shall so to speak, split the difference, and incorporate half of each gap into each of the adjacent classes. This means that we shall now consider the first class as going from $29.995 to $39.995, the second class as going from $39.995 to $49.995, etc. It is interesting to note that this arrangement does not change anything in the given frequency distribution. It is true that the new classifications overlap, but since the values which the intervals may have in common cannot possibly occur among the given data, or any similar type of data, there can be no ambiguities. Indeed, *impossible values are often chosen as the dividing lines between classes in order to avoid such ambiguities.* The dividing lines between two successive classes are called their *class boundaries.* In our illustration the first class has the *lower class boundary* of $29.995 and the *upper class boundary* of $39.995. Similarly, the lower class boundary of the second class is $39.995, while its upper class boundary is $49.995.

The length of a class interval, or simply the *class interval*, is, by definition, the difference between the class boundaries of the given classification. Its *class mark* is defined as the midpoint between the two class boundaries. In our illustration, the length of each class interval was $10, while the class marks were $34.995, $44.995, $54.995, etc. The class marks can always be found easily by averaging the respective class boundaries, i.e., by adding the two class boundaries and dividing their sum by 2. They can, incidentally, also be calculated by means of the averages of the corresponding *class limits*, which are the *smallest* and the *largest* values which can fall into a given class. In our first classification we would thus obtain $30.00 + $39.99 = $69.99, and dividing this sum by 2 we get $34.995, which is the same value which we had before.

A trick which is often employed in the grouping of numerical data involves the use of so-called *open class intervals.* To explain what this means let us suppose, for example, that one of the employees of the ZYX Co. which we have been discussing, namely, the one who made $84.50, had his salary raised to $263.50 a week. Making

the necessary correction in our raw data, we find that the classifications now must cover the much wider interval of approximately $240.
Dividing this total interval by 6, we note that each individual class
now covers about $40. If we group our data accordingly, the
resulting frequency table will be:

Salary (dollars)	No. of employees
30.00– 69.99	36
70.00–109.99	3
110.00–149.99	0
150.00–189.99	0
190.00–229.99	0
230.00–269.99	1

It is apparent that this grouping tells us extremely little about the
distribution of the vast majority of salaries, 90 per cent of them to
be exact, except that they are all less than $70. It is obvious, there-
fore, that this grouping is very unsatisfactory for most practical
purposes.

To solve this dilemma we could either use *more classes,* i.e., a finer
grouping, or we could use *open class intervals.* A classification is
said to be open if, instead of giving both of its class boundaries, we
say either *and over* or *less than.* Using the first of these two types of
open class intervals, putting an open class interval at the top of our
distribution, we can now write the salary distribution as:

Salary (dollars)	No. of employees
30.00–39.99	3
40.00–49.99	15
50.00–59.99	10
60.00–69.99	8
70.00–79.99	3
80.00 and over	1

This gives a much clearer picture than the previous table without
making it necessary to use more than 6 classifications. Besides this
obviously good feature, open class intervals have unfortunately also
some very definite disadvantages. Their brightest feature is that
they can accommodate a wide range of values without requiring the
use of a large number of classifications or classifications which hide
most of the relevant information. Their darkest feature is that they
do not tell us how much *over* or *less than* a given value may fall.
The salary which fell into the open interval of our distribution might,
for all we know, be $2,000 a week. We might also add that open
distributions have the further disadvantage that they present us

with difficulties if we want to present a distribution in graphical form.

Let us remind ourselves that *as soon as we group data we are likely to lose information.* The frequency distributions can tell us that 3 of the employees made anywhere from $30 to $39.99 but it does *not* tell us whether they made $35.67, $38.63, or any value whatsoever within the given interval. On the other hand, the frequency distribution gives us an over-all picture of the salary situation at the ZYX Co. at an easy glance, and it is in this sense that we have put the original data into a more "useful" form. As we shall see later on, the grouping of numerical data can also save considerable time if such a grouping is to be used for the calculation of certain characteristic properties of the original data.

For some purposes it is more convenient to group data in a slightly different form. The president of the ZYX Co. may, for example, be interested in knowing how many of his employees are above or below a certain salary level. In that case, there would be no need for him to know exactly how many employees received salaries which lie in each of the various groupings, but he would rather be interested in knowing the so-called *cumulative frequency distribution* of the salaries. A cumulative frequency distribution can always be constructed in different ways, depending on whether we want a *less than* or an *or more* type of distribution.

Let us now illustrate the meaning of such a distribution by first constructing a *less than* distribution of our salary data. This will not require much additional work, since we already have the ordinary frequency table. We can see, simply by inspecting this table, that no employee made less than $30, and that 3 of them made less than $40. In order to find the number of employees who made less than $50, we must simply add the frequencies of all of the classes which fall below $50, i.e., we have 3 + 15 = 18 employees who made less than $50. Similarly, the number of employees who made less than $60 is 3 + 15 + 10 = 28, etc. The resulting cumulative frequencies can be presented in the following type of frequency table:

Salary (dollars)	No. of employees
less than 30.00	0
40.00	3
50.00	18
60.00	28
70.00	36
80.00	39
90.00	40

Had we been interested in showing how many employees were above or, better, *not below* any given salary level, we could have arranged our data in an *or more* type of cumulative distribution. We know, for example, that every employee made $30 or more. If we want to find the number of employees who made $40 or more, we will have to substract the three employees who were at the bottom of the ladder and who made less than $40. This leaves us 40 − 3 = 37 employees with a salary of $40 or more. The number of employees who made $50 or more is similarly obtained by substracting 15 from the remaining 37, which leaves us 22. The number of employees who made $60 or more is similarly equal to 22 − 10 = 12. The *or more* cumulative frequency distribution is therefore:

Salary	No. of employees
$30.00 or more	40
40.00	37
50.00	22
60.00	12
70.00	4
80.00	1
90.00	0

This cumulative distribution could have been obtained just as well by starting at the other end, adding the frequencies of the respective classes.

Whenever we deal with a large number of individual measurements or observations, we are usually much more interested in knowing what fraction or what percentage of the total number of items fall into a given classification. In that case we can easily change our previous distributions into what we shall call *percentage and cumulative percentage* distributions.

Once a set of data has been classified into an ordinary frequency distribution, it takes very little additional work to convert this into a percentage distribution. We need only divide each class frequency by the total number of cases, and then multiply by 100. If we are willing to write the percentage as a decimal fraction, even this last step is not necessary.

The frequency of the class which contains the salaries from $30.00 to $39.99 can be replaced by a percentage simply by dividing its frequency 3 by 40 (the total number of cases), and then multiplying the result by 100. The resulting percentage distribution can easily be shown to be

Salary (dollars)	Percentage of employees
30.00–39.99	7.5
40.00–49.99	37.5
50.00–59.99	25.0
60.00–69.99	20.0
70.00–79.99	7.5
80.00–89.99	2.5

In identical fashion we can also convert the cumulative frequency distribution into a cumulative percentage distribution. Dividing each cumulative frequency of the *less than* distribution by 40, and multiplying by 100, we get:

Salary (dollars)	Percentage of employees
less than 30.00	0.0
40.00	7.5
50.00	45.0
60.00	70.0
70.00	90.0
80.00	97.5
90.00	100.0

EXERCISES

1. Use Sturges' rule to determine the number of classes which should be used to group

(a)   30 measurements
(b)   250 measurements
(c)   2000 measurements

2. If 500 measurements are given to the nearest tenth of an inch and if the smallest measurement is 14.3 inches, while the largest measurement is 58.7 inches, construct a suitable table into which these measurements could be grouped. Show the class limits and the class marks.

3. The weights of 150 rats which are used in a certain experiment vary from 94 to 207 grams. If these weights are measured to the nearest gram, outline a suitable frequency table into which these measurements could be grouped. Show the class boundaries as well as the class marks.

4. The class limits of a distribution of test scores are 20–24, 25–29, 30–34, 35–39. Find the corresponding class marks and class boundaries.

5. The class marks of a distribution of retail food prices are 13, 20, 27, 34, and 41 cents. Find the corresponding class limits.

6. A group of 120 students who were admitted into a certain medical college had the following indexes for their undergraduate work:

2.47	2.33	2.65	1.82	1.90	2.13
2.05	2.79	2.54	2.00	2.04	3.00
2.05	2.21	2.56	1.84	2.63	1.88
2.20	1.83	2.07	2.26	2.21	2.24
2.43	2.66	2.30	2.45	2.16	2.93

1.75	2.00	2.15	2.09	1.17	1.83
2.34	2.48	2.03	1.97	2.22	1.74
2.85	2.16	2.49	1.90	1.95	1.98
2.18	2.52	2.54	2.13	2.12	2.08
2.56	1.97	2.25	2.34	2.66	2.10
2.09	2.00	1.81	2.61	2.14	2.01
2.32	1.76	2.43	2.25	2.28	2.11
2.34	2.46	2.20	2.30	1.95	1.92
2.34	2.27	2.21	3.00	2.15	2.17
2.45	1.99	2.13	2.17	1.86	1.93
1.82	1.76	1.65	2.14	2.35	2.20
2.05	2.19	2.44	1.73	1.80	2.31
2.34	1.88	1.95	2.72	2.31	2.17
2.75	1.80	2.00	2.36	1.78	2.45
1.93	2.70	2.35	2.36	1.92	2.61

Use these data to construct a frequency distribution and the corresponding percentage distribution.

7. Use the data which have already been grouped in Exercise 6 to construct a cumulative *less than* distribution of the college indexes.

8. The following table contains the grades which 60 students obtained in a final examination in elementary statistics.

64	76	72	85	74	97
68	79	77	83	71	69
87	53	90	93	80	81
94	70	86	84	59	63
76	83	67	72	72	61
75	83	99	88	76	68
78	73	82	85	90	69
64	80	80	74	71	58
67	83	85	77	78	78
89	68	64	83	79	65

Construct a frequency table and the corresponding percentage distribution.

9. Classify the scores of Exercise 8 into a cumulative *or more* distribution and the corresponding cumulative percentage distribution.

10. The following are the prices of 100 houses which were advertised for sale in a Rochester, N. Y., paper in September, 1951.

35,000	8,500	11,400	15,000	8,950
7,200	11,800	7,760	10,500	12,500
6,500	16,500	5,700	11,300	4,500
11,000	19,500	11,300	10,000	14,000
15,000	21,900	18,500	14,200	16,000
3,000	22,500	30,000	25,000	26,000
13,500	15,500	16,000	34,000	8,350
10,500	10,900	4,800	6,000	6,500
8,000	10,000	4,500	9,000	11,000
10,900	12,800	10,800	10,500	3,750

10,250	6,500	8,500	7,950	7,500
11,600	8,000	7,500	16,000	5,700
10,000	6,500	6,500	9,000	10,700
10,500	6,000	12,300	11,600	12,500
13,500	11,500	11,500	12,900	8,500
3,500	10,000	11,500	12,500	11,800
16,500	12,500	15,000	12,300	12,500
13,500	9,500	10,500	8,900	9,600
9,000	11,000	10,800	15,900	11,500
17,000	12,500	27,000	6,500	4,700

Construct a frequency distribution and a percentage distribution.

11. Using the data which have already been grouped in Exercise 10, construct a cumulative *less than* distribution.

12. In an experiment measuring the per cent shrinkage on drying, 40 plastic clay test specimens produced the following results:

19.3	20.5	17.9	17.3
15.8	16.9	17.1	19.5
20.7	18.5	22.5	19.1
18.4	18.7	18.8	17.5
14.9	12.3	19.4	16.8
17.3	19.5	17.4	16.3
21.3	23.4	18.5	19.0
16.1	18.8	17.5	18.2
18.6	18.3	16.5	17.4
20.5	16.9	17.5	18.2

Group these percentages into a frequency distribution and construct the corresponding percentage distribution.

13. Using the same data as in Exercise 12, construct a cumulative *or more* distribution.

14. Take the first two pages of Chapter 1 of this book and construct a frequency table showing how many of the words which are on these two pages begin with the letter *a*, how many begin with the letter *b*, how many with the letter *c*, etc.

15. Cut a deck of cards 50 times, shuffling it after each cut, and make a table of the frequencies with which the four different suits have appeared.

16. Ask 25 people what kind of cigarettes they smoke and construct a table showing the frequencies of the various brands.

2.2 Graphical Presentations

It is well known that many people have mental blocks against anything that is even remotely related to numbers, tables, and formulas. In order to accommodate this human weakness we shall, therefore, have to see how we can put frequency distributions into a more appealing form, i.e., into a form which can be visualized more easily. Even if it were not for this reason, we usually benefit from using graphical methods, particularly in examples in which we compare two or more sets of numerical data. This is because most of us are much better trained to grasp material quickly if it is given to us in pictorial form.

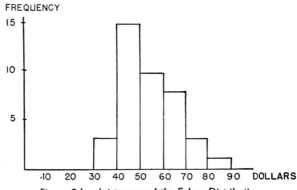

Figure 2.b.   histogram of the Salary Distribution.

The *histogram* is the most common graphical presentation of frequency tables. It is constructed by representing the measurements (in our illustration the salaries in dollars) on a horizontal scale and the class frequencies on a vertical scale, as we have done in Fig. 2.b. The final figure consists of rectangles, the bases of which are supplied by the class intervals, and the heights of which are determined by the corresponding class frequencies.

Among the points which should be watched in the construction of a histogram we find, first of all, that this kind of figure cannot be used if our distribution contains open class intervals at either end. Furthermore, a histogram would be very misleading if our distribution had unequal class intervals and if we did not make some adjustment for the differences in the widths of the rectangles. To illustrate this point let us regroup our salary data by combining all salaries from $50.00 to $69.99 into one classification, leaving the other classes as they were before. The frequency table of the new grouping will be:

Salary (dollars)	No. of employees
30.00–39.99	3
40.00–49.99	15
50.00–69.99	18
70.00–79.99	3
80.00–89.99	1

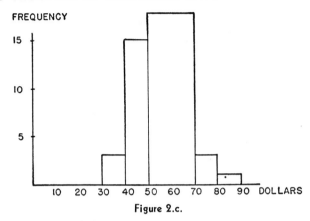

Figure 2.c.

Plotting this distribution as a histogram and giving, as before, the class frequencies by means of the heights of the corresponding rectangles, we would get a histogram like that in Fig. 2.c.

If a stranger were to look at this figure he would get the immediate impression that the bulk of the salaries lies between $50 and $69.99. This is, of course, a considerable mistake, since *less than half* of the salaries belong in this classification. To avoid this mistake, we shall have to make the following minor modification: if one class interval is twice as wide as all others, we will divide the height of its rectangle by two. Similarly, if a class interval is three times as wide as the others, we will correspondingly divide the height of its rectangle by three. *If we follow this suggestion, we are actually representing the*

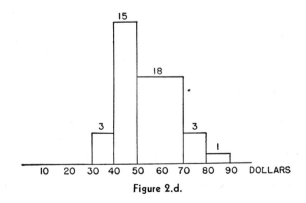

Figure 2.d.

class frequencies by means of the areas of the rectangles instead of their heights. In that case it is better not to indicate the frequency scale, but to give the actual class frequencies as we have done in Fig. 2.d.

Another method of representing frequency distributions in a graphical form involves the use of the so-called *frequency polygon.* A frequency polygon (see Fig. 2.e) is constructed by plotting the class frequencies of the various classes at their respective class marks, i.e., at the midpoints of the class intervals, and then connecting these points by means of straight lines. In order to complete the picture it is often desirable to add one classification to each end of the distribution. Since these extra classes have, evidently, zero frequencies, we can in this manner close the figure with the use of the two additional points.

Frequency polygons can be very misleading if they are incorrectly used to read off frequencies between the successive class marks. We must always remember that the graph was plotted from grouped data, and we must therefore exercise extreme caution in reading, so to speak, between the lines. This difficulty will be explained in more detail in Chapter 3.

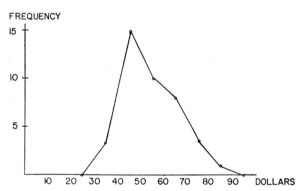

Figure 2.e.   Frequency Polygon of the Salary Distribution.

It should also be noted that frequency polygons present us with the same difficulties which we previously encountered in our study of the histograms of distributions with unequal or open class intervals.

Had we applied the technique of constructing a frequency polygon to a cumulative frequency distribution, we would have obtained a polygon which is generally known as an *ogive.* The main differences between a frequency polygon and an ogive is that we plot the cumulative instead of the ordinary class frequencies and that we plot them at the upper or lower class boundaries, depending on whether the cumulative distribution is a *less than* or an *or more* type of distribution. Figure 2.f gives us the ogive of our previously obtained *less than* distribution of the salaries, and its scale tells us the number of employees whose salaries are less than the corresponding number which

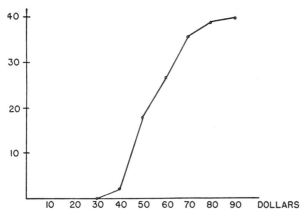

Figure 2.f. Ogive of the Salary Distribution.

is given on the horizontal scale. There are numerous other ways in which statistical data or statistical results can be presented in a graphical or pictorial form. A few of these methods will be mentioned briefly in a later chapter after we have learned more about the most important features of frequency distributions, which we will then be able to display.

In spite of the fact that frequency distributions can take on almost any shape or form, it is rather fortunate that for most practical purposes we can limit our investigation to a relatively small number of more or less standard types. Most often met in scientific investigations is the bell-shaped distribution, shown in Fig. 2.g. Many types of measurements used in everyday life fall into this kind of a distribution. The heights of individuals, their intelligence, and many

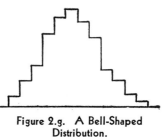

Figure 2.g. A Bell-Shaped Distribution.

other measurable characteristics describe distributions which can roughly be described as bell-shaped.

A frequency distribution can also be either *symmetrical* or *skewed*. It is said to be symmetrical if we can fold its graph (vertically) along some line of symmetry, e.g., the dotted line of Fig. 2.h, and the two halves of the diagram more or less coincide. If, however, a distribution has a tail at either end, such as the distribution which is given in Fig. 2.i, we generally say that it is skewed.

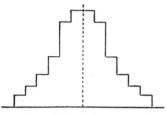

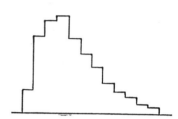

Figure 2.h. A Symmetrical Distribution.

Figure 2.i. A Skewed Distribution.

A good illustration of a skewed distribution is that representing individual incomes. It has a considerable tail at the right-hand side because some incomes, though very few, are extremely large. The most important properties of frequency distributions, such as symmetry, skewness, etc., will be discussed in detail in the next few chapters. However, in order to prevent the reader from getting the erroneous idea that all distributions must necessarily be bell-shaped, let us briefly illustrate some of the other basic types.

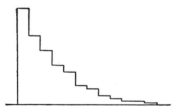

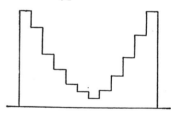

Figure 2.j. A J-Shaped Distribution.

Figure 2.k. A U-Shaped Distribution.

There exist, for example, J-shaped distributions, like the one giving us the number of individuals who own certain numbers of houses. Most people own no houses at all, quite a few own one house each, a smaller number own two each, etc. Another kind of a nonbell-shaped distribution is the U-shaped distribution, illustrated generally by means of the data of the percentage cloudiness recorded in Breslau, Germany. Most of the time the sky is either completely covered or completely clear; less frequently it is covered 10 per cent, 20 per cent, etc. It is true, of course, that this last kind of distribution is not very common, but it will have served its purpose if it has helped to emphasize the point that we cannot always expect to work merely with bell-shaped distributions.

We have illustrated the material of this chapter by means of a set of data which represented the incomes of the employees of a certain factory. *It is important that it be understood clearly that we could as well have used intelligence scores, measurements of the strength of iron bars, ages and weights, or for that matter, any kind of numerical data whatsoever.* The methods which we have discussed and most of the methods which we shall discuss in later chapters are applicable to any kind of numerical data belonging to any field of scientific inquiry.

REFERENCES

F. E. Croxton and D. J. Cowden, *Applied General Statistics*, Prentice-Hall, New York, 1939, Chap. 8.

F. Kafka, *Statistics without Numbers*, Lifetime Editions, New York, 1950, pp. 25–48.

A. E. Waugh, *Elements of Statistical Method*, McGraw-Hill, New York, 1943, Chap. 3.

S. S. Wilks, *Elementary Statistical Analysis*, Princeton University Press, Princeton, 1949, Chap. 2.

EXERCISES

1. Draw a histogram of the following **J**-shaped distributions of the frequencies with which rifle shots hit the given distances from the center of the target.

Distance (cm)	Frequency
0.0–0.5	82
0.5–1.0	61
1.0–1.5	27
1.5–2.0	19
2.0–2.5	7
2.5–3.0	3
3.0–3.5	1

2. Draw a histogram and a frequency polygon of the following distribution of the average old-age pension payments in the 48 states in 1948.

Average payment per recipient (dollars)	Frequency
10.00–19.99	8
20.00–29.99	4
30.00–39.99	13
40.00–49.99	19
50.00–59.99	3
60.00–69.99	1

3. Indicate three different types of data which have skewed distributions.

4. What are three types of measurements, not those given in the text, which can be expected to have a symmetrical bell-shaped distribution?

5. List three types of measurements, other than those given in the text, which have a **J**-shaped distribution.

6. Use the data which have previously been grouped in Exercise 6 on page 19 to construct a histogram, a frequency polygon, and an ogive for the 120 college indexes.

7. Construct a histogram and an ogive for the data of Exercise 8, page 20.

8. Use the prices which are grouped in Exercise 10 on page 20 to construct a histogram, a frequency polygon, and an ogive.

9. Use the data of Exercise 12, page 21, to construct an ogive of the given percentages.

10. Combine the first two classes of the distribution of the rifle shots of Exercise 1 and construct a new histogram, accounting for the difference in the sizes of the class intervals.

3. FREQUENCY DISTRIBUTIONS
II. THEORETICAL
DISTRIBUTIONS

3.1 Continuous Distribution Curves

It is usually quite a temptation to approximate the zigzag appearance of histograms and frequency polygons by means of smooth curves. We mean by this that we are tempted to draw freehand continuous curves which will eliminate, more or less, the irregularities, the grouping effects, of the rectangles of a histogram and the straight lines of a frequency polygon. If we have a relatively small number of measurements, it is usually not advisable to attempt such an approximation, but if we are dealing with large masses of data, we could choose the class intervals smaller and smaller, and approach in this sense a continuous curve.

If we plan to use a smooth curve to represent a set of grouped data, it is for various reasons, which we shall discuss later, more convenient to interpret our distribution as a percentage distribution. This will make no difference, since the shape of the histogram of a percentage distribution is identical with that of the corresponding ordinary frequency table.

Let us now look at the distribution of Fig. 3.a, which represents the ages of a certain group of graduate students. The dotted line, which roughly approximates the distribution, gives us a pretty fair picture of the general shape of the distribution. It is true that the dotted line helps to improve the aesthetic appeal of the figure, but it seems reasonable to ask whether it does not also serve a more practical purpose. We might ask whether it could be used, for instance, to tell us how many, or what percentage of the students are

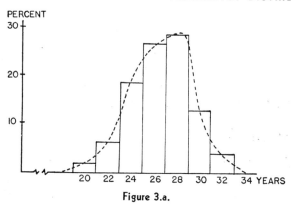

Figure 3.a.

25 years old.   Similarly, we might ask how many of them are 25 years and 3 months.

Checking the number 25 on the horizontal scale of Fig. 3.a, we find that the corresponding percentage on the vertical scale which is read off the dotted curve is close to 24.   Similarly, one might thus think that the percentage of students who are $25\frac{1}{4}$ years old is also in the neighborhood of 24.   It is obvious that something must have gone wrong.   Adding the two percentages which we have thus obtained, we discover that about 48 per cent (almost half of the students) are close to 25 years of age.   In order to understand this mistake, i.e., this evident disagreement with the original distribution, let us recall the difficulties which we had when we tried to plot histograms of distributions with unequal class intervals.   *We pointed out, at that time, that the total frequency or percentage of a given class cannot be understood to belong to any specific value within that class, and that it is therefore best to look at histograms as if the areas of the rectangles, rather than their heights, represent the class frequencies.*   This eliminated the difficulties which confronted us when we had unequal classes, and as we shall see, it will now help us to understand the meaning of a continuous distribution curve.

In order to explain the mistake which we must obviously have made in our calculations of the previous paragraph, let us first ask a simple question: What do we mean when we say that somebody is 25 years old?   Does it mean that he or she is 25 years old to the nearest second or even closer?   If this were how we interpret it, the answer to the question would simply be *0 per cent*.   Even if we have a large group of people, the number of individuals who were born on a particular day, at the same hour, the identical minute, etc., is for all practical purposes negligible, and we can therefore say that the percentage of people belonging to any group who are 25 years old (on the nose) is equal to zero.

It is quite possible that this discussion has seemed somewhat superfluous to the reader who knows, of course, that if we speak about someone who is 25, we mean that he has passed his 25th birthday but has not yet reached his 26th. This is, of course, correct, but our question has nevertheless brought out the mistake which we have made, and we now know that to determine the percentage of students who are 25 in our example, we must see how many, or what percentage, fall between 25 and 26 in Fig. 3.a.

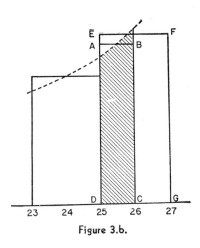

Figure 3.b.

Let us turn, therefore, to Fig. 3.b, which is an enlargement of the needed part of Fig. 3.a. When we discussed histograms in the last chapter, we said that the percentage (frequency) which belongs to a given class is represented by the area of the rectangle which stands on top of that class. Consequently, it follows that we must now look for a rectangle which stands on top of the interval from 25 to 26. Since there is no such rectangle in Fig. 3.a, we will have to construct one which will be in agreement with the original distribution.

To do this we shall, for the moment, drop the word *rectangle* and repeat accordingly that *the percentage (frequency) which belongs to a given class is represented by the area under the smooth curve which is on top of the corresponding class interval.* Just as we have approximated the histogram by means of a smooth curve, we can, similarly, approximate the areas of the rectangles by the corresponding areas under the smooth curve.

The percentage of our students who are 25 is therefore given by the shaded area of Fig. 3.b. Unfortunately, irregular areas of this type cannot be evaluated without the use of calculus, which leaves us no alternative but to resort again to approximate methods. The shaded area of Fig. 3.b is very close to the area of the rectangle $ABCD$, and it is this rectangle which we shall finally use to represent the desired age group.

Since we know that the rectangle $DEFG$ (Fig. 3.b) represents 27 per cent of the students, we can judge roughly that since rectangle $ABCD$ is only slightly smaller than half of rectangle $DEFG$, it represents approximately 12.5 per cent of the students.

Had we used ungrouped data, all this trouble could have been avoided, and we could have counted the 25-year-olds directly. On the other hand, it would not have served our purpose of trying to find out how smooth curves can be used to find the percentage which corresponds to any arbitrary interval of the distribution. Let us repeat therefore that *we have learned that the required percentage is given by the area under the curve which stands on top of the chosen class interval.*

To illustrate this further, let us consider the diagram of Fig. 3.c, which represents a distribution of individual incomes. Let us also suppose that we wish to know what percentage of all of these incomes exceed $5,000 a year. According to what we have just said, this percentage is represented by the shaded area of Fig. 3.c, and we can evaluate its actual size by comparing it with an area which represents

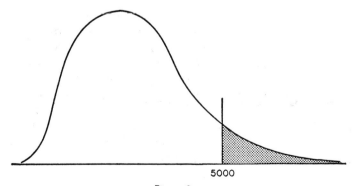

5000

Figure 3.c.

a known percentage. This comparison is most conveniently made with the *total area under the curve,* which must necessarily represent all of the cases, i.e., 100 per cent.

If we thus study the shaded area of Fig. 3.c, we can judge that it is roughly one-twelfth of the total area under the curve, and we can now say that between 8 and 10 per cent of the incomes exceeded $5,000 a year. To make this comparison somewhat more precise, it is customary to choose a scale of measurement which makes the entire area under the curve equal to 1; then we can find the percentage which belongs to a given class directly by measuring the actual area under the curve, e.g., the shaded area of Fig. 3.c. One main reason for making the area under the curve equal to 1 was that we can then compare the area corresponding to any class interval with the total area under the curve without having to perform any actual division.

The study of the smooth curves which can be used to approximate distributions of numerical data leads us to the question whether there exist certain standard types of curves which we might expect to meet most frequently in actual statistical work. Although the answer to this question is in the affirmative, we shall defer our discussion of these special distributions until we have explained what we mean by an expected or a theoretical distribution.

3.2 Expected and Theoretical Distributions

So far we have discussed only distributions which were obtained through the grouping of actual measurements or observations. These distributions are important, but it also happens very often that we are interested in knowing *what kind of a distribution we might expect before the data have actually been collected.* To mention a few examples, an army quartermaster is interested in knowing the distribution of the sizes of incoming recruits, so that he will be able to stock the proper sizes of uniforms and equipment; university officials are usually concerned about the distribution of the students among the various courses, so that they will be able to schedule sufficient sections; and a publishing house may be interested in the distribution of the literary tastes of the general public, in order to print the proper proportion of mysteries, novels, etc.

The distribution of our expectation can be based on previous experience, i.e., previous surveys or experiments, or it can be based on purely theoretical considerations. The three illustrations of the previous paragraph were examples of expected distributions which would have to be based on previous measurements or observations. An elementary and straightforward example of an expected distribution which is based on theoretical principles is the following illustration which deals with the game of heads or tails. Let us assume, for instance, that we flipped a coin 100 times and that we obtained 53 heads and 47 tails. In order to treat the results as a numerical variable, we shall say that we had 0 head 47 times and 1 head 53 times.

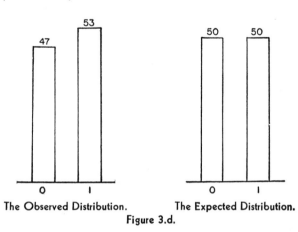

The Observed Distribution.   The Expected Distribution.

Figure 3.d.

If we now want to investigate the distribution of heads and tails which we should have *expected* in 100 tosses of a single coin, we will first have to make an assumption about the "honesty" of the coin. If the coin is honest, i.e., if the chances for heads and tails are the same, we can say that we should expect to obtain about an equal number of heads and tails. The expected distribution of the number of heads is therefore

Number of heads	Frequency
0	50
1	50

It is shown together with the observed distribution in Fig. 3.d. It is important to note that we could never have found these expected frequencies (the expected distribution) if we had not made some assumption about the honesty of the given coin.

Expected distributions play without doubt an extremely important role in a great number of statistical problems. We could, for instance, have used the expected distribution of the 100 flips in order to compare theory with actual practice. Had the discrepancy between the two distributions of Fig. 3.d been small, we might have been able to say that the closeness of the agreement proves that the coin is honest. Had it been large, on the other hand, this disagreement between theory and practice might well be interpreted as an indication that there was something wrong with our assumption that the coin was honest. Although problems of this type are very interesting, they belong to the domain of inductive statistics, and we shall therefore defer their study until we reach Part Two of this book. The above illustration was given merely as a preview of the possible use of a theoretical frequency distribution.

The reader may have noticed that the diagram of Fig. 3.d is neither a histogram nor a frequency polygon, but what is usually called a *bar chart*. The reason why we did not give it as a histogram is that the number of heads (0 or 1) is a *discrete variable*. A variable is said to be *discrete* if it can take on only a definite, limited set of numerical values. In contrast, a variable is said to be *continuous* if it can take on values on a continuous scale of measurement.

In our illustration it is impossible to obtain, for example, one-half or three-quarters head. The only two values which we could possibly have obtained were 0 and 1. In spite of this, it is quite common to represent distributions of discrete variables as histograms, and even to approximate them by means of smooth curves. In order to do this we will have to resort to the following convention: if we say, for example, that a man is 6 ft. 3 in., we mean that he is closer to 6 ft. 3 in. than he is to either 6 ft. 2 in. or 6 ft. 4 in. Consequently, anybody whose height is anywhere from 6 ft. 2.5 in. to 6 ft. 3.5 in. will be classified as being 6 ft. 3 in. In a similar fashion we can spread any discrete variable over a continuous scale. In our previous example we could have done this by considering the number 1 as representing the interval from 0.5 to 1.5, the number 0 as representing the interval from -0.5 to 0.5, etc. Following this procedure we can now represent both of the distributions by means of the histograms of Fig. 3.e.

The illustration which referred to the tosses of a single coin is somewhat too simple to give us a full understanding of the meaning of a theoretical distribution. Let us therefore discuss next what we can expect to happen if we toss 2 or more coins. If we toss 2 coins, 3 possible things can happen: we can get 0 head, we can get 1 head, or we can get 2 heads. These 3 cases can be broken down further if we consider the different ways in which each can occur. Flipping

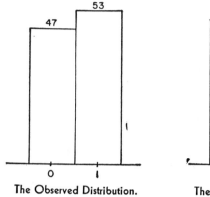

The Observed Distribution.

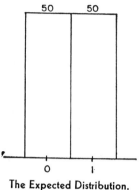

The Expected Distribution.

Figure 3.e.

one coin with each hand and recording first the result of the coin which was flipped with the left hand, we can obtain any one of the following four situations:

$$H \ H, \qquad H \ T, \qquad T \ H, \qquad T \ T$$

If these four cases are to be considered as equally likely, i.e., if we can expect to obtain any one of them about as often as the others, we can then expect to get 0 head one-quarter of the time, 1 head one-half of the time, and 2 heads again one-quarter of the time. The reason why we can expect 1 head twice as often as either of the two other cases is that both H T and T H provide us with 1 head.

If we now flip 2 coins 100 times, the expected distribution of the number of heads will be (see also Fig. 3.f):

Number of heads	Frequency
0	25
1	50
2	25

Here the class frequencies represent one-quarter, one-half, and one-quarter of 100, respectively.

The more coins we use the more complicated our calculations will be. If we had used, for example, 3 coins, the various events which could have happened were

T	T	T	H	H	T
H	T	T	H	T	H
T	H	T	T	H	H
T	T	H	H	H	H

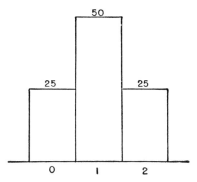

Figure 3.f. The Expected Distribution
of the Number of Heads Obtained in
100 Tosses of Two Coins.

If, as before, we consider these 8 possibilities as equally likely, we will find that we can expect to get 0 head one-eighth of the time, 1 head three-eighths of the time, 2 heads three-eighths of the time, and finally 3 heads again one-eighth of the time.   These fractions were obtained directly from the above table in which the 8 different cases contain 0, 1, 2, and 3 heads, once, three times, three times, and once, respectively.   If we now toss three coins 80 times, the resulting expected frequency distribution will be

Number of heads	Frequency
0	10
1	30
2	30
3	10

This is also shown in the histogram of Fig. 3.g.

3.3 The Binomial Distribution

We have shown in the last section how we can obtain the expected distribution of the number of heads if we are tossing 1, 2, or 3 honest coins.   The method which we have used can easily be generalized to problems in which we want to know how often, or what per cent of the time, certain more general events can be expected to take place. A doctor who knows the mortality of a certain disease may, for instance, be anxious to know *what per cent of the time he can expect 3 out of 10 patients to die from the given disease.*   Similarly, a psychologist may want to know how many answers he can expect a student

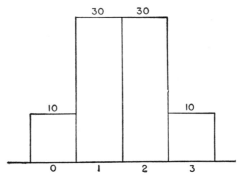

Figure 3.g.   The Expected Distribution of the Number of Heads Obtained in 80 Tosses of Three Coins.

to get in an objective test if he leaves the selection of his answers purely to chance; a soldier may want to know *what per cent of the time he can expect to hit his target with 8 out of 10 bullets.*

Many questions like these can be answered with the use of the theoretical (expected) distribution, which is called the *binomial distribution.* The frequencies of the binomial distribution are usually found by means of a mathematical formula which tells us how to compute the percentage of the time that a certain event can be expected to happen x times out of n.   As we shall see in later chapters, *the probability of the occurrence of a certain event is the same as the fraction (per cent) of the time that the event will (or can be expected to) take place in the long run.*   If the probability of rolling a 3 with one die is $\frac{1}{6}$, for example, this means that in the long run we can expect to get a 3 about one-sixth of the time.   Let us therefore accept this definition for now on a more or less intuitive basis, using the two statements *the probability of the occurrence of an event is equal to p* and *the event will take place in the long run $100 \cdot p$ per cent of the time* as synonymous.

If we expect something to happen about 25 per cent of the time, we shall therefore say that the probability of its occurrence is .25 or $\frac{1}{4}$.   If, for example, it has rained in the past on the Fourth of July 20 per cent of the time, we shall say that the probability that it will rain on this date is .20 or $\frac{1}{5}$.

It follows from these considerations that the binomial formula, i.e., the formula which gives us the distribution of the percentages that an event will take place x times out of n, is actually giving us the *probabilities* that the various eventualities will take place.   It is for this reason that expected distributions, like the binomial distribution, are also called *probability distributions*.

The probability (per cent of the time) that a certain event will happen x times out of n (x times in n trials) is given by the formula

$$p(x;n) = \binom{n}{x}p^x(1 - p)^{n-x} \qquad (3.3.1)^*$$

in which p is the probability that the event will take place in each individual trial. This is only the well-known formula for the probabilities of repeated trials, and it tells us what per cent of the time we can expect to get x successes in n trials.

The symbol $\binom{n}{x}$ which appears in formula (3.3.1) is merely a shorthand symbol for the so-called *binomial coefficients* which are defined as

$$\binom{n}{x} = \frac{n!}{x!(n - x)!}$$

where $n!$ equals $n(n - 1)(n - 2)(n - 3) \ldots 2 \cdot 1$, and is read "$n$-factorial."

In order to simplify the calculations of the percentages and frequencies which can be found with Formula (3.3.1), the binomial coefficients for values of n from 1 to 20 are given in Table VII on page 396. The actual derivation of the formula of the binomial distribution, which is also known by the name of *Newton's formula,* is not particularly difficult, but it requires a more detailed knowledge of the principles of probability than we have at this time. If the reader is interested in checking its derivation, he will find a suitable reference at the end of this chapter. Otherwise, it will suffice for now that our discussion of the binomial distribution, however intuitive it might have been, presented us with a concrete illustration of a theoretical frequency distribution.

To illustrate how the binomial distribution is used, let us investigate the following problem. Four people have the same disease, and their doctor wants to know what per cent of the time he can expect all of them to survive; what the chances are that exactly 1 patient will die; how often it will happen that exactly 2 out of 4 will die, etc. The doctor knows that the mortality rate of the disease is .10. This means that the doctor wants to know *how the chances of the occurrence of the various possibilities are distributed.*

It is important to note that although the binomial distribution is given by a single mathematical formula, it still gives us the entire distribution of the percentages (frequencies) which are associated with the various cases, if we calculate its values for the different values of x.

Returning now to our example, let us first find the probability that all patients will survive, i.e., that no patient will die. Putting $n = 4$, $x = 0$, and $p = .10$ into formula (3.3.1), we have

$$p(0;4) = 1(.10)^0(.90)^4 = .6561$$

which means that about 65.6 per cent of the time all 4 patients can be expected to survive. Next we shall put $x = 1$, keeping n and p the same as before, and we have

$$p(1;4) = 4(.10)^1(.90)^3 = .2916$$

which tells us that exactly 1 out of 4 patients will die under these circumstances almost 30 per cent of the time. Finally, putting x equal to 2, 3, and 4, respectively, we can also find that

$$p(2;4) = 6(.10)^2(.90)^2 = .0486$$
$$p(3;4) = 4(.10)^3(.90)^1 = .0036$$
$$p(4;4) = 1(.10)^4(.90)^0 = .0001$$

which means that we can expect exactly 2 of 4 patients to die about 5 per cent of the time, 3 will die about $\frac{1}{3}$ of 1 per cent of the time, while the chances that all will die are $1/100$ of 1 per cent (or 1 in 10,000). The over-all picture of this binomial distribution, which is a percentage distribution rather than a frequency distribution, is given by the histogram of Fig. 3.h. To clarify our calculations we might add, perhaps, the binomial coefficients 1, 4, 6, 4, and 1 were obtained from the table on page 396.

The formula of the binomial distribution could also have been used in the determination of the probability of getting, for example, 1 head with 2 coins. Putting $x = 1$, $n = 2$, and $p = .50$, we have

$$p(1;2) = 2(.50)^1(.50)^1 = .50$$

which is the identical answer that we had before.

The binomial distribution has many important applications other than those which we have discussed so far. Since these further applications belong to inductive statistics, however, we shall delay their treatment until Chapters 9 and 10.

The binomial distribution is by no means the only theoretical distribution which we shall meet in our future studies. Another theoretical distribution is the so-called *Poisson distribution*, named after the famous French mathematician who is one of the forefathers

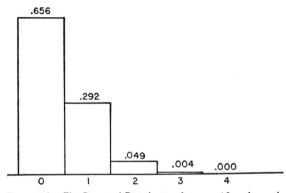

Figure 3.h. The Binomial Distribution for $p = .10$ and $n = 4$.

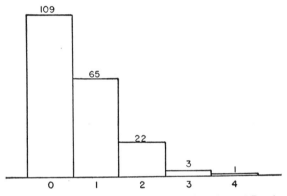

Figure 3.i. The Distribution of the Number of Deaths Resulting from the Kick of a Horse per Year per Army Corps of the Prussian Army.

of modern statistics. The Poisson distribution, which is in many respects quite similar to the binomial distribution, provides us with the probabilities (percentages) of getting x successes whenever the probability p of the occurrence of each single event is very small, while the exposure, i.e., the number of trials or the number of times which the event could possibly take place, is very large. Although we shall not give the actual formula of the Poisson distribution, it will nevertheless be instructive to consider a few simple illustrations. The classical example of the type of data which might be expected to follow a Poisson distribution is the distribution of the number of deaths resulting from the kick of a horse per year per army corps of the Prussian army. This illustration fits the conditions which we stated for the Poisson distribution because the probability that any one soldier is kicked to death by a horse is *very small*, while on the other hand, the exposure to the risk is *very large* because there were a great many soldiers.

Other applications of this distribution deal, for example, with the inspection of manufactured products. The number of defective bottles which we may find in large lots of manufactured beer bottles can be expected to fit a Poisson distribution, since the percentage of defectives is usually *very small* while the total number of bottles is *very large*. Another important application can be found in problems of radiation in physics. The probability that a small particle hits a certain tiny designated area is *very small*, yet the number of particles is *very large*. Finally, the number of fish caught by fishermen per day on a certain lake, and the number of automobile accidents per car owner per year, are both variables which can reasonably be expected to follow a Poisson distribution.

3.4 The Normal Curve

No study of theoretical frequency distributions, no matter how modest, can be complete without mention of the so-called *normal curve*, which in many respects is the cornerstone of modern statistical theory. It has long been known that large masses of measurements of the same quantity present an astonishing degree of regularity and orderliness. As early as the eighteenth century it was observed that errors of measurements seemed to fall into a very definite pattern which was then attributed to the laws of chance. The mathematical basis of this normal law of chance was first studied by Pierre Laplace (1749–1827), Abraham de Moivre (1667–1745), and Carl Gauss (1777–1855). We shall not concern ourselves in this chapter with the mathematical derivation of the normal distribution or with its theoretical assumption, save for some brief comments on its relation to the binomial distribution.

It can be shown that if we take a binomial distribution, put p equal to $\frac{1}{2}$ and let n become larger and larger, the resulting theoretical distribution will come closer and closer to the bell-shaped distribution which is known as the normal curve. A nice illustration of this approximation is provided by the normal curve machine (Fig. 3.j), models of which can be found in the science exhibits of many museums. This machine, if we may call it that, operates as follows. A large number of small pellets are dropped into an opening which is at the top of a large inclined or vertical board. Pegs are spaced on this board in such a manner that the dropping pellets will bounce on the pegs and distribute themselves among the compartments which make up the bottom portion of the machine in a pattern which comes very close to the shape of a normal curve.

In order to demonstrate the relationship between the distribution of the pellets and the binomial distribution, let us imagine that some pellets are dropped through the opening at the top of the diagram of Fig. 3.j. The dropping pellets will then hit some of the pegs which are lettered A, B, C, D, E, and F, traveling along the dotted paths of the diagram. This means that each time a pellet hits one of the pegs it can fall either to the left or to the right, and it must thus hit one peg on each level. At the end of its path, at the bottom of the machine, each pellet must fall into one of the compartments which are labeled 1, 2, 3, and 4. Let us now ask for the total number of different paths which a pellet can take in order to arrive in any one of the four compartments. There is only *one* way in which a pellet can land in compartment 1: it must travel along the path $ABD1$ (see Fig. 3.j). A pellet can reach compartment 2 in *three* different

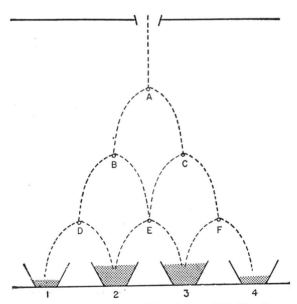

Figure 3.j. Model of a Normal Curve "Machine."

ways by taking either path $ABD2$, path $ABE2$, or path $ACE2$. Compartment 3 can be reached also via *three* different paths, namely, $ABE3$, $ACE3$, and $ACF3$; and finally, compartment 4 can be reached only by *one* path, namely, $ACF4$. There are, therefore, all in all *eight* different paths which a pellet can choose after it has been dropped into the machine.

Assuming that it is equally likely that a pellet will take any one of the 8 paths, the fraction of the pellets which can be expected to arrive in compartment 1 is $\frac{1}{8}$; in compartment 2 we can expect $\frac{3}{8}$; $\frac{3}{8}$ in compartment 3; and again $\frac{1}{8}$ in compartment 4. The reader will note that this distribution is precisely the same as the binomial distribution for the number of heads obtained with 3 honest coins.

No machine which works with pellets can ever be expected to give us anything but a discrete distribution since, after all, the normal curve is a smooth continuous curve, and although we may increase the number of pegs and compartments, we will still have a grouped distribution. This does not matter, however, so long as we remember that it was our purpose merely to show that the binomial distribution comes very close to a normal curve if the number of pegs and compartments becomes very large, i.e., when the n of formula (3.3.1) becomes very large.

As we shall see later, there exist problems in which we can actually expect, on the basis of theoretical considerations, that our data will fall into the pattern of a normal curve. In actual practice we will usually be satisfied, however, with merely showing that the data which we have collected come close to a normal curve, without giving any theoretical reasons.

In general, the normal curve (an illustration of which is given in Fig. 3.k) is a continuous bell-shaped curve which has many interesting mathematical properties. It is of tremendous importance to the scientist in the study and analysis of his data, and there can be no

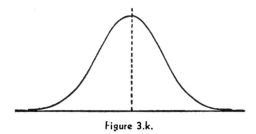

Figure 3.k.

doubt that it plays a vital role in the majority of the decisions which are based on experimental results. It is necessary to add a word of caution, however, because the indiscriminate use of the normal curve and its theory can lead to ridiculous and highly misleading results. There exist many problems, a few of which will be studied in later chapters, in which we have good rea ons to expect theoretical distributions which are *not* normal curves. Just to mention a few, there are the chi-square distribution and the *t* distribution which form the basis of many problems of estimation and prediction.

REFERENCES

C. H. Sisam, *College Algebra*, Holt, New York, 1940, Chap. 18.

EXERCISES

1. Draw a freehand curve to fit the histogram of any one of the sets of data which were given in Exercises 6, 8, 10, or 12 on page 20. Use the area under this curve to estimate roughly above which value we can expect to find the highest 10 per cent of the cases and below which value we can expect to find the lowest 25 per cent.

2. Draw a freehand curve to fit the histogram of the distribution of the pension payments which were given in Exercise 2 on page 27, and decide on the basis of the area under this curve what percentage of the payments were above $45.

3. State whether each of the following is a discrete or a continuous type of variable:

    (a) Number of children per family
    (b) Measurements of the velocity of sound
    (c) Savings deposits
    (d) The weight of mice
    (e) Test grades
    (f) Prices of second-hand cars
    (g) Number of fatal automobile accidents
    (h) Measurements of the intensity of light

4. Use formula (3.3.1) to calculate the percentage distribution (probabilities) for the number of heads for repeated tosses of 4 coins.

5. Toss 4 coins 64 times and compare the observed frequencies of the number of heads with the expected frequencies which are obtained by multiplying the percentages of Exercise 4 by 64.

6. Roll one die 120 times and record the frequencies with which the various faces of the die appeared. What is the corresponding expected distribution? Compare the two distributions.

7. If 50 per cent of all children born are boys, what percentage of the families having 5 children can we expect to have

  (a) All boys
  (b) Two boys and 3 girls
  (c) One boy and 4 girls?

8. If the probability that a plane gets shot down during a raid is .05, what per cent of the time can we expect 8 out of 10 planes to return?

9. A short quiz consists of 8 multiple-choice questions, each permitting 3 alternatives. If a student who has not studied for this test simply guesses his answers, what per cent of the time can we expect him to get 6 answers correct? Use formula (3.3.1).

10. If a sharpshooter can hit a distant target 90 per cent of the time and if he fires 100 rounds of 5 shots, how many times can we expect him to get a perfect round?

4. DESCRIPTIVE MEASURES
I. MEASURES OF
CENTRAL TENDENCIES

4.1 Introduction

The grouping of numerical data and their presentation as histograms or other visual representations are the first step in the statistical treatment of experimental results or observed data. As we have pointed out before, measurements are grouped or classified in order to put them into a form which lends itself more readily to further studies, and in order to avoid the unpleasant job of having to consider directly hundreds or even thousands of individual numbers.

In everyday life it is customary to describe what we observe by means of a few well-chosen descriptions. In the program of a football game we will find, for example, the age, height, and weight of the various athletes, together with the number of years which they have played the game. This does *not* tell us whether they are blonde or brunette, and good or bad at their studies. However, the above information may well be sufficient to enable us to evaluate the comparative merits of the two teams. Similarly, frequency distributions are descriptive of the sets of data which they represent inasmuch as they tell us how the measurements are distributed among the various groupings. Again we have only a partial description, but as we shall see, much can be learned about the original data if we proceed by asking for a description of the distribution, i.e., *by asking for a description of this description.* This is really not as complicated as it may sound. A photograph describes a certain individual just as a histogram or a frequency table describes a given set of numerical data. If we can then describe the individual as skinny or chubby, pleasant or grouchy, *simply by looking at this picture*, we can similarly describe a large set of numerical data as spread out or bunched, symmetrical or skewed, *by looking at the frequency table or histogram*.

Just as we can describe a person directly, or by looking at his or her picture, we can similarly describe a set of numerical data *by either looking at the raw data, or by looking at their distribution*. Since a direct description is bound to be more accurate than a description which is based on a photograph, we can also say that a description which is based on the raw data is likely to be more accurate than a description which is based on the corresponding frequency table. It is for this reason that we shall distinguish in this and the following chapters between descriptive measures which are obtained directly from the raw data, and the corresponding descriptive measures which are obtained from the grouped distributions.

It is obvious that since we can never give a complete description of anything, we must again limit ourselves to the most important features and characteristics. Following the customary procedure we shall, therefore, investigate the four fundamental types of descriptive measures which are: measures of *central tendencies,* measures of *variation*, measures of *symmetry,* and measures of *peakedness.* Measures of central tendencies will tell us something about the center of a given set of numerical data; measures of variation will describe their spread, dispersion, or variation. Measures of symmetry will tell us to what degree our data are balanced; and measures of peakedness point out how flat or peaked our distribution may be.

4.2 Measures of Central Tendencies

The remainder of this chapter will be devoted to the first of these four types of descriptions, namely, to the measures of central tendencies. The term itself implies that we are trying to locate the center or the middle of a set of data. The vagueness of this term is quite appropriate because there are actually a great many different ways in which we can *define* the center of a distribution. If we speak about the center of a sphere, there can be no doubt as to what we mean; if we say that a politician is ideologically in the center, we know at least that he does not belong to either political extreme; if we speak about a center of attraction, we know that we are speaking about a definite focal point of interest. The center of a set of data, on the other hand, is not as well defined, and we can interpret it in a variety of different ways, each of which describes a property of the data which might reasonably be called a central tendency. It must be understood, therefore, that the center of a set of data must be *defined*, and this can be done in a variety of ways.

4.3 The Arithmetic Mean, Ungrouped Data

The *arithmetic mean* of a set of numbers x_1, x_2, x_3, . . . , x_n is what most laymen call their *average*, and it is defined as their sum divided by their number, i.e., the sum of the x_i divided by n. It is usually denoted by the symbol $\bar{x}$ (*x*-bar) and we can write it symbolically as

$$\bar{x} = \frac{\sum_{i=1}^{n} x_i}{n} \qquad (4.3.1)^*$$

To save time, we shall abbreviate this term and call it simply the *mean*. Since there exist also a *geometrical mean* and a *harmonic mean*, it must be understood that whenever we speak of the *mean* we are actually referring to the arithmetic mean which is defined by formula (4.3.1). This formula, which gives us the mean of ungrouped data, has the very desirable property that it is easy to compute. If we have, for example, the 6 examination grades 92, 53, 87, 41, 88, and 80, their mean is easily found to be

$$\bar{x} = \frac{92 + 53 + 87 + 41 + 88 + 80}{6} = 73.5$$

Other advantageous properties of the mean are that it always exists, it can always be calculated, for any kind of data; it always gives a unique answer; and it takes into account every individual measurement. Whether or not this last property is really desirable is open to question, because a single extreme (very large or very small) value can affect the mean to such an extent that it is doubtful whether it is actually representative of the center of our data.

Let us consider, for example, the ages of the guests at grandfather's birthday party, which were 18, 23, 25, 24, and 22, while grandfather himself was 92. The mean of these ages including that of grandfather can readily be found to be equal to 33. Although this mean is *by definition* a measure of the center of the 6 numbers, it is hardly representative or descriptive of the ages which belonged to this group. If somebody were to hear that the average age of the guests was 33, he would hardly receive the impression that most of the people were close to 20 years of age.

Since our reason for computing a measure of central tendencies is to get a quick description of a set of numerical data, we could hardly say that we have accomplished this purpose with the computation of the mean of the 6 ages. It is actually quite difficult to say when a measure is good and when it is bad because *its suitability depends largely on what we intend to do with the descriptive measure after it has been obtained.* If, for example, every guest at the party including the host had received as a door prize an amount of money equal to his or her age, the mean (or the total sum of their ages) would have been the information needed in order to provide sufficient funds. Consequently, whenever we represent a set of data, so to speak, by a single number, we must always be careful that it is clearly understood what is expressed by that number. Furthermore, we should also make sure that its meaning is understood by others who might want to use our results. Fortunately, most people know what is meant by a mean although they may not actually call it by that name.

The following property is another advantageous feature of the arithmetic mean: if we have the means of a number of separate groups of data, these means can readily be combined into an over-all mean without going back to the original raw data. Let us suppose, for example, that one set of measurements consists of n_1 numbers whose mean is $\bar{x}_1$; a second set consists of n_2 measurements with a mean of $\bar{x}_2$; and a third set consists of n_3 measurements with a mean of $\bar{x}_3$. With the use of this information we can calculate the combined mean of all of the measurements by means of the formula

$$\bar{x} = \frac{n_1\bar{x}_1 + n_2\bar{x}_2 + n_3\bar{x}_3}{n_1 + n_2 + n_3} \qquad (4.3.2)$$

For example, if one group of 20 students received an average (mean) grade of 63, a second group of 18 students received an average of 57, while a third group consisting of 12 students averaged 58, the over-all mean of the combination of the three groups is

$$\bar{x} = \frac{20 \cdot 63 + 18 \cdot 57 + 12 \cdot 58}{20 + 18 + 12} = 59.6$$

Formula (4.3.2) can be derived fairly easily. Let us write the sum of the scores of the students of the first group as Σ_1, the sum of the scores of the second group as Σ_2, and that of the third group as Σ_3. Since the over-all mean is defined as the sum of all of the scores divided by their number, we can write

$$\bar{x} = \frac{\Sigma_1 + \Sigma_2 + \Sigma_3}{n_1 + n_2 + n_3}$$

in which the numerator represents the total of the scores, while the denominator stands for the total number of scores. According to our original definition of the mean we can also write

$$\bar{x}_1 = \frac{\Sigma_1}{n_1}, \quad \bar{x}_2 = \frac{\Sigma_2}{n_2}, \quad \bar{x}_3 = \frac{\Sigma_3}{n_3}$$

Multiplying these three equations by n_1, n_2, and n_3, respectively, we get

$$n_1\bar{x}_1 = \Sigma_1, \quad n_2\bar{x}_2 = \Sigma_2, \quad n_3\bar{x}_3 = \Sigma_3$$

Substituting these last values into our previous expression for the over-all mean we finally have

$$\bar{x} = \frac{n_1\bar{x}_1 + n_2\bar{x}_2 + n_3\bar{x}_3}{n_1 + n_2 + n_3}$$

which agrees with formula (4.3.2), which we wanted to prove.

If we consider an arbitrary number, say k, separate groups of data, the over-all mean can easily be shown to be equal to

$$\bar{x} = \frac{\sum_{i=1}^{k} n_i\bar{x}_i}{\sum_{i=1}^{k} n_i} \qquad (4.3.3)*$$

where n_i is the number of individuals who belong to the ith group, and $\bar{x}_i$ is its arithmetic mean.

Further advantages of the mean will become apparent in later chapters when we shall discuss the mean of a sample which is to be used for predictions and estimations. The mean will then prove itself to be very reliable, which means that it is a relatively stable measure and does not vary much from sample to sample. As we have said before, most people do understand what we mean by a *mean*, at least as long as we call it an *average*. Unfortunately the same cannot be said for most other statistical measures.

EXERCISES

1. The lowest prices charged for a $3\frac{1}{2}$-oz can of tuna fish on the same day in 10 different stores were 27, 45, 35, 29, 36, 33, 25, 27, 25, and 36 cents. Compute the mean of these prices.

2. A 10-ml pipet was calibrated and found to deliver the following volumes: 9.97, 9.94, 9.98, 9.92, and 9.95 ml. Find the mean of these measurements.

3. The body weights of 10 rats, used in a study of vitamin deficiencies, were

123 g	127 g
135	94
142	134
146	126
158	110

Compute the mean of these weights.

4. The grades which 18 students obtained in a short quiz were 7, 9, 6, 10, 10, 8, 9, 10, 10, 4, 3, 10, 6, 7, 9, 8, 2, 10. Find the mean of these scores.

5. The following are the number of defective pieces which were produced by a certain machine in 8 successive days: 4, 1, 6, 3, 5, 2, 8, 6. Calculate the mean.

6. Find the mean of the college indexes which were given in Exercise 6 on page 19.

7. What is the average (mean) price of the houses given in Exercise 10 on page 20?

8. The average weight of the 7 linesmen of a football team is 208 lb, while the average weight of the 4 backs is 186. Find the average (mean) weight of the entire team.

9. Department store A pays to its 1200 employees an average wage of $42.18, department store B pays an average of $45.72 to 860 employees, while department store C pays to its 940 employees an average wage of $41.53. What is the over-all mean of these salaries?

10. The following table shows the average regents grades obtained by students of 5 different schools. Compute the over-all mean of the grades.

	Number of students	Mean
School A	237	82.1
School B	149	78.5
School C	195	86.4
School D	256	82.3
School E	91	72.5

4.4 The Arithmetic Mean, Grouped Data

The mathematical operations which are required for the calculation of a mean do not go beyond addition and division. However, if we were asked to compute the mean of a great number of measurements, the necessary calculations would entail a considerable amount of work. For this reason it is usually advisable to group our data first and then compute the mean from the resulting distribution.

Let us recall that if we group data, each individual measurement loses, so to speak, its identity. Instead of knowing the precise value of each measurement we are left with a distribution which tells us how many of the numbers fall into each class, but which does not tell us what the measurements really are. Since we will then no longer know the actual values of the measurements, it may seem impossible to calculate their mean. This is indeed what happens, unless we are willing to make some assumption concerning the distribution of the measurements within each classification and content ourselves, thus, with an approximation. Let us assume, for example, that *all measurements which fall into a given class are located at its class mark, i.e., at the midpoint of the class interval.* This assumption is not as unreasonable as it may seem, because there is usually a considerable amount of compensation between the measurements which fall above the class marks and those which fall below. The error which is introduced by this assumption, namely, the error of considering each measurement as if it were located at the class mark, will be discussed further in Section 4.13.

To illustrate the calculation of the mean from grouped data, let us consider again the distribution of the salaries of the 40 employees of the ZYX Co. which was

Salary (dollars)	Class mark	Frequency
30.00–39.99	34.995	3
40.00–49.99	44.995	15
50.00–59.99	54.995	10
60.00–69.99	64.995	8
70.00–79.99	74.995	3
80.00–89.99	84.995	1

According to the assumption which we have just made, these salaries will be treated as if 3 were $34.995, 15 were $44.995, 10 were $54.995, etc. Very little accuracy would be lost if we were to round these class marks to $35.00, $45.00, etc., and it would be quite reasonable to do so in this case.

In order to compute the *mean* of this distribution we must, as before, find first the total of all the salaries. This means that we must add *three* times $34.995, *fifteen* times $44.995, *ten* times $54.995, etc. In general, denoting the class mark of the ith classification by the symbol x_i, and its corresponding class frequency by f_i, we can write the grand total of all the salaries as

$$\sum_{i=1}^{6} x_i f_i$$

This summation goes from 1 to 6 because we have grouped the salaries into that number of classifications, and written in full, it is equivalent to the sum $x_1 f_1 + x_2 f_2 + x_3 f_3 + x_4 f_4 + x_5 f_5 + x_6 f_6$.

Substituting this summation into formula (4.3.1), which defined the mean, we find that the mean of the salaries is given by the expression

$$\bar{x} = \frac{\sum_{i=1}^{6} x_i f_i}{n} \qquad (4.4.1)$$

where n stands for the total number of salaries, which in this case is equal to 40. This total can be written symbolically as $\sum_{i=1}^{6} f_i$. The mean of our grouped data can now be computed with the use of the following schema:

Class mark x_i	Frequency f_i	Their product $x_i f_i$
34.995	3	104.985
44.995	15	674.925
54.995	10	549.950
64.995	8	519.960
74.995	''	224.985
84.995		84.995
		$\Sigma x_i f_i = 2195.800$

The mean salary is equal to 2195.8/40 = \$53.995, or \$54.00 to the nearest cent, which is the identical result which we would have obtained if we had rounded the class marks to the nearest cent.

If we are interested in determining the error which was introduced by the grouping and the subsequent assumption that the salaries are located at the respective class marks, we must find the actual mean of the salaries from the raw data. Adding the salaries which are given on page 13 we obtain a total of \$2178.77, and dividing this total by 40, we obtain the actual mean, which is \$54.47 to the nearest cent. *The 47-cent difference between the two means must be attributed to the fact that we are likely to lose accuracy and discard information whenever we group data.*

Formula (4.4.1) can easily be generalized to fit the calculation of

the mean of any arbitrary set of grouped data. If a grouping consists of k classifications, we can write

$$\bar{x} = \frac{\sum\limits_{i=1}^{k} x_i f_i}{\sum\limits_{i=1}^{k} f_i} \qquad (4.4.2)^*$$

where the denominator is equal to the total number of cases, and
could be written as n.

The calculation of the mean of a set of grouped data can still be
a lot of work, particularly if the class marks x_i are large numbers, or
if they are given to many decimals. To reduce the work which is
entailed in the calculation of $\bar{x}$ from grouped data, we shall use the
standard trick of changing the scale of measurement.

Let us consider Fig. 4.a, which represents again the histogram of
the distribution of the salaries. The horizontal scale, which measures
the salaries, is denoted the *x scale*. To simplify the numbers with
which we shall have to work, let us pick up the *x scale* without changing the remainder of the diagram, and let us substitute in its place
a new scale which, in Fig. 4.a, is called the *u scale*. The new scale

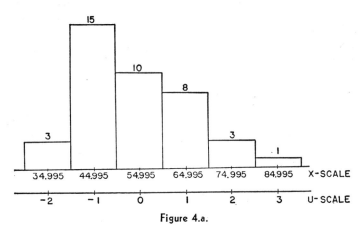

Figure 4.a.

was chosen (and it must be understood that this choice is completely
arbitrary) in such a manner that *the class marks of the distribution
coincide with the units of the new scale.* The zero point of the new
scale was conveniently placed in line with the class mark of the
third class.

It is by no means unusual to measure identical quantities with two or more different scales of measurement. For example, we can measure the length of a room in feet or we can measure it in meters. A well-known example of a physical quantity which is often measured by two different scales is temperature, which can be given either in the Fahrenheit or in the centigrade scale. Figure 4.b shows a thermometer on which the centigrade scale is given on the left and the Fahrenheit scale on the right. Since many calculations are easier to perform in the centigrade scale, it is often quite helpful to change measurements from one scale to the other. This can be done by means of the well-known formula

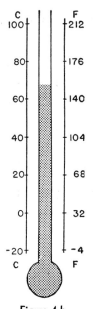

$$F = \tfrac{9}{5}C + 32 \tag{4.4.3}$$

What we plan to do in our original problem with the x and the u scales (see Fig. 4.a) is precisely the same. In order to simplify the calculations we express the class marks in terms of the new scale, the u scale, which was chosen specially for this purpose. If we want our final answer to be again in the x scale, we convert our results with the use of some formula like (4.4.3). It can easily be shown that this must be

Figure 4.b. $x_i = 10u_i + 54.995 \tag{4.4.4}$

where x_i is the measurement in the x scale which corresponds to the measurement u_i in the u scale. It was necessary in (4.4.4) to multiply the measurement of the u scale by 10 because this is the distance between the successive class marks in the original scale. The number 54.995, which was added to the product, is simply the value of the x scale which was chosen as the zero point of the new scale.

In general, if we introduce a new scale by assigning successive integers to the class marks of a distribution, and if we choose one of the class marks as the zero of the new scale, the corresponding formula which will enable us to change from one scale to the other is

$$x_i = c \cdot u_i + x_0 \tag{4.4.5}$$

In this formula c stands for the class interval (in the old scale), and

x_0 stands for the value of the class mark (in the old scale) which was
chosen as the origin of the new scale.

Since the calculation of the mean from grouped data makes it
necessary for us to find the products $x_i f_i$ and their sum, let us now
multiply both sides of formula (4.4.5) by the frequencies f_i. This
gives us

$$x_i f_i = c u_i f_i + x_0 f_i \qquad (4.4.6)$$

in which we are now using x_i and u_i to denote the class mark of the
ith class in both scales. *We have, therefore, an equation like (4.4.6)
for each class mark of the distribution.* Adding equals to equals,
we can now add the corresponding sides of these equations. Written
with summations, this gives us

$$\sum_{i=1}^{k} x_i f_i = \sum_{i=1}^{k} (c u_i f_i + x_0 f_i) \qquad (4.4.7)$$

where k is, as before, the number of classifications. Using Theorems
A and B of Chapter 1, we can rewrite this as

$$\sum_{i=1}^{k} x_i f_i = c \sum_{i=1}^{k} u_i f_i + x_0 \sum_{i=1}^{k} f_i \qquad (4.4.8)$$

Since the total number of cases n is equal to the sum of the class
frequencies, we can write

$$\sum_{i=1}^{k} f_i = n \qquad (4.4.9)$$

Substituting this expression into (4.4.8), and dividing both sides of
the equation by n, we finally have

$$\frac{\sum_{i=1}^{k} x_i f_i}{n} = \frac{c \sum_{i=1}^{k} u_i f_i}{n} + x_0 \qquad (4.4.10)$$

The left-hand side of this equation is *by definition* the mean of the
grouped data, and we can therefore give *the short formula for the
calculation of the mean from grouped data* as

$$\bar{x} = \frac{c \sum_{i=1}^{k} u_i f_i}{n} + x_0 \qquad (4.4.11)*$$

Returning now to our illustration, let us compute the mean of the
grouped salaries with the use of Formula (4.4.11). This is most
conveniently done by means of the following schema.

| Class marks | | Frequency | Their product |
x scale	u scale	f	uf
34.995	−2	3	−6
44.995	−1	15	−15
54.995	0	10	0
64.995	1	8	8
74.995	2	3	6
84.995	3	1	3
		40	−4

Substituting the total of the frequencies and the total of the products $u_i f_i$ into the short formula for the mean (4.4.11), we finally have

$$\bar{x} = \frac{10(-4)}{40} + 54.995$$
$$= -1 + 54.995 = \$53.995$$

which is precisely the same result which we obtained before, using the long formula (4.4.2).

The short method for computing the mean of grouped data is so simple and saves so much time and energy that it should always be used. In order to reduce the work to a minimum, the zero point of the u scale is usually chosen somewhere near the middle of the distribution, preferably at the class mark which has the highest frequency.

The short formula cannot be used for distributions which contain unequal class intervals, although there exists a modified form which applies also in that case. Finally, it cannot be used if our distribution contains open class intervals at either end. This emphasizes even more strongly than before why unequal and open class intervals are not very desirable.

EXERCISES

1. The following is the distribution of 1000 aptitude scores:

Scores	Frequency
11– 20	5
21– 30	14
31– 40	52
41– 50	117
51– 60	188
61– 70	233
71– 80	202
81– 90	112
91–100	61
101–110	12
111–120	4

Compute the mean of this distribution using (1) formula (4.4.2), and (2) formula (4.4.11). Time yourself on the two parts of this problem to check how much time is saved by using the short method.

2. Find the mean of whichever data you grouped among those of Exercises 6, 8, 10, or 12 on page 19.

3. Calculate the mean distance which the rifle shots of Exercise 1, page 27, hit from the center of the target.

4. Find the mean of the pension payments which were given in Exercise 2 on page 27.

5. An experiment consisting of 100 tosses of 10 coins produced the following result:

Number of heads	Frequency
0	1
1	2
2	3
3	12
4	23
5	17
6	18
7	19
8	2
9	3
10	0

Calculate the mean to find the average number of heads. Use formula (4.4.2) since little is to be gained by introduction of a new scale.

4.5 The Median, Ungrouped Data

The arithmetic mean defines the middle of a distribution in the sense of a center of gravity. The *median*, which is our second measure of central tendencies, defines the center of a set of data as the point (number) which divides the measurements into two groups containing an equal number of the measurements which are arranged according to size. This means that there must be as many measurements below the median as there are above it, and that in order to find the median we first must arrange our measurements according to size. This is not always a pleasant task, particularly if we are dealing with a great number of scores or measurements.

If we are working with an *odd* number of measurements, there is no problem in finding the one measurement which satisfies our definition of the median. In a set of 11 measurements, for example, the 6th largest is the median; 5 measurements are larger, and 5 are smaller. In general, the median of n numbers is given by the

$\dfrac{n+1}{2}$ th, provided of course, that they are ordered by size. In a set of 17 measurements, for instance, the $\dfrac{17+1}{2}$ th or the 9th largest is by definition equal to the median.

If two or more measurements are alike, it does not matter which is written first. The median of the numbers 8, 10, 10, 6, and 10 is simply 10 and *there is no sense in asking which of the three tens is to be designated the median.*

Among an even number of measurements there will *not* be one which divides the data into two equal parts, and the median will, consequently, have to be defined somewhat differently in this case. In a set of 10 numbers, we could pick any number which lies between the 5th and 6th largest, and this number would satisfy the condition that there are as many measurements which are larger as there are measurements which are less. It seems quite reasonable, therefore, to define the median of an *even* number of measurements as the average (mean) of the two middle values. The median is thus halfway between the two central values of the ordered set of data, and it can easily be checked that the formula $(n+1)/2$ will again give us the *position* of the measurement which is to be designated as the median. If we have, for example, 40 measurements, the median will be the $\dfrac{40+1}{2}$ th or the 20.5th, which means that it is halfway between the 20th and 21st of the ordered measurements.

To calculate the median of the salaries which we have been using as an illustration, we arrange them first according to size. This gives us

34.60	37.55	38.75	40.75	41.13	41.33	44.65	45.20
45.42	45.50	45.60	45.60	46.32	46.50	47.23	47.25
47.65	49.50	52.29	53.25	53.39	55.12	56.75	57.30
57.42	57.50	58.75	59.50	61.25	63.44	63.50	63.79
65.42	65.75	65.75	67.12	72.57	75.25	78.68	84.50

Looking directly at this array of numbers, we find that the 20th salary is \$53.25, while the 21st is \$53.39. The median of these salaries is therefore equal to

$$M = \frac{53.25 + 53.39}{2} = \$53.32$$

It should not surprise the reader that the median of these numbers is not equal to their mean, for the simple reason that the two measures of central tendencies define the center of the set of data in a different manner; they actually describe slightly different features of the same set of data. Indeed, the very fact that in our example the mean and the median differed by as little as .68 can possibly be interpreted as indicative of another property of these numbers, namely, of their symmetry.

Beginning students often commit the error of mistaking the expression $(n + 1)/2$ for a formula which gives them the median. This is, of course, not the case. The formula tells us only how many of the numbers we must count in our ordered series of measurements until we reach the particular measurement (or midpoint between measurements) which is defined as the median.

A definite advantage of the median is that it involves practically no mathematical calculations. On the other hand, it requires that we arrange our data according to size, and this can be very cumbersome. Another interesting property of the median which, incidentally, it does not share with the mean, is that the median is *not* easily affected by extreme values. To illustrate this point, let us consider again the ages of the guests at the birthday party which we had previously given as 18, 22, 23, 24, 25, and 92. The median of this set of numbers is 23.5 and it is, in a sense, much more descriptive of the majority of these ages than the mean, which was 33. Even if the oldest member of this group had been 75, 99, or 45, or if the youngest had been only 13, this would not have changed the value which we originally obtained for the median.

Another advantage of the median lies in the fact that the median of a set of grouped data can be found *even if the distribution is open at either end.* Furthermore, and this is quite important, the median lends itself even to define the middle of a number of objects, properties, or qualities which do not permit a quantitative description. It is possible, for example, to arrange a group of our friends in the order in which we like them best, and to determine the median of this ordered group precisely as we found the median of our numerical data. In a similar fashion we can order our preferences for radio or television programs, colors, types of food, etc., and we can indicate the middle of each of these ordered quantities by pointing to the one which occupies the position of the median. For example, if we like apple pie, chocolate cake, ice cream, cup cakes, and pudding in the given order of preference, we can say that ice cream represents the median. It is important to remember that the mean is not even defined for examples of this kind.

Among the unpleasant properties of the median we find, next to the fact that we have arranged the numbers according to size, that it does not lend itself to further manipulations. This means, for instance, that if we have the median of two or more separate sets of data, we *cannot* find the over-all median without going back to the raw data. The median of the numbers 15, 18, and 21 is equal to 18, while the median of the numbers 16, 40, and 43 is equal to 40. Knowing only the values of these two medians, we would never have been able to find that the over-all median is 19.5. In order to determine this value we would have to reorder the combined set of 6 numbers according to size, and then find the median of this new arrangement. The reader can easily verify that the result is 19.5.

A further property of the median which makes it considerably less desirable than the mean is that it is less stable, i.e., less reliable than the mean, if it is used for the purpose of estimation or prediction. Since problems of this type really belong to inductive statistics and will be discussed in detail later on, we shall content ourselves for the moment with a more or less intuitive idea of what is meant by the reliability of a statistical measure.

Let us consider, for example, the following illustration. Three biologists undertake to determine the average length of a given type of insect, and they decide to base their estimates on samples of 3 measurements each. The results which they obtained were

> Biologist A: .09,   .10,   and   .41 cm
> Biologist B: .15,   .25,   and   .35 cm
> Biologist C: .19,   .20,   and   .30 cm

Had all three of them used the *mean* to estimate the average length of this type of insect, their respective results would have been .20, .25, and .23 cm. If, on the other hand, they had used the *median*, their estimates would have been .10, .25, and .20 cm. We see from these results that whereas the three means were all relatively close to one another (they all fell on the interval from .20 to .25), the three medians were spread over the much wider interval from .10 to .25. It is in this sense that we say that the mean is more stable, i.e., it is subject to less chance variation.

4.6 The Median, Grouped Data

The calculation of the median from grouped data makes it again necessary to make some assumption about the distribution of the individual measurements within each class interval.   The significance of the median of a set of grouped data is, perhaps, most easily understood with the aid of a diagram like that in Fig. 4.c.   The median of

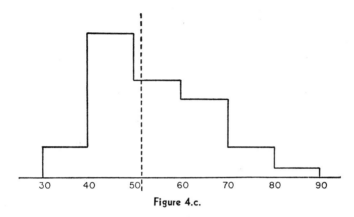

Figure 4.c.

a frequency distribution is *by definition* that point of the horizontal scale which if we draw a vertical line through it, the line will divide the total area of the rectangles of the histogram in half.   This means that the sum of the areas of the rectangles (or parts of rectangles) which are to the left of the dotted line of Fig. 4.c must equal the sum of the corresponding areas which are to its right.

In order to find this dividing line which, like the median of ungrouped data, divides our data into two equal parts, we must see first into which of the classes the median will fall.   If we have a total of n measurements, we now must count $n/2$ of them (and not $(n + 1)/2$ as we did before) until we reach the median.   This change is necessary to satisfy the conditions which we have imposed on the median of the grouped data, namely, that the area of the histogram which lies to the left of the median must equal the area which lies to its right.

If we now return to our illustration, and if we start counting at the left end of the distribution (histogram), we find that 18 of the salaries are less than \$49.995, whereas 28 of them are less than \$59.995.   Since we need altogether $\frac{40}{2} = 20$ of the measurements, this means that the median must lie somewhere in the interval from \$49.995 and \$59.995, and that we must take 2 more than the 18 numbers which fell to the left of \$49.995.   Assuming that the salaries are *evenly distributed* within each class interval, we will find the median by adding a certain portion of the class interval from \$49.995 to \$59.995 to its lower class boundary. Since we need 2 of the 10 cases which fell into this class, we will have to add $\frac{2}{10}$ of this class interval to its lower boundary, which was \$49.995. When we said that the salaries were evenly distributed within the class, we meant that if we were to subdivide the class into any number of equal subintervals, their respective frequencies would all be the same.

The median of a set of grouped data is therefore given by the lower class boundary of the class into which the median must fall *plus* a certain fraction of its class interval which depends on the number of cases which we still lacked when we reached its lower class boundary. The median of our grouped salaries is thus equal to

$$M = 49.995 + 10 \cdot \frac{2}{10} = \$51.995$$

or \$52.00 to the nearest cent. In general, if L is the lower class boundary of the class which contains the median, f_M its class frequency, c the class interval, and j the number of cases which we still lacked when reaching L, the median is given by the formula

$$M = L + c \cdot \frac{j}{f_M} \qquad (4.6.1)^*$$

This formula should always be used for the calculation of the median of a set of grouped data.

Had we begun to count the necessary 20 cases from the *other end* of the distribution, we could have used the same formula to find the median but we would have had to write U (the upper class boundary) instead of L, and we would have had to subtract (instead of add) the necessary fraction $c(j/f_M)$. We would thus have found that 12 of the salaries were above \$59.995, and that we would need another 8 cases in order to reach the median. We would then have had

$$M = 59.995 - 10 \cdot \frac{8}{10} = \$51.995$$

which is identical with our previous result. In general, if the median is computed in this fashion we can write corresponding to (4.6.1) the formula

$$M = U - c \cdot \frac{j}{f_M} \qquad (4.6.2)^*$$

The class into which the median must fall is most conveniently found from the cumulative distribution. If our data are not grouped into such a distribution, however, we will simply have to keep adding the frequencies of the consecutive classes (starting at either end) until we reach $n/2$ of the cases. This procedure is illustrated by means of the following distribution of 661 examination grades:

Examination grades	Frequency
10–14	12
15–19	59
20–24	143
25–29	217
30–34	168
35–39	54
40–44	7
45–49	1

Beginning at the top of this distribution (starting with the smallest grades) we will have to count $661/2 = 330.5$ of the grades until we reach the median. Since the first three classes contain a total of $12 + 59 + 143 = 214$ of the cases, we will need $330.5 - 214 = 116.5$ more of the 217 grades which are contained in the next class. The median of this distribution is therefore, according to formula (4.6.1),

$$M = 24.5 + 5 \cdot \frac{116.5}{217} = 27.28$$

It is important to note that unless the distribution has extremely few classes or unless it has such an odd shape that the median will fall into the first or last classification, open class intervals will not interfere with its computation.

4.7 The Mode, Ungrouped Data

A third measure of central tendencies is defined as the value which occurs with the highest frequency. This measure, which is called the *mode*, applies to numerical as well as to categorical groupings. For example, if more people live in 4-room apartments than in any other size of apartment, we say that 4 rooms is the *modal size* of an apartment; if more people die of heart disease than of any other disease, we can say that heart disease is the *modal* cause of death; and if the *mode* in an examination is 53, this means that more students received a 53 than any other grade. These three illustrations should suffice to give the reader a pretty fair idea of what we mean by a mode.

No calculations are necessary for determination of a mode, because we merely count the cases and then select the value (or category) which has emerged the most often. In a sense, the mode is the most descriptive measure of central tendencies because *it tells us which value is the most common.* Unfortunately, the mode does not always exist or, at least, it is not always uniquely defined. If we have very few measurements, it happens quite often that no two are alike, which means that none can rightfully be called a mode. It is easy to make up an example in which there is no mode. If the weights of a number of people are 185, 135, 136, 140, 177, 194, 148, and 166, these 8 numbers do not define a mode.

While some sets of data may have no mode at all, it can also happen that there are two or more values which satisfy our definition of a mode. This possibility is illustrated by the following numbers: 63, 65, 65, 65, 70, 72, 74, 79, 79, 79, 82, 82, and 93, among which both 65 and 79 occur three times. This is not uncommon if we are dealing with a small set of measurements. The values 63, 70, 72, 74, and 93 each occurred once, 82 occurred twice, and 65 and 79 each occurred three times. We have, consequently, two modes, and it is customary to say in a case like this that the set of data is *bimodal.*

It can, of course, happen that we will have an even greater number of modes, in which case we shall say that our data are *multimodal.* In general, the mode is considered to be a very useful measure in problems which involve discrete distributions or categorical groupings. As a matter of fact, qualitative descriptions do not permit the use of the mean, and it is generally preferable to describe the middle of such groupings in terms of the mode. If we want to investigate, for example, what colors are preferred by different groups of people, we can compare the modes of the different groups, i.e., compare the color which is, in each group, preferred by the greatest number of people. In a society in which majorities and pluralities play an important role, the mode is an indispensable concept in politics, in business, and in everyday life. Although relatively few people are familiar with the term *mode*, most people will have no difficulty in learning what it means and how it can be used.

In view of these facts it is unfortunate that the disadvantages of the mode seem to outweigh its desirable features. As we have said before, there exist a great number of cases in which the mode simply does not exist. Moreover, the mode is an extremely unstable measure of the middle of a distribution if it is to be used for purposes of prediction and estimation, and finally, it does not lend itself to further manipulations.

If we deal with continuous measurements, it will be necessary for us to group our data before we can attempt to determine a mode, since it is evidently unlikely that any one value will occur more than once.

4.8 The Mode, Grouped Data

If we fit a smooth curve to the histogram of a distribution, it seems only reasonable to define the point at which the curve is the *highest* as the mode of the distribution. In Fig. 4.d, for instance, which gives us a distribution of incomes, the maximum value of the curve occurs at approximately $2,500, and this value is said to be the mode.

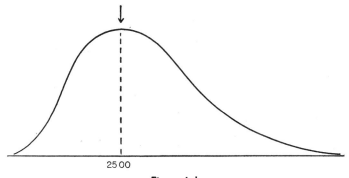

25 00

Figure 4.d.

If, instead of a smooth curve, we have a histogram, however, it is not quite so obvious which point of the scale should be chosen as the maximum point of the distribution.

The class which has the greatest frequency, and which is obviously not very difficult to find, is called the *modal class* of the distribution. The question still remains as to what point within this modal class should be chosen to represent the mode. In our illustration which dealt with the salaries of the 40 employees of the ZYX Co., the modal class is the class which goes from $39.995 to $49.995 (see Fig. 4.e). It would be very easy to define the mode of the distribution simply as the class mark of the modal class, but if we want the mode to correspond to the highest point of the ideal curve which might be fitted to our data, the class mark of the modal class would at best present us with a crude approximation. In our illustration, the frequency of the class which follows the modal class, i e., the class which goes from $49.995 to $59.995, is considerably larger than that which

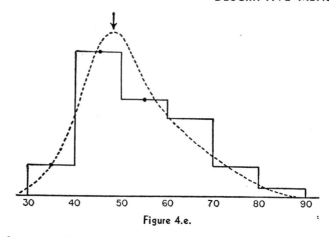

Figure 4.e.

precedes the modal class. As a matter of fact, these two frequencies which we shall denote as f_1 and f_{-1} are equal to 10 and 3, respectively. Consequently, it would seem proper (see Fig. 4.e) to shift the mode somewhat to the right of the class mark of the modal class. Whenever f_1 is greater than f_{-1}, the mode should be given somewhere to the right of the class mark of the modal class. Conversely, it must be placed to its left whenever f_{-1} is greater than f_1. It follows from this that the actual position of the mode will have to depend to some extent on the frequencies of the adjacent classes, and it therefore must be *defined* by means of some method of interpolation. A relatively simple way of defining the *mode of grouped data*, accounting to some extent for the frequencies of the classes which are adjacent to the modal class, is provided by the formula

$$\text{Mode} = L + c \cdot \frac{f_1}{f_1 + f_{-1}} \qquad (4.8.1)^*$$

where L and c are, as before, the lower class boundary and the class interval of the modal class, respectively. The mode of our example is thus

$$\text{Mode} = 39.995 + 10 \, \frac{10}{10 + 3} = \$47.687$$

or \$47.69 to the nearest cent.

It must be remembered that the above definition of the mode for grouped data was, fundamentally speaking, *arbitrary* and designed to accomplish the specific task of accounting for the differences in the frequencies of the two classes which are adjacent to the modal class.

It is quite possible that there exist better approximations of the mode which might be obtained, for example, by fitting a parabola through the three points which are marked on Fig. 4.e, and by subsequently finding the maximum point of this curve. For most practical purposes, however, formula (4.8.1) provides a sufficiently accurate measure of the mode, and the use of more exact methods would involve mathematical complications which would, in most cases, not be offset by a corresponding increase in accuracy.

A pronounced disadvantage of the mode which we have not yet discussed is that it is greatly affected by the choice of the groupings, a change of which can rearrange the entire picture to such an extent that the mode may vary by a considerable amount. Let us consider, for example, the following distribution of the ages of a certain group of individuals.

Ages	Frequency
10–19	6
20–29	15
30–39	12
40–49	10
50–59	6
60–69	3

The mode of this distribution is according to formula (4.8.1) equal to

$$\text{Mode} = 19.5 + 10 \cdot \frac{12}{12 + 6} = 26.17$$

If we now regroup these data into wider classes as we have done in the following table,

Ages	Frequency
10–29	21
30–49	22
50–69	9

we find that the mode has been changed to

$$\text{Mode} = 29.5 + 20 \cdot \frac{9}{9 + 21} = 35.50$$

and that it differs from the previously obtained value by almost 10 years. It is for this reason that we say that the choice of the groupings can have a considerable effect on the mode.

The fact that a distribution has *more than one mode* is often interpreted as indicative of the fact that we are dealing with heterogeneous data, i.e., that our data consist of the superposition of several distinct distributions.

The mean, median, and mode will generally more or less coincide *if* we are dealing with a symmetrical distribution. Otherwise, the median will usually fall somewhere between the mean and the mode. If a distribution is moderately skewed, the three measures of central tendencies which we have discussed are approximately related as in formula (4.8.2), which enables us to get a rough idea of any one of the three measures of central tendencies if we know the other two.

$$\text{Mode} = 3(\text{Median}) - 2(\text{Mean}) \qquad (4.8.2)$$

and if we had used it to find the modal salary, we would have obtained

$$\text{Mode} = 3(51.995) - 2(53.995) = \$47.995$$

which does not differ by very much from the value of the mode which we obtained previously by means of formula (4.8.1).

EXERCISES

1. Find the median of each of the given three samples of the lengths of young-of-the-year fresh-water drum, caught near Rattlesnake Island in Lake Erie (measurements are given in millimeters).

Sample 1	Sample 2	Sample 3
92	89	78
88	86	71
85	81	71
82	66	95
81	75	86
86	61	84
100	78	84
83	76	88
75	91	72
67	82	81
72	82	64
63	78	71
80	82	58
92	86	60
82	96	81
71	61	73
67	62	67
69	59	85
56	80	89
89	65	75
95	70	79
77	86	77
77	78	65
71		

2. Find the median of the weights of the rats which were given in Exercise 3 on page 52.

3. Find the median of the test grades which were given in Exercise 4 on page 52.

4. Determine the median of the ungrouped college indexes of Exercise 6, page 19.

5. Find the mode of each of the following sets of numbers (if it exists).

(a) 4, 7, 8, 6, 7, 9, 7, 7, 5, 5, 6, 8, 6.
(b) 23, 31, 27, 35, 48, 22, 46, 30, 54, 39, 57.
(c) 11, 15, 13, 14, 13, 12, 10, 11, 12, 13, 11, 13.
(d) 1, 5, 5, 8, 8, 6, 4, 5, 2, 8, 5, 8, 9.

6. Find the mode of the grades which the 18 students obtained in Exercise 4 on page 52.

7. The following are observations of the time required for sound to travel between two points (measurements given in seconds).

1.50	1.65	1.45	1.50	1.30
1.40	1.60	1.65	1.75	1.50
1.50	1.60	1.50	1.45	1.55
1.55	1.50	1.50	1.45	1.60

Find the median and the mode.

8. Calculate the median and the mode of the distribution of the aptitude scores which is given in Exercise 1 on page 58.

9. Calculate the median and the mode of whichever data were grouped among Exercises 6, 8, 10, and 12 on page 20.

10. Calculate the median of the distances given in Exercise 1 on page 27.

11. Find the median and the mode of the distribution of the pension payments of Exercise 2, page 27.

4.9 The Geometric and Harmonic Means

The final two measurements of central tendencies which we shall mention very briefly in this section are the *geometric* and the *harmonic means*. Given a set of numbers x_1, x_2, x_3, . . . , x_n, their geometric mean is defined as the nth root of their product, i.e.,

$$\text{Geometric mean} = \sqrt[n]{x_1 \cdot x_2 \cdot x_3 \cdot x_4 \cdot \ldots \cdot x_n} \qquad (4.9.1)^*$$

Since the use of this formula will evidently involve a considerable amount of work, it is reasonable to ask why and when this complicated expression should be used. In actual practice, the geometric mean is used primarily in problems which measure *rates of change*, particularly index numbers, which will be discussed in Chapter 18. To illustrate the calculation of a geometric mean let us consider the following example. The population of a small mining town was a mere 3000 in 1947. In 1948 uranium deposits were discovered in its vicinity, and the population rose in that year to 24,000. In the following year, in 1949, the population doubled in size, and 48,000 people were living in this town. On the basis of this information we are now asked to determine the average change in the size of the population from 1947 to 1949. In 1948 the population had become 8 times of what it was in 1947, while in 1949 the population had merely doubled in size. Calculating the mean of these two numbers we get $(8 + 2)/2 = 5$ which, as we shall see, can easily lead to serious misunderstandings. If a stranger would come to this town and if he were told that for the past two years the size of the population has on the average multiplied by 5, he might very well reason that since the original population was 3000, the population in 1948 must have been about $5 \cdot 3000 = 15,000$, and that the population in 1949 must, consequently, be $5 \cdot 15,000 = 75,000$. Checking back with our original information, we find that this result differs considerably from the actual size of the population in 1949.

If we calculate the geometric mean, on the other hand, we get $\sqrt{8 \cdot 2} = \sqrt{16} = 4$, and repeating the reasoning of the stranger, but substituting the geometric mean in place of the mean, we can now say that if the original population was 3000, then the population for 1949 must be 4 times 4 times 3000. This equals 48,000, which is the correct number of people who lived in the town in 1949.

The figures which we have used in this illustration are, of course, somewhat exaggerated to suit our particular purpose, but they nevertheless point out the type of problem, namely, the averaging of rates in which the geometric mean is a more suitable, a less misleading average than the ordinary mean.

The *harmonic mean* of a set of numbers is defined by the formula

$$\text{Harmonic mean} = \frac{n}{\sum_{i=1}^{n} 1/x_i} \qquad (4.9.2)*$$

and it is found by dividing n, the total number of measurements, by the sum of their reciprocals. Although this formula may not be quite as difficult to compute as the geometric mean, its use is again limited to a specific type of problem.

Let us consider, for example, the problem of finding the *average speed* of a car which has traveled the first 10 miles of a trip at 30 miles per hour, and the second 10 miles at 60 miles per hour. Without thinking, most people are bound to say that the average speed was the mean of 30 and 60 which is 45 miles per hour. If we recall that an average speed is usually defined as the total distance divided by the total time, it follows immediately that this answer was incorrect. At 30 miles per hour, it took the car 20 minutes to travel the first 10 miles; at 60 miles per hour it took the car only 10 minutes to travel the second 10 miles. Consequently, the car traveled a total of 20 miles in 20 + 10 = 30 minutes, and its average speed was 40 miles per hour. This answer could have been obtained directly with the use of the harmonic mean. Substituting the two velocities into formula (4.9.2), we get

$$\text{Average speed} = \frac{2}{1/30 + 1/60} = 40$$

To complicate matters we might add that the arithmetic mean would have given us the correct average speed *if the car had traveled at the two speeds for equal intervals of time instead of for equal distances.*

The harmonic mean is used mostly for the averaging of prices in the construction of index numbers. If we buy, for example, $10 worth of eggs at 50 cents a dozen in one store, and another $10 worth at 40 cents a dozen in a second store, the average price per egg is correctly determined by the harmonic mean of the two prices. It is equal to $2/(\frac{1}{40} + \frac{1}{50}) = 44\frac{4}{9}$ cents per dozen.

Since both of these means are very limited in their application, we shall not devote much time to their study. We have given the above illustrations primarily to caution the reader against the careless and indiscriminate use of the most common measures of central tendencies.

4.10 The Weighted Mean

The *weighted mean*, which is used only in certain specific kinds of problems, involves a slight modification of the ordinary mean. *It must be used whenever we are trying to average quantities which are of different importance, i.e., which carry different weights.* What we mean by a *difference in importance* is illustrated by the following example. The students of a given college buy their English books for $2.75, their mathematics books for $3.50, and their physics texts for $4.25. The ordinary mean of these three prices is $(2.75 + 3.50 + 4.25)/3 = \$3.50$, and it would be a satisfactory measure of the average price per book if the students were to buy an *equal number* of books of each kind. However, if they were to buy 600 English books, 400 mathematics books, and 100 physics books, this "average" would no longer be correct. The average price per book would then be

$$\frac{600(2.75) + 400(3.50) + 100(4.25)}{600 + 400 + 100} = \$3.16$$

to the nearest cent. This result is the *weighted mean* of the prices of the books. It was necessary to multiply the price of each book by a certain weight, in this case the number of books sold, in order to account for the difference in their importance.

In general, if we want to average a set of numbers $x_1, x_2, \ldots, x_n$ and give them the respective weights of $w_1, w_2, \ldots, w_n$, their weighted mean is given by the expression

$$\bar{x}_w = \frac{\sum_{i=1}^{n} x_i w_i}{\sum_{i=1}^{n} w_i} \qquad (4.10.3)^*$$

Although the choice of the weights did not present any difficulties in our previous illustration, their selection is not always so obvious, and must usually be based on additional considerations. If we want to construct a *cost-of-living index*, for example, we will have to worry about the roles played by the various commodities in the average budget. The weights which are most frequently used in such a problem are the *quantities* of the various items which are either consumed, sold, or produced.

Weighted means must also be used in the averaging of percentages or rates. If we learn, for example, from an actuarial table that 7.4 per cent of all 75-year-olds can be expected to die within the period of 1 year and, similarly, $\frac{1}{4}$ of 1 per cent of all of those who are 25, it would be a serious mistake to conclude that we can expect the mean, i.e., $(7.5 + .25)/2 = 3\frac{7}{8}$ per cent, to die in the two groups combined. There are many more people who are 25 than there are people who are 75, and consequently we would have to weight the two percentages by the relative sizes of the two groups. It is for the same reason that we cannot take the mean of the indexes of a number of college students without weighting them by the total number of credit hours on which they were based. Also, if we look back at formulas (4.3.2) and (4.3.3), we find that we have weighted the means of the various groups by their respective size.

EXERCISES

1. Find the geometric mean of the numbers 10 and 1000, and the harmonic mean of the numbers 60 and 90.

2. Find the geometric mean of the numbers 2, 2, and 16, and the harmonic mean of the numbers 20, 40, and 40.

3. A student answered 16 out of 100 questions correctly on the first try; 24 out of 100 on the second try a week later; and 81 out of 100 on the third try a week after that. In the second try he did, therefore, $\frac{24}{16} = 1.50$ times as well as in the first try. Use formula (4.9.1) to find the average rate of improvement between the successive tries.

4. If somebody buys $24 worth of butter at 60 cents a pound and $24 worth of a different brand at 80 cents a pound, calculate the harmonic mean of 60 and 80 in order to find the average price per pound.

5. The following table shows the *batting averages* and the *number of times at bat* of 5 baseball players:

Batting average	Number of times at bat
.320	200
.400	80
.310	300
.340	250

Use formula (4.10.3) to find their combined batting average.

6. If Mr. Brown buys 12 gallons of gasoline at 27 cents per gallon, 14 gallons at 24 cents per gallon, and 15 gallons at 25 cents per gallon, what is the average price per gallon?

4.11 Quartiles, Deciles, and Percentiles

Besides the median, which by definition divides an ordered series of measurements into two equal parts, there exist certain similar measures which divide the numbers into 4, 10, and even 100 equal parts. In spite of the fact that such measures can scarcely be called measures of central tendencies, we shall discuss them in this chapter because of their similarity to the median. Just like the median they are measures of position, i.e., they provide us with points above or below which we can find certain fractions of the total set of data. Since there would obviously be no sense in dividing very small sets of data into 10 or even into 100 equal parts, we shall discuss these measures only for grouped data.

The three *quartiles* are defined as the three dividing lines which separate our ordered set of data into four equal parts. Twenty-five per cent of the data must fall below the *first quartile*, which is written as Q_1; 50 per cent of the numbers must fall below the *second quartile* Q_2, which, incidentally, is equal to the median; and 75 per cent of the data must fall below the *third quartile*, which is accordingly written as Q_3.

These quartiles are useful descriptions inasmuch as they tell us, for example, where to find the middle 50 per cent of a set of data, where to find the highest 25 per cent, etc. (See Fig. 4.f.)

The steps which we must take for the calculation of the quartiles are practically identical with those which were needed for the determination of a median. The only difference is that we will now have to count $n/4$ cases to find Q_1, and $3n/4$ cases to find Q_3, starting at the bottom of the distribution.

To illustrate calculation of the quartiles, let us again consider the salary distribution which was used also to illustrate the determination of the median. Since $40/4 = 10$ and $3(40/4) = 30$, we must count this many of the salaries in order to reach Q_1 and Q_3. As in the case of the median, we first must find the two classes into which these two

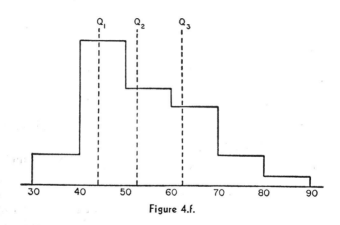

Figure 4.f.

quartiles will fall, and then we must add to the lower class boundaries of these classes whatever fractions of the respective class intervals are still needed. Since only 3 of the salaries fall below \$39.995, we will need 7 of the 15 salaries which lie in the next class in order to reach Q_1. Devising a formula which is practically equivalent to (4.6.1), we find that

$$Q_1 = 39.995 + 10 \cdot \frac{7}{15} = \$44.66$$

Similarly, since 28 of the salaries are below \$59.995, we need 2 of the 8 salaries of the class which goes from \$59.995 to \$69.995 until we have counted the necessary 30 measurements which lead us to Q_3.

Analogous to the method which we used to find the median, we obtain therefore

$$Q_3 = 59.995 + 10 \cdot \frac{2}{8} = \$62.50$$

If we use formula (4.6.1) for the determination of Q_1 and Q_3, it must be understood that the L must stand for the lower class boundary of the class which contains the respective quartile, and that f_M (we might now call it f_Q) stands for its corresponding frequency.

Deciles are numbers which, by definition, divide a given set of numbers into 10 equal parts, and they are calculated in precisely the same manner as the median and the quartiles. We shall write the *first decile*, below which there must be the lowest 10 per cent of our data, as D_1; the *second decile*, below which there must be the lowest 20 per cent, as D_2; and in general, the *ith decile*, which marks off the lowest *10 times i per cent* of our data, as D_i.

In order to find any one of the D_i (i can be either 1, 2, 3, . . . , or 9) we must count $i \cdot n/10$ of the total number of cases, and then use again a formula analogous to (4.6.1). It is actually of little value to compute a decile if we are dealing with as few as 40 measurements, but to illustrate the general method we shall again refer to the distribution of the 40 salaries. In order to find D_1, for example, we must count $1(40/10) = 4$ of the salaries, starting from the bottom, and we will find that

$$D_1 = 39.995 + 10 \cdot \frac{1}{15} = \$40.66$$

Three of the salaries were below \$39.995, and we therefore needed one more of the 15 which were in the next highest class. Similarly, D_6 is determined by counting $6(40/10) = 24$ of the cases starting from the bottom, or by counting 16 from the top of the distribution. Using both methods we obtain

$$D_6 = 49.995 + 10 \cdot \frac{6}{10} = \$55.995$$

or

$$D_6 = 59.995 - 10 \cdot \frac{4}{10} = \$55.995$$

which must, of course, be the same.

Quartiles, deciles, and also the percentiles which we shall discuss next, are used mainly in educational and psychological statistics. If we know Q_3, for instance, we can easily check whether any one of the scores falls into the highest 25 per cent; if a value falls above D_9, we know that it is among the highest 10 per cent; if a grade falls below D_3, we know that it is one of the lowest 30 per cent, etc.

Percentiles are, by definition, the points (numbers) which divide our data into 100 equal parts according to size. They are again calculated by means of a formula which is analogous to (4.6.1). If we want to find, for example, the 37th percentile P_{37}, we must look for a number which is such that it separates our data into the lowest 37 and the highest 63 per cent. We will therefore have to count $37(n/100)$ of the n measurements which, in our example, gives us $37(40/100) = 14.8$. Since 3 of the salaries lie below $39.995 we have

$$P_{37} = 39.995 + 10 \cdot \frac{11.8}{15} = \$47.86$$

This tells us that the lowest 37 per cent of the data fall below $47.86. Since our distribution consisted of as few as 40 salaries, it is somewhat questionable whether this percentile is of any value at all. Anyhow, it has served the purpose of demonstrating the general method for calculation of percentiles. If we want to find one of the higher percentiles, e.g., the 95th percentile P_{95}, above which we will find the highest 5 per cent of our data, it will be advisable to count from the top instead of from the bottom of the distribution.

EXERCISES

1. Find Q_1 and Q_3 for the distribution of aptitude scores which was given in Exercise 1 on page 58.
2. Calculate the quartiles of the distribution of pension payments which is given in Exercise 2 on page 27.
3. Calculate the quartiles of whichever data were grouped among those given in Exercises 6, 8, 10, and 12 on page 20.
4. Find D_1, D_8, and D_9 of the same data which were used in the previous exercise.
5. Find all deciles of the distribution of the aptitude scores of Exercise 1, page 58.
6. Find D_3 and D_7 of the salary distribution which was used as an illustration in the text.
7. Calculate P_{70}, P_{75}, and P_{95} of the aptitude scores of Exercise 1, page 58.
8. Calculate P_{35} and P_{65} of the data which were used in the previous exercise.

4.12 The Arithmetic of Approximate Measurements

A question which often baffles the beginning student is the problem of how accurate, i.e., to how many decimals, it is generally advisable to state our results. It is difficult to give any general rules, since they must depend, first of all, on whether we are working with numbers which are approximate measurements or with numbers which are exact. If a test grade is equal to 65, this means that it is precisely 65 and no other number; however, if we say that the length of a certain object is 65 inches to the nearest inch, this means that the length of this object can be anywhere between 64.5 and 65.5 inches.

Whenever we deal with exact numbers there is, logically speaking, no limit to the number of decimals which may be carried, although a relatively small number is usually dictated by practical reasons. If we are interested, for example, in the mean of the scores 10, 15, 8, 12, 9, 11, and 14, we could state our result as 11.285714. . . . , but for most practical purposes we would be just as well off giving it simply as 11.3.

If we are working with approximate numbers it is much more difficult to decide how much accuracy we should carry throughout our work. In the *addition or subtraction* of approximate numbers it helps to remember that a chain is only as strong as its weakest link. If we were asked to add, for example, the following column of numbers:

$$25.8743$$
$$3.45$$
$$1005.2$$
$$16.8$$

which are all approximate measurements, we should give our final result to at most one decimal as 1051.3, or perhaps better as 1051, since we cannot be sure even of the .3. It would have been utterly ridiculous to state the answer as 1051.3234, since 1005.2 alone stands for any number between 1005.15 and 1005.25. Furthermore, we should always remember that we cannot expect our final result to be more accurate than the raw data with which we began.

In the *multiplication and division* of approximate numbers it is important to watch the so-called significant digits. The number of significant figures is the number of digits (supposedly accurate) after we have discarded all zeros which may be to the left of the first non-zero digit (if the number is less than 1), and possibly also some of the zeros which are to the right. The number 93.475 has 5 significant digits, 0.0034 has 2, while 90 can have either 1 or 2, depending on what we mean by the zero which is to the right of the nine. For example, if 90 cm stands for a length somewhere between 89.5 and 90.5, this number has 2 significant digits. If, on the other hand, it stands for any measurement between 85 and 95 cm, only one of its digits is said to be significant. A number like 3,560,000 can thus stand for a variety of different things, depending on how many of the zeros are significant.

We can now state a rule which should always be followed in the multiplication and division of approximate numbers. It is simply that our final result should never have more significant figures than any one of the numbers with which we began. For example, the product of 7.6 and 3.8445 should be given as 29 and not as 29.21820.

If the reader will follow these general rules and use some common sense, he will not only avoid ridiculous answers, but he will also save himself a good deal of time which would otherwise be wasted on meaningless and unnecessary computations.

4.13 Grouping Errors

As we have seen in several of our illustrations, a change in the choice of the groupings can produce a considerable change in the values of the mean, median, or mode. When we calculated the mean from grouped data we assumed that all measurements which belonged to a given class were located at its class mark. In order to calculate the median of grouped data we assumed, on the other hand, that the measurements were evenly distributed within each class interval. Either of these two assumptions could have been used for the calculation of the mean because, as the mathematically inclined reader can easily verify, the results would have been exactly the same. The error which may be caused by the process of grouping is usually fairly small, because there is generally a sufficient compensation between the values which fall above and below the class marks. As we have shown on page 69, however, this error can be considerable in the case of the mode.

It is always good to remember that the grouping of any kind of data is likely to introduce an element of arbitrariness which can affect our results. The same can be said for the assumptions which we might make about the distribution of the values which lie within the class intervals of a given distribution.

All the measures of central tendencies which we have studied have good as well as bad features. It is difficult to say which particular measure should be used at any particular time, since this choice will depend largely on the specific property of our data which we want to describe. It must always be remembered that the choice of an average, i.e., a measure of central tendencies, is, fundamentally speaking, nothing but a more or less arbitrary definition. It would be completely nonsensical to ask for a true average since such a quantity simply does not exist. Different averages may be more desirable than others in particular problems, but even then any such preference is dictated only by practical reasons.

REFERENCES

M. M. Blair, *Elementary Statistics*, Holt, New York, 1944, Chap. 9.

E. B. Mode, *The Elements of Statistics*, Prentice-Hall, New York, 1941, Chaps. 5, 6.

C. H. Richardson, *An Introduction to Statistical Analysis*, Harcourt, Brace, New York, 1944, Chap. 3.

A. E. Waugh, *Elements of Statistical Method*, McGraw-Hill, New York, 1943, Chaps. 4, 5.

5. DESCRIPTIVE MEASURES II. MEASURES OF VARI-ATION AND SYMMETRY

5.1 Introduction

The mean, median, and mode each supplies a single number which we, so to speak, substitute for the entire set of measurements. They supply a specific kind of information about our data which cannot possibly give us a complete picture. This information may be sufficient in a limited number of problems, but we will find that, in general, we must describe other features of our distributions as well. Among these we shall discuss first the *variation, spread,* or *dispersion* of a set of numbers. We need not look far to find examples in which it is evident that our knowledge of the mean or some other measure of central tendencies must be supplemented by a statistical measure which tells us something about the interval over which our data are distributed, or what extent they are spread out or bunched.

Let us look, for example, at a teacher who wants to evaluate his students' abilities on the basis of the grades which they received in a number of tests. One of his students scored 30, 60, and 90, while a second student received the corresponding grades of 58, 60, and 62. In order to get an over-all picture of their abilities, the teacher first computes the two means, and discovers that both had an average (mean) score of 60. Stopping at this point, the teacher might well decide that they are equally good, and that they should therefore be treated in an equal fashion. A slightly more careful analysis of these scores shows, however, that while the second student was fairly consistent, the first one was extremely erratic in his performance. The grades which the second student obtained in these tests were all very close to 60, which seems to indicate a balanced, though mediocre, performance. The scores of the first student, on the other hand, varied over such a considerable range that it would seem advisable to give him some special attention.

Another illustration which demonstrates clearly the importance of knowing the variation of a set of numerical data deals with measurements of the compressive strength of structural steel. Let us suppose, for example, that construction of a certain bridge requires steel with a minimum strength of 40,000 pounds per square inch. To play safe, we inform several plants that we will need steel with an average strength of 60,000 psi, and each plant is requested to submit a sample of its product on the basis of which we will be able to decide where to buy the steel. Company A sent in a sample which was tested and which showed the following measurements of compressive strength:

$$56{,}000, \quad 57{,}500, \quad 61{,}000, \quad 62{,}350, \quad 63{,}150,$$

The corresponding measurements for the steel produced by Company B were

$$40{,}000, \quad 44{,}250, \quad 68{,}400, \quad 69{,}000, \quad 78{,}350,$$

Although information which consists of as few as 5 observations is seldom conclusive, comparison of the above two sets of numbers will reveal some interesting results. Both samples meet the required average strength, since both had a mean of 60,000 psi, and we would therefore not be able to differentiate between these two products on the basis of the mean alone. If we then look at the *variations* of these two sets of numbers, we will note that there is a considerable difference. Whereas the first product was consistently close to 60,000, the second varied from 40,000 to over 78,000, which seems to indicate that if we buy steel from Company B, it could happen that some would be below minimum strength.

So far we have used the idea of variation as a more or less intuitive concept, expressing the spread of a set of numerical data. Our next step will therefore consist of defining statistical measures which will describe the property which we have just discussed, and we will observe that, as in the case of the measures of central tendencies, we can define different statistical measures, all of which might reasonably be called measures of variation.

5.2 The Range

The most widely understood and the most easily calculated measure of variation is undoubtedly the *range*. The range of a set of numbers is defined simply as the difference between the largest and the smallest numbers which belong to the set. The smallest salary received by an employee of the ZYX Co. was $34.60, the largest salary was $84.50, and the range is therefore 84.50 − 34.60 = $49.90. Similarly, the range of the compressive strength of the steel of Company A was 63,150 − 56,000 = 7,150 psi, while the range of the steel of Company B was 78,350 − 40,000 = 38,350 psi.

Although the range is a measure of variation which is easy to understand and which does not require any lengthy calculations, it is not truly a measure of variation or dispersion, and its usefulness is outweighed by far by its undesirable properties. It is really used mainly if we are interested to obtain a quick, though possibly not very accurate, picture of the variation.

The range is a poor measure of the dispersion of a set of data, because it is based exclusively on the two extreme values, telling us nothing about any remaining measurements. If we take, for example, the numbers

$$3, \quad 10, \quad 10, \quad 10, \quad 10, \quad 10, \quad 10, \quad 10, \quad 10, \quad 10$$

the numbers

$$3, \quad 3, \quad 3, \quad 3, \quad 3, \quad 10, \quad 10, \quad 10, \quad 10, \quad 10$$

and the numbers

$$3, \quad 4, \quad 5, \quad 6, \quad 6, \quad 7, \quad 7, \quad 8, \quad 9, \quad 10$$

we can easily see that although all three sets have the identical range' their dispersions are by no means the same. In the first set all numbers but one were 10's; in the second set half of the numbers were 3's, while the other half were 10's; and in the last set the numbers are spread all over the interval from 3 to 10.

A further disadvantage of the range is its instability in problems of sampling. This is again due to the fact that the range is based on the two extreme values, which in most cases are subject to much chance variation, and which are most easily affected by erratic mistakes. Last but not least, the range cannot be found for grouped data.

These numerous shortcomings of the range make it evident that we must look for alternative measures of variation which will account for more than the mere difference between the extremes.

5.3 The Mean Deviation

Since the dispersion of a set of data is evidently small if they are bunched closely around the mean, and since it is large if the values are spread over a considerable distance from the mean, this suggests that we might look for a measure of variation which is based on *the distances by which the various numbers depart from their mean.* If we write the distance (deviation) of a measurement x_i from the mean $\bar{x}$ as their difference $x_i - \bar{x}$, a possible measure of the variation of the x's would be given by *the mean of their deviations from the mean.* Symbolically we could write this statistic as

$$\frac{\sum_{i=1}^{n} (x_i - \bar{x})}{n} \qquad (5.3.1)$$

which is nothing but the average of the deviations. Applying now Theorems A and B of Chapter 1, we find that

$$\frac{\sum_{i=1}^{n} (x_i - \bar{x})}{n} = \frac{\sum_{i=1}^{n} x_i - \sum_{i=1}^{n} \bar{x}}{n} = \frac{\sum_{i=1}^{n} x_i}{n} - \bar{x}$$

and since by definition

$$\bar{x} = \frac{\sum_{i=1}^{n} x_i}{n}$$

we discover that *the formula which was supposed to supply us with a measure of variation must always be equal to 0.* Obviously, it does not accomplish what we set out to do.

The original idea of expressing the variation of a set of data in terms of the deviations from the mean, i.e., in terms of the quantities $x_i - \bar{x}$, was really not a poor one. As it happened, we made the unfortunate choice of using their average, which turned out to be equal to 0. One way of eliminating this difficulty is to ignore the minus signs of the negative differences and to define a measure of variation in terms of their *absolute values.* The absolute value of a positive number is simply the number itself, but the absolute value of a negative number equals the number *without its minus sign.* It is customary to write the absolute value of a number x as $|x|$, and we have, for example,

$$|15| = 15 \quad \text{and} \quad |-15| = 15$$

We can now define the following measure of variation, which is called *the mean or the average deviation*.

$$\text{Mean deviation} = \frac{\sum_{i=1}^{n} |x_i - \bar{x}|}{n} \qquad (5.3.2)^*$$

In order to calculate the mean deviation we must first locate the mean of our data, then determine the deviations $x_i - \bar{x}$ and their absolute values $|x_i - \bar{x}|$, and finally substitute the sum of these absolute values into formula (5.3.2). To illustrate, let us calculate the mean deviation of the following 10 numbers which are insurance premiums given in dollars.

26.   35.   48   57,   61,   68,   73,   85,   90,   92

The various steps which are needed for the calculation of a mean deviation are shown in the table below. Actually, it is not necessary to write down the deviations $x_i - \bar{x}$ as well as their absolute values, but it is a good check to see whether the sum of the deviations is equal to zero.

x_i	$x_i - \bar{x}$	$|x_i - \bar{x}|$
26	−37.5	37.5
35	−28.5	28.5
48	−15.5	15.5
57	−6.5	6.5
61	−2.5	2.5
68	4.5	4.5
73	9.5	9.5
85	21.5	21.5
90	26.5	26.5
92	28.5	28.5
635	0	181.0

$$\bar{x} = \frac{635}{10} = 63.5; \qquad \text{mean deviation} = \frac{181}{10} = 18.1$$

This result tells us that on the average the insurance premiums deviated from the mean by $18.10.

Calculation of the mean deviation is usually quite cumbersome, particularly if the measurements are large and if the mean must be given to several decimals. Although there exist several methods of obtaining an approximation of the mean deviation, there are no real short cuts which will give us an exact answer.

Some people prefer to define the mean deviation in terms of the *deviations from the median* instead of the deviations from the mean. In that case we would have

$$\text{Mean deviation} = \frac{\sum_{i=1}^{n} |x_i - M|}{n}$$

and the result would be slightly different unless, of course, the median just happens to coincide with the mean.

The formula which defined the mean deviation can also be generalized to apply to grouped data. If we again assume that all measurements which lie within a given class are located at the respective class mark, we can write

$$\text{Mean deviation} = \frac{\sum_{i=1}^{k} |x_i - \bar{x}| \cdot f_i}{n} \qquad (5.3.3)^*$$

where x_i stands for the class mark of the ith class, f_i for its class frequency, and k for the number of classifications.

In spite of its relative simplicity, the mean deviation is neither an important nor a very useful measure of variation. Since it involves absolute values, it does not lend itself to further mathematical treatment, and it is consequently difficult to study its applicability to problems of sampling. The main reason why we have studied the mean deviation at all is that it is the logical stepping stone to the most important measure of variation, the standard deviation.

EXERCISES

1. Find the range of the college indexes of Exercise 6, p. 19.
2. What is the range of the percentages which were given in Exercise 12 on page 21?
3. Find the ranges of each of the three samples of Exercise 1, p. 70.
4. Find the mean deviation of the weights of the rats which were given in Exercise 3, p. 52.
5. What is the mean deviation of the number of defective pieces which were discussed in Exercise 5 on page 52?
6. Calculate the mean deviation of the pension payments of Exercise ? p. 27.
7. Calculate the mean deviation of whichever data were grouped among Exercises 6, 8, 10, and 12, p. 20.

5.4 The Standard Deviation, Ungrouped Data

The most widely used measure of variation is the so-called *standard deviation*, which will be denoted by the letter s. This measure of variation has been accepted almost universally as the most suitable descriptive measure of the variability of a set of numerical data. Its advantages are so numerous that they outbalance by far the unfortunate fact that its calculation is quite involved.

Before we give the formula which defines the standard deviation, let us recall that when we defined the mean deviation we were forced to use absolute values *in order to eliminate the minus signs which appeared in those deviations in which x_i was less than $\bar{x}$*. This goal can also be accomplished if we *square* each deviation from the mean, since the squares of real numbers are always positive. *Using this alternative technique of eliminating the minus signs of the negative deviations, we shall define the standard deviation as the square root of the mean of the squared deviations.* This means that in order to calculate s we first must find the mean, then the deviations and their squares, and finally the square root of the mean of the squared deviations. We defined the standard deviation as the *square root* of this average because we are, in this fashion, compensating for the fact that we originally squared each deviation. Symbolically, we can therefore write the standard deviation as

$$s = \sqrt{\dfrac{\displaystyle\sum_{i=1}^{n}(x_i - \bar{x})^2}{n}} \qquad (5.4.1)$$

To illustrate the use of this formula, let us again consider the 10 insurance premiums for which we computed the mean deviation in the previous section. Since we already know that the mean is equal to \$63.5, we can arrange the necessary work in the following manner:

x_i	$x_i - \bar{x}$	$(x_i - \bar{x})^2$
26	−37.5	1406.25
35	−28.5	812.25
48	−15.5	240.25
57	−6.5	42.25
61	−2.5	6.25
68	4.5	20.25
73	9.5	90.25
85	21.5	462.25
90	26.5	702.25
92	28.5	812.25
		4594.50

and
$$s = \sqrt{\dfrac{4594.5}{10}} = \sqrt{459.45} = \$21.4$$

It is evident from this illustration that calculation of the standard deviation involves a considerable amount of arithmetical detail, especially if $\bar{x}$ is not an integer, in which case it is quite a task to square all deviations. Consequently, it would seem desirable to check whether simplifications exist. Starting with the formula for s^2 which, incidentally, is also known as the *variance*, we have

$$s^2 = \frac{\sum_{i=1}^{n} (x_i - \bar{x})^2}{n} = \frac{\sum_{i=1}^{n} (x_i^2 - 2x_i\bar{x} + \bar{x}^2)}{n}$$

Using Theorems A and B of Chapter 1, we can write this also as

$$s^2 = \frac{\sum_{i=1}^{n} x_i^2}{n} - 2\bar{x}\frac{\sum_{i=1}^{n} x_i}{n} + \frac{\sum_{i=1}^{n} \bar{x}^2}{n}$$

and with the use of Theorem C, Chapter 1, and formula (4.3.1) we finally have

$$s^2 = \frac{\sum_{i=1}^{n} x_i^2}{n} - \bar{x}^2 = \frac{\sum_{i=1}^{n} x_i^2}{n} - \left(\frac{\sum_{i=1}^{n} x_i}{n}\right)^2$$

The simplified formula for the standard deviation of ungrouped data is therefore

$$s = \sqrt{\frac{\sum_{i=1}^{n} x_i^2}{n} - \left(\frac{\sum_{i=1}^{n} x_i}{n}\right)^2} \qquad (5.4.2)^*$$

It is important to note that by use of this formula we can find the standard deviation *without having to determine the actual deviations from the mean*. Furthermore, this formula is *not* an approximation, and it will give us the same result as if we had used formula (5.4.1).

Applying this short method to the insurance premiums which we used before, we have

x_i	x_i^2
26	676
35	1225
48	2304
57	3249
61	3721
68	4624
73	5329
85	7225
90	8100
92	8464
635	44917

$$s = \sqrt{\frac{44917}{10} - \left(\frac{635}{10}\right)^2} = \sqrt{4491.7 - 4032.25} = \$21.4$$

The advantage of the short method is that we need only find the sum of the x's and the sum of their squares. These sums can easily be found by use of tables or, better, by use of a computing machine. As a matter of fact, it is possible to find both summations *at the same time* on almost any standard machine.

Formula (5.4.2) should always be used for calculation of the standard deviation from ungrouped data. Formula (5.4.1), which was not starred for this reason and which will, of course, give us the identical results, will from now on serve only to define the meaning of the standard deviation. While formula (5.4.1) gives us a clearer picture of what is meant by a standard deviation, formula (5.4.2) enables us to find it with much greater ease.

A further simplification, which can usually save us a good deal of time in the calculation of a standard deviation consists of *adding or subtracting any arbitrary number* from each measurement. It is not difficult to give a rigorous proof that addition or subtraction of a constant will not affect the value which we will get for the standard deviation, but it should be evident even without formal proof that the dispersion (spread) of a set of data will not change if a constant is added to every number. If we had done this, for example, with our insurance premiums, we could have subtracted \$60 from every premium and we would then have had the numbers

$$-34, \quad -25, \quad -12, \quad -3, \quad 1, \quad 8, \quad 13, \quad 25, \quad 30, \quad 32$$

Calculating the sum and the sum of the squares of these premiums we obtain

$$\sum_{i=1}^{n} x_i = 35 \quad \text{and} \quad \sum_{i=1}^{n} x_i^2 = 4717$$

Substituting these results into formula (5.4.2) we obtain $s = 21.4$, which is the same value which we had before. The advantage of this trick rests in the fact that we can work with much smaller and more convenient numbers.

Before we proceed to the discussion of the standard deviation of grouped data, let us indicate briefly some of the many important uses of the standard deviation. When we compared the grades of the two students who had 58, 60, 62, and 30, 60, 90, respectively, we said that the grades of the first were much more consistent than those of the second. We can now find the two standard deviations, which are 1.63 and 24.49, and we are in a much better position to make a precise comparison of the two variations.

An important use of the standard deviation is based on the fact that if we have normally distributed data, i.e., data which fit closely to a normal curve, 68 per cent of the measurements will fall within *one* standard deviation on either side of the mean, and about 95 per cent within *two* standard deviations on either side of the mean. This knowledge is helpful in the following type of problem. If the students of a certain school average 62 in a given test and if Jones, who is one of them, scores 71, this information alone does *not* tell us very much about Jones's position relative to the other students except that he is somewhat above average. Had we known, however, that the standard deviation of the grades of all students was equal to 8, we would then be able to say that Jones is among the highest 16 per cent, *provided, of course, that the grades do follow the pattern of a normal curve.* This follows because the deviation of Jones's score from the mean is $71 - 62 = 9$, which is slightly more than one standard deviation.

Since it is often helpful to know how many standard deviations a certain measurement is above or below the mean, we shall now introduce the so-called *standard units, standard scores,* which are generally denoted by the letter z. *If a measurement x belongs to a set of data which has the mean $\bar{x}$ and the standard deviation s, it is given in standard units as*

$$z = \frac{x - \bar{x}}{s} \tag{5.4.3}*$$

The grade which Jones obtained in the test is therefore in standard units equal to $(71 - 62)/8 = 1.125$.

Further important applications of the standard deviation will be discussed in the next few chapters, in which we shall give, among other things, a more thorough treatment of the normal curve. To avoid the confusion which might arise from the different names which have been given to the standard deviation, it should do no harm to mention that it is referred to by some writers as the *root-mean-square deviation*, which is an outdated and unnecessarily long name.

5.5 The Standard Deviation, Grouped Data

The formula which gives us the standard deviation of grouped data is again based on the assumption that all measurements which belong to a given class are located at its class mark. With this assumption we can write this standard deviation as

$$s = \sqrt{\frac{\sum_{i=1}^{k} (x_i - \bar{x})^2 f_i}{n}} \qquad (5.5.1)$$

which is the square root of the *mean* of the squared deviations from $\bar{x}$, weighted by the class frequencies f_i. The squared deviations $(x_i - \bar{x})^2$ were added f_i times in this summation, to account for the f_i values which belonged to the respective classes.

This formula is important *only* inasmuch as it *defines* the standard deviation of grouped data. It will not be used for actual computations, however, because there are simplifications which can save us a tremendous amount of time and labor. These simplifications are based on the same *change of scale* which we have used previously in the derivation of the short formula for the mean of grouped data. Choosing, therefore, again one of the class marks as the zero point of the new scale, and the old class marks as its successive units, we can write according to (4.4.5)

$$x_i = cu_i + x_0$$

where x_i and u_i are the class marks in the two respective scales, while x_0 is the zero point and c is the class interval in the old scale. Since we have by definition

$$\bar{u} = \frac{\sum_{i=1}^{k} u_i f_i}{n}$$

which is only the mean of the u's for grouped data, we can write formula (4.4.11) as

$$\bar{x} = c\bar{u} + x_0 \qquad (5.5.2)$$

Subtracting equals from equals, i.e., the corresponding sides of equation (5.5.2) from those of equation (4.4.5), we have

$$x_i - \bar{x} = cu_i + x_0 - c\bar{u} - x_0 \qquad (5.5.3)$$
$$= c(u_i - \bar{u})$$

Squaring both sides of this equation, and multiplying both sides by f_i, we obtain

$$(x_i - \bar{x})^2 f_i = c^2 (u_i - \bar{u})^2 f_i \qquad (5.5.4)$$

Finally, adding, as we did on page 57, *equals to equals* by summing both sides of the equation, we get

$$\sum_{i=1}^{k} (x_i - \bar{x})^2 f_i = c^2 \sum_{i=1}^{k} (u_i - \bar{u})^2 f_i \qquad (5.5.5)$$

and dividing both sides of this equation by n, we discover that the left-hand side of (5.5.5) represents *the square of the standard deviation of the x's*, while its right-hand side is equal to c^2 times the square of the standard deviation of the u's. If we now, to avoid confusion, write the standard deviation in the x scale as s_x and the corresponding standard deviation of the same measurements in the u scale as s_u, we have

$$s_x^2 = c^2 s_u^2 \quad \text{or} \quad s_x = c s_u$$

This tells us that the standard deviation in the x scale is equal to c times the corresponding standard deviation in the u scale. Using formula (5.4.2) adjusted for grouped data, *the short formula for the standard deviation of grouped data* can finally be written as

$$s = c \sqrt{\frac{\sum_{i=1}^{k} u_i^2 f_i}{n} - \left(\frac{\sum_{i=1}^{k} u_i f_i}{n} \right)^2} \qquad (5.5.6)^*$$

It is true that this formula looks fairly complicated, but it unquestionably makes it much easier to compute the standard deviation of grouped data. It is really necessary only to find the two summations $\sum_{i=1}^{k} u_i f_i$ and $\sum_{i=1}^{k} u_i^2 f_i$, and substitute them into formula (5.5.6). It is interesting to observe that it is unnecessary, with this formula, to calculate first the mean and the deviations.

The following table shows how easy it is to find a standard deviation of grouped data by use of formula (5.5.6). Using the distribution of the weights of a group of 1000 children, we have

x_i	f_i	u_i	$u_i f_i$	$u_i^2 f_i$
26.5	3	−4	−12	48
30.5	11	−3	−33	99
34.5	61	−2	−122	244
38.5	147	−1	−147	147
42.5	258	0	0	0
46.5	276	1	276	276
50.5	135	2	270	540
54.5	73	3	219	657
58.5	32	4	128	512
62.5	4	5	20	100
	1000		599	2623

Substituting these totals into formula (5.5.6) we get

$$s = 4 \sqrt{\frac{2623}{1000} - \left(\frac{599}{1000}\right)^2} = 4 \sqrt{2.623 - .359} = 6$$

Had we done this problem with the use of formula (5.5.1), the resulting computations would have been outlandish. If the reader does not believe this statement, he is welcome to convince himself by going to the trouble of calculating the standard deviation without using the short-cut method.

Since it is always necessary to find squares and square roots in the calculation of a standard deviation, suitable tables are provided at the end of this book (Table VIII, pp. 397–405).

The standard deviation of grouped data was defined on the assumption that all measurements which belong to a class are located at its class mark. The error which is introduced in this fashion, and which is appropriately called the *grouping error*, can at times be fairly large, particularly if the class intervals are very wide. A correction, *called Sheppard's correction*, tells us that we can compensate for these errors by writing the adjusted standard deviation as

$$s' = \sqrt{s^2 - \frac{c^2}{12}} \tag{5.5.7}*$$

It is generally not advisable to use this correction unless we are sure that the accuracy of our measurements warrant such an additional refinement. In general, it would be advisable to delay use of this formula until we have reached a deeper understanding of the problems which are involved in the grouping of numerical data. We have given this formula at this time merely to impress the reader again with the fact that the grouping of data *can* introduce an error into our calculations. Had we used Sheppard's correction in our last example, the adjusted standard deviation would have become

$$s' = \sqrt{36 - \frac{16}{12}} = 5.9$$

EXERCISES

1. Find the standard deviation of the following 8 numbers using (a) formula (5.4.1), and (b) formula (5.4.2). (Time yourself on the two methods and check how much time is saved by using the short formula).

$$11, \quad 9, \quad 13, \quad 12, \quad 6, \quad 15, \quad 10, \quad 17$$

2. Find the standard deviation of the following 10 proportions:

$$.85, \quad .43, \quad .61, \quad .59, \quad .28, \quad .77, \quad .13, \quad .08, \quad .26, \quad .51$$

3. Calculate the standard deviation of the first sample of the lengths of the fish of Exercise 1, p. 70.
4. Calculate the standard deviation of the 10 weights of Exercise 3, p. 52.
5. Calculate the standard deviation of the 5 calibrations of Exercise 2, p. 51.
6. Calculate the standard deviation of whichever data were grouped among those of Exercises 6, 8, 10, and 12, p. 20.
7. Calculate the standard deviation of the aptitude scores of Exercise 1, p. 58.
8. Find the standard deviation of the pension payments of Exercise 2, p. 27.
9. Calculate the standard deviation of the distances which the rifle shots of Exercise 1, p. 27 hit from the center of the target.

5.6 The Quartile Deviation

It is sometimes convenient to use a measure of variation which, on the one hand, is easier to find than the standard deviation, yet which, on the other hand, is more descriptive and more accurate than the range, which accounted for nothing but the two extreme values. Since the definition of a descriptive measure is, fundamentally speaking, arbitrary, we can define a *third measure of variation which is based on the position of the middle 50 per cent of our data.* This measure of variation, which is known as the *quartile deviation* or as the *semi-interquartile range*, is defined as

$$Q = \frac{Q_3 - Q_1}{2} \qquad (5.6.1)^*$$

An advantageous feature of the quartile deviation is that it accounts for the spread of the middle and, in that sense, most significant part of our data. This means that it will not be affected by the chance fluctuations of the extreme values.

The difference $Q_3 - Q_1$ alone gives us the interval which contains the middle 50 per cent of our data, and it is correspondingly called the *interquartile range*. Although this interquartile range itself would be a perfectly acceptable measure of variation, it seems to be more desirable to take half of this distance, which represents *the average distance by which the two quartiles deviate from the median.* If we know, for example, that a set of data has a median of 55 and a quartile deviation of 20, we can then say that (if the distribution is fairly symmetrical) the middle 50 per cent of the data fall between 35 and 75.

5.7 Measures of Relative Variation

The standard deviation is used in many problems as an indication of the accuracy of a set of measurements. If we measure the same quantity, for example, the weight of a bird or the height of a tree, *several times*, it would be asking for too much to expect an identical result in each case. Consequently we use the standard deviation to express the accuracy of such repeated measurements. Had we measured a number of *different* quantities, on the other hand, the variation of our measurements could then be due either to the inaccuracies of our method of measurement or to an actual difference between the objects which we are trying to describe.

Let us suppose, for instance, that we are investigating a problem in biology and that a set of repeated measurements produced a standard deviation of .10 cm. *Does this information enable us to decide whether our measurements are accurate or not?* It is evident that this question can only be answered *if we know the size of the object which we are trying to measure.* Had we measured the height of an elephant, for example, a standard deviation of .10 cm would imply that our measurements have been very accurate. Had we measured the size of the head of a very small insect, however, this standard deviation would obviously imply that our methods of measurement were extremely inaccurate.

This illustration should make it clear why there is a definite need for a measure of variation which expresses the magnitude of the variation *relative to the quantity which is being measured.* This suggests a measure of *relative variation* which should give us the actual variation as a percentage of the average size of the measurements. Describing the center of the distribution by use of the mean, and the variation of the distribution by use of the standard deviation, we can define the *coefficient of variation* as

$$V = \frac{s}{\bar{x}} \cdot 100 \qquad (5.7.1)^*$$

This formula gives us the standard deviation as a percentage of the mean, and it is easy to find in problems in which we have already calculated $\bar{x}$ and s.

For example, if the average (mean) salary of a group of electricians is \$75 a week, with a standard deviation of \$12, then the coefficient of variation is

$$V = \frac{12}{75} \cdot 100 = 16 \text{ per cent}$$

It is advisable to employ the coefficient of variation whenever it is necessary to compare the dispersions of two or more sets of data. This is true particularly if we have to compare the variation of several sets of measurements which are given in different units of measurement or in different scales. The usefulness of the coefficient of variation in problems of this type is due to the fact that it gives us a percentage which is thus independent of the scale of measurement.

A second measure of relative variation can be defined in terms of the quartile deviation and the median, instead of the standard deviation and the mean. The resulting formula would be

$$\frac{(Q_3 - Q_1)/2}{M} \cdot 100$$

but to simplify matters, it has been the custom to use the midpoint between Q_1 and Q_3 in place of the median, and the *coefficient of quartile variation* is therefore defined as

$$V_Q = \frac{Q_3 - Q_1}{Q_3 + Q_1} \cdot 100 \qquad (5.7.2)^*$$

This formula provides a convenient alternative to the coefficient of variation in problems in which we have calculated the quartiles instead of $\bar{x}$ and s.

EXERCISES

1. Find the quartile deviation and the coefficient of quartile variation, using the results of Exercise 1, p. 78.

2. Use the quartiles which were calculated in Exercise 2 on page 78 to find the quartile deviation and the coefficient of quartile variation of the pension payments.

3. Find the quartile deviation and the coefficient of quartile variation of the data which were used in Exercise 3, p. 78.

4. Find the coefficient of variation of the numbers which are given in Exercise 1 on page 95.

5. Find the coefficient of variation by use of the results of Exercise 4, p. 95.

6. Compute the coefficient of variation of whichever data were used in Exercise 6, p. 95.

7. Calculate the coefficient of variation for each of the three samples of Exercise 1, p. 70, and compare the three values.

5.8 Measures of Symmetry

Let us now turn briefly to the third type of descriptive statistics, namely, to those which exhibit the *symmetry or skewness* of a set of data. We mentioned earlier that the mean, median, and mode are the same for a perfectly symmetrical distribution. This is not true, however, if a distribution has a tail at either end, i.e., if it is skewed (see Figs. 5.a and 5.b). It can easily be shown that *if the tail of the distribution is at the right*, the mean will generally exceed the median, which in turn can be expected to be larger than the mode. Obviously this order will be reversed if the tail of the distribution is at the other side.

This discrepancy between the mean, median, and mode provides an easy way to express the symmetry or lack of symmetry of a distribution with the so-called *Pearsonian measures of symmetry and skewness*. Since the symmetry and skewness of a distribution are properties of its *shape*, it is desirable to make these measures of skewness independent of the scale of measurement. This can be accomplished, as in the case of the coefficient of variation, by dividing the chosen differences between the respective measures of central tendencies by the standard deviation. *The Pearsonian coefficient of skewness* can therefore be defined as

$$SK = \frac{\bar{x} - \text{mode}}{s} \qquad (5.8.1)^*$$

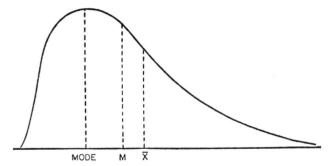

Figure 5.a.   A Positively Skewed Distribution.

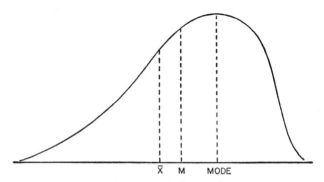

Figure 5.b.   A Negatively Skewed Distribution.

which, together with formula (4.8.2), can also be written as

$$SK = \frac{3(\bar{x} - M)}{s} \qquad (5.8.2)^*$$

These formulas are often used to determine whether or not it is permissible to treat a distribution as if it were symmetrical. If a distribution is symmetrical, its skewness, as measured by (5.8.1) or (5.8.2), must, of course, be equal to 0, since the mean, median, and mode will then be the same.

Applying both formulas to the distribution of the salaries of the employees of the ZYX Co., we will find that since the mean, median, mode, and standard deviation were equal to 54, 52, 47.7, and 11.8, respectively, formula (5.8.1) gives us

$$SK = \frac{54 - 47.7}{11.8} = .53$$

while formula (5.8.2) gives us

$$SK = \frac{3(54 - 52)}{11.8} = .51$$

It should not be surprising that both values were not the same, since formula (4.8.2) is, after all, only an approximation.

There exist several other measures of symmetry, some of which are based on quartiles, others on deciles and percentiles, but the most important and the most widely used measure of symmetry is α_3 (*alpha three*) which is based on the so-called moments about the mean. Since the *moments* of a distribution are, mathematically speaking, quite involved, we shall be satisfied for now with simply giving α_3 as

$$\alpha_3 = \frac{\frac{1}{n} \sum\limits_{i=1}^{n} (x_i - \bar{x})^3}{s^3} \tag{5.8.3}$$

This means that *alpha three* is the average of the cubed deviations from the mean divided by the cube of the standard deviation. The corresponding formula for grouped data is

$$\alpha_3 = \frac{\frac{1}{n} \sum\limits_{i=1}^{k} (x_i - \bar{x})^3 f_i}{s^3} \tag{5.8.4}$$

which, with a suitable change in scale, can be written as

$$\alpha_3 = \frac{c^3}{s^3} \left[\frac{\sum\limits_{i=1}^{k} u_i^3 f_i}{n} - 3 \left(\frac{\sum\limits_{i=1}^{k} u_i^2 f_i}{n} \right) \left(\frac{\sum\limits_{i=1}^{k} u_i f_i}{n} \right) + 2 \left(\frac{\sum\limits_{i=1}^{k} u_i f_i}{n} \right)^3 \right] \tag{5.8.5}*$$

In spite of the fact that this formula may look quite involved to the nonmathematician, its use is really not difficult. If we have already found the summations $\sum\limits_{i=1}^{k} u_i f_i$ and $\sum\limits_{i=1}^{k} u_i^2 f_i$ in the calculation of the standard deviation, we now have to find *only* the additional summation $\sum\limits_{i=1}^{k} u_i^3 f_i$, and substitute the various values into formula (5.8.5). The work which is necessary for the calculation of α_3 of the distribution of the salaries is shown in the following table.

f_i	u_i	$u_i f_i$	$u_i^2 f_i$	$u_i^3 f_i$
3	-2	-6	12	-24
15	-1	-15	15	-15
10	0	0	0	0
8	1	8	8	8
3	2	6	12	24
1	3	3	9	27
40		-4	56	20

from which we find that

$$\alpha_3 = \frac{1000}{11.8^3} \left[\frac{20}{40} - 3\left(\frac{56}{40}\right)\left(\frac{-4}{40}\right) + 2\left(\frac{-4}{40}\right)^3 \right] = .56$$

It follows from the definitions of the various measures of symmetry and skewness which were given by formulas (5.8.1), (5.8.2), and (5.8.3) that the skewness of a distribution is positive if the median or mode is to the *left* of the mean. A distribution is therefore said to be *positively skewed* if its tail is at the right-hand side of the distribution, and it is said to be *negatively skewed* if its tail is at the left.

5.9 Measures of Peakedness

Another important use of the moments of a distribution, in this case the fourth moments about the mean, is in the definition of α_4 (*alpha four*) which measures the *peakedness* or *kurtosis* of a distribution. This statistic is defined as

$$\alpha_4 = \frac{\frac{1}{n} \sum_{i=1}^{n} (x_i - \bar{x})^4}{s^4} \tag{5.9.1}$$

in which the numerator is the mean of the fourth powers of the deviations from the mean.

It is interesting to note in connection with these measures of skewness and kurtosis that the α_4 of a normal curve is always equal to 3, while the α_3 is always equal to 0. Consequently, if we have a set of data for which $\alpha_3 = 0$ and $\alpha_4 = 3$, we have a fairly good indication that our data will fit the shape of a normal curve.

If a curve is very peaked (see the dotted curve of Fig. 5.c) its value of α_4 will be greater than 3, and it is said to be *leptokurtic*; if it is flatter than the bell-shaped normal curve, however, its α_4 will be less than 3, and it is then said to be *platykurtic*. The statistic α_4 is usually found only for grouped data, in which case there exists a short formula analogous to that for α_3.

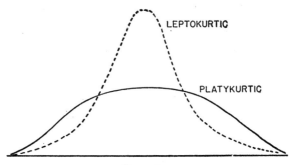

Figure 5.c.

This completes our preliminary study of the various statistics which are used to describe the properties of frequency distributions or ungrouped data. It has been our purpose to emphasize throughout this discussion that descriptive measures are essentially arbitrary, and that they must consequently be chosen to fit the needs of particular problems. This would make it evident why a person who uses these formulas should know what they mean and in what kinds of problems they can be used.

REFERENCES

M. M. Blair, *Elementary Statistics*, Holt, New York, 1944, Chap. 10.
E. B. Mode, *The Elements of Statistics*, Prentice-Hall, New York, 1941, Chaps. 8, 9.
C. H. Richardson, *An Introduction to Statistical Analysis*, Harcourt, Brace, New York, 1934, Chaps. 4, 5.
A. E. Waugh, *Elements of Statistical Method*, McGraw-Hill, New York, 1943, Chaps. 6, 8.

EXERCISES

1. Find both Pearsonian measures of skewness for the distribution of the aptitude scores of Exercise 1, p. 58.
2. Calculate both Pearsonian measures of skewness for whichever data were grouped among those of Exercises 6, 8, 10, and 12 on page 20.
3. Calculate α_3 for distribution of the aptitude scores of Exercise 1, p. 58.
4. Find α_3 for the distribution of the pension payments of Exercise 2, p. 27.

6. DESCRIPTIVE MEASURES
III. THEORETICAL
DISTRIBUTIONS

6.1 Introduction

The various statistics which we have used for the description of grouped and ungrouped sets of numerical data can be used also for the description of theoretical or expected distributions. Since the mean, median, standard deviation, and other measures of theoretical distributions have, logically speaking, the same meaning which they had for the distributions of numerical data, it seems unnecessary to devote much time to the mathematical detail of the corresponding descriptive measures of theoretical distributions.

Before going into a detailed study of the most general properties of theoretical distributions, let us briefly review some of their features which were discussed in Chapter 3. There we pointed out that theoretical distributions should be looked upon as distributions of proportions inasmuch as they give us the proportion (fraction) of the total number of cases rather than the actual frequency which is associated with a given class. In this sense, we can also say that theoretical distributions are *probability* distributions since the two statements: "the interval contains 20 per cent of the cases" and, "the probability that any one value will fall into this class is .20" mean exactly the same.

Until we reach Chapter 7, we shall treat the concept of probability on a more or less intuitive basis, interpreting it as the proportion of the time that a certain event is going to, or can be expected to take place. If the reader does not approve of this informal approach, he may read Chapter 7 before continuing his study of the remainder of this chapter. We have not put a detailed study of probability and chance into Part One of this book because it has been our aim to draw as sharp a line as possible between the problems of inductive and of descriptive statistics. Although the word *probability* may have appeared in previous chapters, our work has not yet gone beyond the study of pure descriptions.

We stressed in Chapter 3, in our discussion of expected and theoretical distributions, that *the fraction of the cases which fall into any given class is represented by the area under the distribution curve which is on top of this class.* Having made the total area under the curve equal to 1, we then saw that the fraction (proportion) of the cases was measured directly by the area under the curve. To illustrate this again, let us consider the distribution of Fig. 6.a, which represents

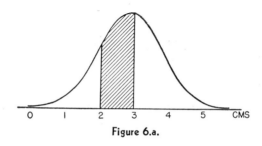

Figure 6.a.

the distribution of the lengths of a certain species of fish. If the total area under the curve is equal to 1, the shaded area of this diagram measures the percentage of the fish which have a length from 2 to 3 cm; making a rough guess, we would not be far off in saying that it is about 30.

It is customary to make the area under theoretical distributions equal to 1, representing thus 100 per cent. This makes it possible to use the same expected or theoretical distribution regardless of whether we want to compare it with a distribution of 40 measurements or with one of 5000. We have only to convert an observed distribution into a *distribution* of proportions, and we are then ready to make a comparison. All theoretical distributions are therefore distributions of proportions, and the proportion which belongs to a given class interval is given simply by the corresponding area under the curve.

The study of theoretical distribution requires a slight change in the symbolism which we have used in the previous chapters. We may want to distinguish, for example, between *the mean of a set of data* and *the mean of a theoretical distribution which we plan to fit to the given data.* This and similar problems are of great importance in the next few chapters, in which we shall try, among other things, to compare *the mean of a sample* with *the mean of a theoretical distribution.* To avoid confusion, it will therefore be necessary to use different symbols to denote the various means. Following customary procedure, we shall denote the mean of a theoretical distribution by the letter m, reserving the symbol $\bar{x}$ for the mean of a set of observed data. Similarly, we shall write the standard deviation of a theoretical distribution as σ (sigma), and the standard deviation of a set of numerical data as s.

6.2 The Normal Curve and the Use of Normal Curve Tables

The *normal curve* which we introduced in Chapter 3 with the illustration of the pegs and the pellets has the interesting feature that the entire curve (its shape, its area, etc.) is determined if we know the values of its mean and standard deviation. This means that for a given value of m and a given value of σ there exists *one and only one corresponding normal curve.* Due to this interesting and convenient property, we can find the normal curve which corresponds to any set of numerical data on the basis of $\bar{x}$ and s alone. Having found this normal curve, we can then compare it with the observed distribution and decide whether or not the original data fit a normal distribution.

The normal curve is a bell-shaped curve which extends indefinitely in both directions. This means that although the curve comes closer and closer, it will never come all the way down to the horizontal axis, no matter how far we go from the mean. To give a complete picture of the normal curve it would therefore be necessary to draw its two tails, which go infinitely far in both directions. Fortunately, this will not be necessary because the percentage of cases which deviate from the mean by more than 4 or 5 standard deviations is so small that it is usually ignored.

Before we continue this study of the properties of the normal curve, it will be better to investigate first how we can convert any distribution into its so-called *standard form.* It is in this standard form that we will later be able to compare any distribution with the corresponding normal curve. A distribution is changed into its standard form by means of a change of scale like that shown in Fig. 6.b, in which the x scale is the scale in which the measurements were originally obtained. If the mean and standard deviation of the observed distribution are $\bar{x}$ and s, we can choose a new scale, the z scale, whose zero point is at $\bar{x}$ and whose unit of length is equal to the distance from $\bar{x}$ to $\bar{x} + s$ (see Fig. 6.b). Studying the original distribution in the *new scale*, we find that its mean is 0 and its standard deviation is equal to 1.

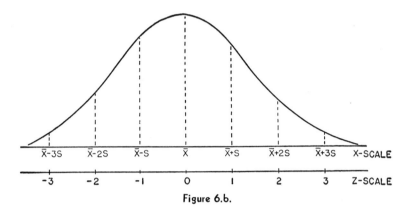

Figure 6.b.

A distribution which has a zero mean and a standard deviation of 1 is said to be in its standard form. It is possible to change any curve into its standard form by the change of scale which is pictured in Fig. 6.b. If we want to find the z value of a measurement which originally was obtained in the x scale, we need a formula analogous to (4.4.3) or (4.4.5). It can easily be seen that this formula must be

$$z = \frac{x - \bar{x}}{s} \qquad (6.2.1)^*$$

This is formula (5.4.3), which we used in the previous chapter to convert measurements into standard scores. The significance of standard units or standard scores must now be apparent, because *changing measurements into standard units is precisely what we do when we put a distribution into its standard form.* Since it is easy to convert a set of measurements into the corresponding standard scores, or standard units, we can thus put any distribution into its standard form, and to make comparisons, we will need only the one normal curve which has a zero mean and a standard deviation of 1.

Since it is important to know what proportion of cases fall into any class, and since this proportion is given by the corresponding area under the normal curve, the areas under the normal curve are given in Table I, p. 389, for values of z from 0 to 3.09. In this table, the area which is said to correspond to a given value of z is *the area under the normal curve which goes from 0 to z.* Such an area is given, for example, by the shaded area of Fig. 6.c. Areas which belong to

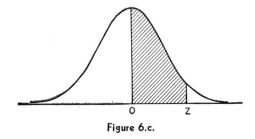

Figure 6.c.

negative values of z (which correspond to measurements which are smaller than the mean) are not given in Table I, because we can treat them *as if they were positive,* thanks to the symmetry of the normal curve. If we have, for example, $z = -1.5$, we can find the corresponding normal curve area by looking up $z = 1.5$ in Table I. We must remember, of course, that the area which we have thus obtained is the area which is bounded at the left by $z = -1.5$ and at the right by $z = 0$, i.e., the mean (see Fig. 6.d).

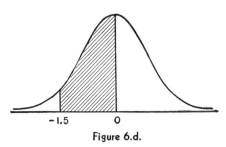

Figure 6.d.

If we are interested in finding the area, the proportion of cases which falls to the *right* of a positive value of z (see Fig. 6.e), we cannot obtain this value directly from Table I. However, since the total area which lies to the right of the mean is .5000 (the curve is symmetrical), we can find the area in which we are interested by first looking up the area which corresponds to the given value of z and then subtracting this value from .5000. If we want to find, for

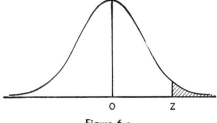

Figure 6.e.

example, the area which falls to the right of $z = .35$, we take the corresponding value from Table I and subtract it from .5000. This gives us, in this case, $.5000 - .1368 = .3632$ (Fig. 6.f).

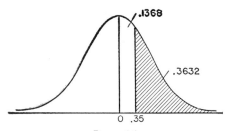

Figure 6.f.

Had we asked instead for the area under the normal curve which falls to the *left* of a positive value of z, as for example, $z = .35$, our answer would have been $.1368 + .5000 = .6368$. Our reason for *adding* .5000 to the tabular value can easily be seen from the diagram of Fig. 6.g. Whenever we want to find an area to the left or to the

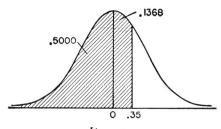

Figure 6.g.

right of a *negative value of z*, it is best to study the situation by drawing a diagram like those in Figs. 6.c to 6.g. Once we have such a diagram it is easy to decide whether we must add .5000 to the tabular value, whether we must subtract it from .5000, or whether we can leave it as given in Table I.

There are also problems in which we will be interested in the area under the normal curve which lies *between* two given values of z. If both z's are on the same side of the mean, our answer will be given by the *difference* of the tabular values which correspond to the given z's. For example, the area between $z = .73$ and $z = 1.64$ (see Fig. 6.h)

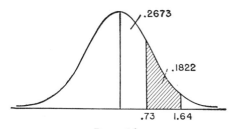

Figure 6.h.

is given by the difference .4495 − .2673 = .1822. If two values of z lie on opposite sides of the mean, i.e., if one z is positive and the other is negative, we *add* the values which are given in Table I (see Fig. 6.i), in order to obtain the area which lies between them. The

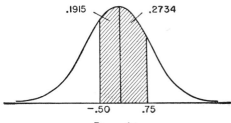

Figure 6.i.

area under the normal which lies between $z = -.50$ and $z = .75$, for example, is equal to .1915 + .2734 = .4649.

Once we have learned how to find areas to the left, to the right, and between given values of z, we can apply this knowledge to a great number of problems which utilize the table.

EXERCISES

1. The distribution of the grades which a group of students obtained in statistics has a mean of 63 and a standard deviation of 12. Convert each of the following grades into standard scores.

(a) 85	(d) 61
(b) 75	(e) 92
(c) 24	(f) 57

2. The mean and standard deviation of a set of measurements are 38.6 and 3.7 cm, respectively. Change each of the following measurements into standard units.

(a) 42.5	(d) 46.8
(b) 27.9	(e) 40.0
(c) 34.3	(f) 39.3

3. Find the normal curve areas which lie
(a) To the right of $z = 1.73$.
(b) Between $z = -.33$ and $z = .57$.
(c) To the right of $z = -1.24$.
(d) To the left of $z = -.85$.
(e) Between $z = 0$ and $z = .22$.
(f) Between $z = -2.83$ and $z = -1.64$.
(g) Between $z = 1.20$ and $z = 1.61$.
(h) Between $z = 0$ and $z = -1.14$.

4. Find z if
(a) The normal curve area to the right of z is .2643.
(b) The normal curve area between 0 and z is .4929.
(c) The normal curve area to the left of z is .9756.
(d) The normal curve area between $+z$ and $-z$ is .7888.

6.3 Applications of the Normal Curve Areas

In our discussion of the uses of the standard deviation we mentioned in Chapter 5 that 68 per cent of a normally distributed set of measurements fall within one standard deviation on either side of the mean. This claim can now be verified by use of Table I. If a measurement is one standard deviation *above* the mean, its z value is equal to 1 (see Fig. 6.b) and if it is one standard deviation *below* the mean, its z value is -1. The normal curve area which, according to Table I, corresponds to $z = 1$ is .3413, and the area between $z = 1$ and $z = -1$ is therefore equal to $.3413 + .3413 = .6826$. This means that a little more than 68 per cent of the cases fall into the interval which covers the range of *one standard deviation* on either side of the mean. Using the identical argument we will find that

95.46 per cent of the cases fall within *two standard deviations*, and 99.73 per cent of the cases fall within *three standard deviations* on either side of the mean (see Fig. 6.j). The interval which covers one

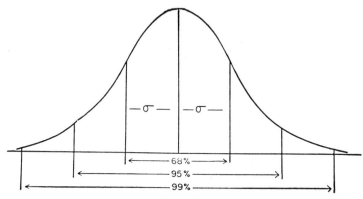

Figure 6.j.

standard deviation on either side of the mean is often referred to as the *one-sigma range*. Similarly, we can speak of a *two-sigma range* and a *three-sigma range*, referring to the corresponding intervals which are described in Fig. 6.j. The three percentages which are associated with these three intervals play an important role in many applied problems, and they are usually rounded off to 68, 95, and $99\frac{1}{2}$, which is a sufficiently close approximation for most practical purposes.

In the examples which we shall discuss next it must always be assumed that the data with which we are concerned are normally distributed. *Obviously, there can be no justification for using either normal curve areas or percentages unless we have good reason to believe that our data fit closely to a normal curve.*

Example 1. A certain kind of bug has an average (mean) length of .30 inch with a standard deviation of .02 inch. If these lengths are normally distributed, what percentage of the bugs can be expected to have a length of .35 inch or more?

The measurements with which we are dealing in this problem are for all practical purposes measured with a continuous scale. Consequently, we need only find the z value for $x = .35$, check the corresponding area in Table I, and subtract it from .5000. Formula (6.2.1) gives us

$$z = \frac{.35 - .30}{.02} = 2.5$$

The corresponding normal curve area is .4938, and our answer is .5000 − .4938 = .0062, or slightly more than 6/10 of 1 per cent.

> *Example 2.* The average density of a number of glass bricks is 2.510, with a standard deviation of 0.02. If these measurements of density are normally distributed, below what density can we expect to find the lightest 10 per cent of the bricks?

This problem differs from Example 1 inasmuch as we are now given the percentage and we are asked to find the corresponding z or x. If we check .5000 − .1000 = .4000 (see Fig. 6.k) in the area columns

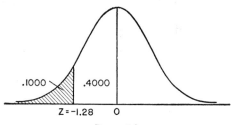

Figure 6.k.

of Table I, we will find that the area which is closest to .4000 has a z value of 1.28. Substituting this z value into (6.2.1), not forgetting, of course, to make it minus, we have

$$-1.28 = \frac{x - 2.510}{0.02}$$

Solving this equation for x, we get $x = 2.484$. This implies that the lightest 10 per cent of the bricks have a density of .2484 or less.

> *Example 3.* The grades which were given in a final examination in geometry showed a mean of 69 and a standard deviation of 9.3. Assuming that the grades describe a more or less normal curve, what per cent of the students can be expected to have received a grade of 76, 77, 78, or 79?

The fact that grades given in an examination are usually *integers* makes it necessary for us to treat the grade of 75 as if it covered the interval from 74.5 to 75.5, the grade of 76 as if it covered the interval from 75.5 to 76.5, etc. This spreads the grade distribution over a continuous scale, and we can now solve the problem by finding the

area under the corresponding normal curve which falls between 75.5
and 79.5.   The two z values which correspond to the ends of this
interval are

$$z_1 = \frac{75.5 - 69}{9.3} = .70 \quad \text{and} \quad z_2 = \frac{79.5 - 69}{9.3} = 1.13$$

and the respective tabular values are .2580 and .3708.   The answer
is then given by the difference .3708 − .2580 = .1128, and we can
say that about 11.3 per cent of the students can be expected to have
had scores from 76 to 79.

Example 4.   An introvert-extrovert test which was standardized on
a group of students showed a mean score of 75 and a standard deviation
of 12.   If we want to designate the highest 15 per cent as *extrovert,* the
next 20 per cent as *moderately extrovert,* the middle 30 per cent as *average,*
the next 25 per cent as *moderately introvert,* and the lowest 10 per cent
as *introvert,* what ranges of scores will be covered by these five designa-
tions, assuming that they follow the pattern of a normal curve?

As in all problems which involve areas under the normal curve, it
is best to begin by drawing a diagram.   This has been done in Fig. 6.1,

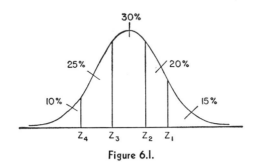

Figure 6.I.

in which the dividing lines between the five classifications are given
as z_1, z_2, z_3, and z_4.   Next we find the areas which lie between the
mean and *each* of the four z's.   This is easy once we have drawn the
diagram, and it can be seen by inspection that these areas are .3500,
.1500, .1500, and .4000, respectively.   Checking these areas in

Table I, and taking care of the appropriate signs, we find that the z's which are closest to these areas are

$$z_1 = 1.04, \quad z_2 = .39, \quad z_3 = -.39, \quad z_4 = -1.28$$

Finally, using formula (6.2.1) to convert these z's into the corresponding grades, we find that

$$1.04 = \frac{x_1 - 75}{12}, \quad .39 = \frac{x_2 - 75}{12},$$

$$-.39 = \frac{x_3 - 75}{12}, \quad -1.28 = \frac{x_4 - 75}{12}$$

and $x_1 = 87.48, \quad x_2 = 79.68, \quad x_3 = 70.32, \quad x_4 = 59.64$

Rounding these scores to the nearest integers, we can now classify the grades as follows:

Extrovert	88 or more
Moderately extrovert	80 to 87
Average	71 to 79
Moderately introvert	60 to 70
Introvert	59 or less

6.4 The Use of Normal Curve Graph Paper

We have repeatedly stressed the fact that normal curve theory and normal curve tables can be used *only* if our observed distributions come reasonably close to a normal curve. This raises the important question *how we can ever know whether a given distribution is really sufficiently close to warrant the use of the tables of the normal curve.*

The criterion which is commonly used as the basis for this decision requires a much deeper knowledge of statistics than we have at this time. Consequently, until we discuss this criterion in Chapter 16, let us be satisfied with a much cruder method which has the advantage that it involves practically no calculations at all. This method is based on a special kind of graph paper, called *normal curve paper* or *probability graph paper* (see Fig. 6.m) which has been designed for this particular purpose.

If we plot the cumulative *less than* distribution of a set of observed data on this kind of paper, *we can say that our data are normally distributed if the resulting curve is close to a straight line.*

To illustrate the use of this paper, let us consider the following (fictitious) distribution of the weights of 300 army recruits:

Weights (to the nearest pound)	Frequency
150–158	9
159–167	24
168–176	51
177–185	66
186–194	72
195–203	48
204–212	21
213–221	6
222–230	3
	300

Converting this table into a cumulative percentage distribution, using the class boundaries instead of the class limits, we have

Weights	Cumulative percentages
less than 149.5	0
158.5	3
167.5	11
176.5	28
185.5	50
194.5	74
203.5	90
212.5	97
221.5	99
230.5	100

Before we plot this cumulative distribution, let us first investigate the scales of the normal curve paper. The cumulative percentage scale is already marked off on this paper in the special pattern which makes it so suitable for our problem. The other scale consists of equal subdivisions which are not numbered, and they can therefore be used in our problem to represent the class boundaries of 149.5, 158.5, etc.

If we now plot the cumulative distribution of the weights, as in Fig. 6.m, the reader will note that the first and last points had to be omitted *because a normal curve never reaches 0 or 100 per cent unless we go infinitely far in both directions.* Judging by the graph of Fig. 6.m, it seems quite reasonable to say that the distribution of the weights of the recruits is close to a normal curve.

Normal curve paper has the additional feature that it makes it easy for us to *estimate* the standard deviation of a distribution without having to go through all the necessary calculations. We know from

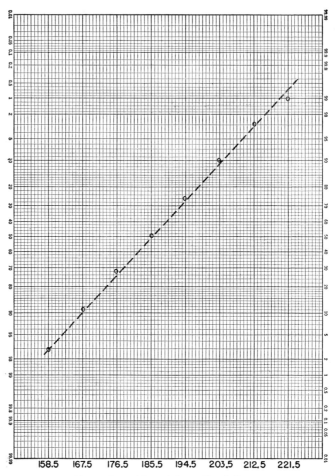

Figure 6.m. Normal Curve Graph Paper.

our discussion of the previous section that in a normal curve 68 per cent of the cases fall inside of the one-sigma range. This means that $50 + \frac{68}{2} = 84$ per cent of the cases fall below a z value of 1 and that $50 - \frac{68}{2} = 16$ per cent of the cases fall below a z value of -1. Checking 16 and 84 per cent on the vertical scale of the normal curve paper of Fig. 6.m, we can judge by the straight line which we have drawn through our points that the corresponding points on the horizontal scale are approximately 172 and 201. By construction, the distance between these two points must cover a one-sigma range, i.e., it must actually cover *two standard deviations*. We can, therefore, estimate the standard deviation of our distribution by dividing the difference between 201 and 172 by 2, and this gives us $(201 - 172)/2 = 14.5$. If we went to the trouble of calculating the actual value of the standard deviation by means of formula (5.5.6), we would find that its value is 14.54. This is amazingly close to the result which we have just obtained with the much less laborious approximate method. It is true that we cannot always expect our results to be as close as this, but the use of normal curve paper is nevertheless a very convenient and fairly accurate way of finding the standard deviation of a distribution *provided that our data do fall into the pattern of a normal curve.*

6.5 The Fitting of a Normal Curve to a Set of Observed Data

Another interesting problem which can be solved by means of the areas of Table I is posed by the question: *Given the distribution of a certain set of measurements, how can we find the normal curve which has the same mean and the same standard deviation as the original distribution?* This question is usually referred to as the problem of fitting a normal curve to an observed distribution.

If such a normal curve could be found, we would be able to compare it with our observed distribution and thus be able to decide whether we have a good fit, i.e., whether our distribution comes close to a normal curve. We have already said that there exists *only one* normal curve which we can fit in this fashion; there exists only one normal curve for given values of $\bar{x}$ and s.

Let us illustrate this fitting of a normal curve by use of the distribution of the weights which was given on page 115. This distribution has a mean of 184.3 and a standard deviation of 14.54. Before tackling the problem as a whole, let us first indicate the general approach which we shall use, by calculating the normal curve area which corresponds to any one of the classes, say the one which goes from 204 to 212. This problem is similar to Example 3 of page 112, because we are again interested in finding the area which falls between two given values of z. Because the class limits of our chosen class are 203.5 and 212.5, their respective z values are $(203.5 - 184.3)/14.54 = 1.32$ and $(212.5 - 184.3)/14.54 = 1.94$. The normal curve areas which, in Table I, agree with these z's are .4066 and .4738, and their difference is .0672. This means that 6.72 per cent of the weights could be expected to fall into the chosen class *if our distribution is a normal curve.* Since 6.72 per cent of 300 (the total number of recruits) is about 20.2, we can now say that the corresponding *normal curve frequency* of the class is 20.2. It is interesting to note that this is close to the observed frequency of the same class, which was 21.

Generalizing this method to the entire distribution, we can now arrange our work in the following kind of table:

Class interval (1)	L (2)	z (3)	Areas (4)	Differences (5)	Normal curve frequencies (6)
	149.5	−2.39	.4916		
150–158				.0300	9.0
	158.5	−1.77	.4616		
159–167				.0846	25.4
	167.5	·1.16	.3770		
168–176				.1716	51.5
	176.5	−.54	.2054		
177–185				.2373	71.2
	185.5	.08	.0319		
186–194				.2261	67.8
	194.5	.70	.2580		
195–203				.1486	44.6
	203.5	1.32	.4066		
204–212				.0672	20.2
	212.5	1.94	.4738		
213–221				.0210	6.3
	221.5	2.56	.4948		
222–230				.0045	1.4
	230.5	3.18	.4993		

The second column of this arrangement contains the class boundaries L, and the third contains their corresponding z's. Column (4) contains the normal curve areas from Table I corresponding to each of the z's, while column (5) is obtained by taking the *differences* of the areas of column (4), except for the class which has one class boundary above and the other below the mean, in which case we take the *sum* of the respective areas of column (4). The last column, which represents the *normal curve frequencies*, is finally obtained by multiplying each value of column (5) by the total number of cases n, in this example by 300.

Once we have calculated the frequencies which we *should* have had if our distribution were a normal curve with the same mean and standard deviation, we can compare the observed frequencies with the corresponding frequencies of the normal curve which we have fitted to our data. This comparison is generally put on a precise basis by means of the chi-square criterion which we shall discuss in this connection in Chapter 16.   For the time being we shall be satisfied with a visual comparison of the histograms of the two distributions. Figure 6.n, which shows the superimposed histograms of the actual distribution of the weights and of the normal curve which we have fitted, seems to indicate that we have indeed an excellent fit.   It would therefore be quite reasonable to treat the observed distribution as if it were a normal curve.

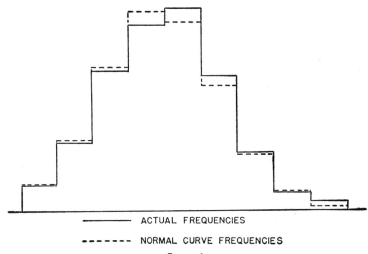

————— ACTUAL FREQUENCIES

– – – – – – NORMAL CURVE FREQUENCIES

Figure 6.n.

REFERENCES

F. E. Croxton and D. J. Cowden, *Applied General Statistics*, Prentice-Hall, New York, 1939, Chap. 11.

W. J. Dixon and F. J. Massey, *Introduction to Statistical Analysis*, McGraw-Hill, New York, 1951, Chap. 5.

A. E. Waugh, *Elements of Statistical Method*, McGraw-Hill, New York, 1943, Chap. 7.

S. S. Wilks, *Elementary Statistical Analysis*, Princeton University Press, Princeton, 1949, Chap. 8.

EXERCISES

1. If the ages of a group of teachers are normally distributed with a mean of 41 and a standard deviation of 8, what percentage of this group is 35 years or older?

2. The grades which a number of students obtained in a test had a mean of 71 and a standard deviation of 10.   Find (1) what percentage of the stu-

dents scored 64 or less; (2) what percentage scored 90 or more, (3) what percentage had either 75, 76, 77, or 78.   Assume that the grades are normally distributed.

3. The heights of a number of students are normally distributed, with a mean of 68 inches.   If 10 per cent are 71 or more inches tall, what is the standard deviation of this distribution?

4. A set of final examination scores is normally distributed, with a mean of 64 and a standard deviation of 15.   If the lowest 15 per cent of the students are to get F's, which score will be the highest F?   If the highest 10 per cent are to get A's, what is the lowest A?

5. A set of measurements is normally distributed with a mean of 12.8 cm and a standard deviation of 1.7 cm.   Find the quartiles of this distribution.

6. If the average lifetime of a certain kind of battery is 300 hours, with a standard deviation of 27 hours, what percentage of these batteries can be expected to last anywhere from 250 to 350 hours?   Assume that these lifetimes are normally distributed.

7. Plot on normal curve paper the distribution of whichever data were grouped among those of Exercises 6, 8, 10, and 12 on page 20.   Check whether the distribution is close to a normal curve.

8. Plot on normal curve paper the distribution of the aptitude scores of Exercise 1, p. 58.   Check whether the distribution is close to a normal curve.

9. Plot on normal curve paper the distribution of the pension payments of Exercise 2, p. 27, and decide whether or not it is reasonable to treat this distribution as a normal curve.

10. Fit a normal curve to the distribution of whichever data were grouped among those of Exercises 6, 8, 10, and 12 on page 20.   Draw the two histograms and decide whether it is a good fit.

11. Fit a normal curve to the distribution of the aptitude scores of Exercise 1, p. 58.   Compare the two distributions and decide whether it is a reasonably good fit.

12. Fit a normal curve of the distribution of the number of heads obtained in the 100 tosses of 10 coins of Exercise 5, p. 59.   Should we expect a good fit?

PART TWO:

*PROBABILITY
AND SAMPLING*

7. PROBABILITY

7.1 Introduction

The statistical methods which we have introduced to the reader in Part One of this book have all belonged to the field of *descriptive statistics*. They can reasonably be described as safe inasmuch as the only errors to which we exposed ourselves were mistakes in arithmetic, the selection of a wrong formula, and the misreading of a tabular value. Although this constitutes in all probability a sufficient risk to most beginning students, we now face an entirely different kind of risk consisting of errors which cannot be eliminated through the cure of a few careless habits. *This new kind of error appears the very moment that we use partial information and derive general conclusions.* It is true, of course, that we need not expose ourselves to this new kind of error, but if we limit ourselves to the statistics which we have discussed so far, we will be burying our heads in the sand. We would thus deprive ourselves of one of the most powerful sources of knowledge which mankind ever had, namely, the scientific method.

Science is based on *inductive procedures* which in most logic books are described as "reasoning from the particular to the general." A standard example of this kind of reasoning is: *All swans which we have seen were white; hence, all swans are white.* Although the reader may be indifferent towards the color of swans, he will soon discover that the *structure* of this kind of thinking is basic to all scientific thought. Scientific knowledge consists of generalizations which are based on observation and experimentation. If we were to refrain from making generalizations we might be able to report what we have seen and what we have measured, *but we would never be able to put this information to work.* Therefore, if we want to learn from experience and use knowledge of the past for predictions of the future, we must face the gamble which is intrinsic in inductive statistics and the scientific method.

One primary task of inductive statistics consists of the development of methods which enable us to calculate and subsequently minimize the risks which must be assumed in every problem of prediction or estimation. A considerable part of our study will therefore be devoted to the evaluation of these risks, *because it is the use of the calculated risk which makes the work of the scientist superior to that of the fortune teller.*

Granting that it is virtually impossible to understand the factors of chance which form the basis of inductive statistics without a sound understanding of the concept of probability, we shall devote the next few pages to a more or less philosophical discussion of the meaning of probability.

7.2 The Meaning of Probability

One of the most annoying obstacles which we must face in our discussion of the meaning of the word *probability* is the multiplicity of meanings which everyday language has given to such words as *possible, probable, likely,* and *chance.* As long as we limit ourselves to conversational language it does not matter much whether we use vague terms which may add color to an argument or which may impress someone who is less informed than we. However, if we want to make *precise* scientific statements, we must limit ourselves to the use of well-defined and meaningful terms. Since we shall use *probability* as a basic scientific term, we must explain its meaning in a manner which is sufficiently clear to avoid ambiguities and misunderstandings. The controversy about the meaning of probability and chance has filled many volumes of philosophical discussions. As we have no intention of exposing the reader to the beclouded depths of philosophical analysis, we shall limit ourselves in this chapter to a few simple and basic considerations.

Let us remember, first, that *all definitions are really arbitrary.* If we were to decide suddenly that *probability* would be a much nicer name for the kind of pastry which is normally called apple pie, we would most likely create a good deal of confusion. However, if we were to insist on using this term again and again, it is conceivable that we might finally be presented with the appropriate dessert. It is true that this illustration is far-fetched and that there is nothing to be gained by using *probability* instead of the well-established *apple pie.* On the other hand, let us recall that

> That which we call a rose
> By any other name would smell as sweet.

This tells us that names or terms are unimportant as long as we know the concepts or ideas for which they stand.

Statisticians use the term *probability* for the important scientific concept of the *relative frequency*, or to be more exact, the *limit of a relative frequency*. If other writers prefer to use the word in a different sense, this is a privilege which we cannot deny, although it is regrettable that this term does have so many different connotations. Prior to explaining what we mean by a relative frequency or by the limit of a relative frequency, it will clarify matters if we first investigate how probabilities are usually defined in most standard texts. The customary "definition" reads as follows: *If an event can lead to the occurrence of n equally likely results of which s are denoted as successes, the probability of a success is given by the ratio s/n.*

We have advisedly given the word *definition* in quotes because this is actually no definition at all. It cannot be accepted as a definition of probability, because it explains it in terms of events which are supposedly *equally likely*, without telling us what *equally likely* means. If two events are said to be equally likely, this is usually meant to imply that they are equally probable (they have the same probability), and consequently we are using in this definition the word which we are trying to define.

Although the expression s/n is *not a definition* of probability, it does enable us to calculate probabilities in many problems, once we *know* or once we *have assumed* that the various alternatives are equally likely. If we assume, for example, that a coin is honest, we assume that heads and tails are equally likely, and we can then say that the probability of heads is $\frac{1}{2}$. Similarly, we can use the same argument to arrive at the conclusion that the probability of rolling a 4 with one die is $\frac{1}{6}$, *assuming* that all six faces are equally likely.

The problem of deciding whether or not we can consider events as equally likely has led to some very unreasonable, even absurd, types of thinking. Laplace's famous *rule of indifference*, also called the *rule of equal ignorance*, states that if there is no reason why one event should be more likely than another, the two events are to be considered as equally likely. The not unusual mistake of considering events as equally likely, simply because they are the only alternatives and we know nothing about them, has led to some very strange thinking. We might say, for instance, that the name of a man whom we do not know is either Henry Jones or it is not Henry Jones; there are two alternatives, we know nothing about the man; hence the probability that his name is Henry Jones is $\frac{1}{2}$.

A good illustration of the difficulties in which we may find ourselves if we indiscriminately use the principle of Laplace is the following variation of the classical problem of the three chests. Let us suppose that we are packing three lunch baskets. Into the first we put *two* ham sandwiches, into the second we put *one* ham and *one* cheese, and into the third we put *two* cheese sandwiches. Getting hungry later on, we decide to pick at random one of the three baskets and take out one sandwich without looking at the other. If the sandwich which we happen to choose is ham, we can ask for the probability that the sandwich which is left in the basket is of the same kind. Many people would reason as follows: the second sandwich is either a ham sandwich or a cheese sandwich; hence the chances are fifty-fifty, and the probability is $\frac{1}{2}$.

If we look at this problem a little more closely, we discover that this *obvious* solution is incorrect. It seems reasonable to say that before we ever made our first choice, each of the six sandwiches had an equal chance of being picked. Consequently, we can now study this problem with the following scheme:[1]

	The sandwich which was chosen	The sandwich which remained
Basket 1 $\{$	H_1	H_2
	H_2	H_1
Basket 2 $\{$	H	C
	C	H
Basket 3 $\{$	C_1	C_2
	C_2	C_1

Looking at this table we find that among the three cases in which a ham sandwich was chosen first, the second sandwich was also ham *two out of three times*. This means that under the stated conditions the correct probability is $\frac{2}{3}$ and not $\frac{1}{2}$. The moral of this story is that one cannot be too careful in accepting events as equally likely.

Let us remember, therefore, that the formula s/n can be used only if we already know or assume that the various alternatives have the same probability, and that it can never serve as a definition of the term probability itself.

---

[1] The subscripts are needed to differentiate between the like sandwiches which are in the same basket.

When we first discussed theoretical distributions in Chapters 3 and 6, we introduced the concept of probability on a more or less intuitive basis as the percentage of the time that certain things would, or could be expected to take place. If we say, for example, that the probability of a tulip bulb coming to bloom is .75, we mean that 75 per cent of the bulbs can be expected to bloom. What we have so far described as the *fraction or proportion of the time* is in more precise language called the *relative frequency.* For example, if, on the average, 8 out of 10 bombing missions are successful, we can say that the relative frequency of successful missions is $\frac{8}{10}$ or .80; if 186 students graduate out of a freshman class of 300, we can say that the relative frequency with which students finish college is .62.

If we flip an honest coin, we expect heads to appear with a relative frequency of .50. This does *not* mean that if we flip a coin 10 or 20 times, we must necessarily always get 50 per cent heads and 50 per cent tails. It would not take more than one or two experiments to convince any skeptic that even the most honest coin will not come up with precisely that same number of heads and tails in every case. In other words, we cannot expect an equal number of heads and tails every time, *but if we flip a coin a sufficient number of times, we will usually come fairly close to 50 per cent heads and 50 per cent tails. It is this relative frequency in the long run which we shall define as the probability of the occurrence of a given event.* Since the expression *in the long run* can hardly be described as a precise scientific term, we shall speak instead of the *limit of the relative frequency,* which as far as we are concerned, really means exactly the same. Therefore it is the limit of the relative frequency which is defined as the probability of a given event, and as we can easily see, this is only the intuitive definition which we introduced in Chapters 3 and 6. Since the idea of a limit belongs to the study of calculus, we shall not burden ourselves with this complex notion, and use instead the more intuitive, yet easily understood expression *in the long run.*

It is evident that since the number of successes or, better, the proportion of successes can never be negative, and since it can also never exceed 100 per cent or a relative frequency of 1.00, *a probability must always lie between 0 and 1.* Although a probability of 0 does *not* mean that an event is beyond the realm of possibility, it is generally understood to imply that the event is extremely unlikely. We usually assign a probability of 0 to events which in colloquial terms would not happen in ten million years. If, for example, we let a monkey play around with a typewriter, it is not impossible that he might type Plato's *Republic* word for word without a mistake, but we most certainly would never expect it to happen. Similarly, if we assign to an event a probability of 1, this does not mean that the event has to happen, but that it is practically certain that it will happen almost all of the time. We are practically certain, for example, that all New Yorkers are not going to decide suddenly to take a trip to Alaska, although logically speaking, it could, of course, happen.

The role which is played by probability in modern science is that of a substitute for certainty and truth. As we shall see, it is not only a poor substitute if we compare it with the customary notion of certainty, but it is also a far cry from what most people understand by truth. The relationship between probability and certainty is easy to see by means of an illustration of the following kind. Let us suppose that a farmer has planted a certain crop and that he wants to consult an agricultural expert about his chances of its being a success. If the expert could tell him *for sure* that his crop would succeed, the farmer would know precisely where he stands. Similarly, a negative reply, though perhaps regrettable, would also tell him exactly what to expect. On the other hand, the kind of answer which he will actually get will merely tell him that his chances may be pretty good, average, or fairly poor. Before trying to interpret the meaning of such a reply in the light of what we have said about probabilities, let us first ask the expert for a more precise evaluation of the farmer's chances. Let us suppose, for instance, that he tells us that the probability that the farmer will have a successful crop is .90. Where do we stand now? Would this entitle us to say that the expert was right if the crop succeeds, wrong if the crop fails? In order to answer either question we must check what the expert meant by a probability of .90. According to the definition which we gave above, a probability of .90 means that in the long run we can expect something to happen about 90 per cent of the time. Consequently, when the expert told us that the probability of a successful crop was .90, he meant to say that *among a large number of similar crops and under the same conditions as to weather, etc., about 90 per cent can be expected to succeed.*

This implies that if we want to discuss the probability of a certain event, we will always have to refer to what will happen in the long run to a large number of similar events. This state of affairs is usually viewed with great skepticism by those who are unwilling to settle for anything but *absolute certainty* or *absolute truth*. On the other hand, if we want to be scientific, i.e., if we want to obtain knowledge from observations and experiments, we must resign ourselves to the fact that all scientific predictions are precisely of this type.

The reader may have received the impression that, according to what we have said in the last paragraph, it is perfectly safe to make scientific predictions, *since nobody can ever prove them right or wrong on the basis of a single event.* If a meteorologist tells us, for example, that the probability that it will rain is .80, we cannot say whether he was right or wrong, regardless of what happens on the day to which he referred. As we have said before, it is impossible to check whether a probability is correct referring to only a single event, because the meteorologist really said only that under similar conditions we can expect it to rain about 8 times in 10.

This does not mean, of course, that since nobody can prove that we are wrong, we should go ahead and make wild predictions about single events. We should always remember that it is as important in everyday life as it is in scientific work to make the correct predictions and the correct decisions *as often as possible.* It is necessary, therefore, to know in each case which are the proper odds, i.e., which are the correct probabilities. For example, if the chances of our catching a cold at a football game are .30 if we do not wear a coat, while they are .15 if we are properly dressed, we would be smart to *play the odds* by wearing a coat. *Naturally, this will not protect us from catching a cold, but in the long run we will catch fewer colds if we act according to the alternatives which afford us the best odds.* Similarly, we can always expect the greatest success ratio if we bet (or act according to) **the** best odds. Since the probabilities provide us with these odds, it is reasonable to say that although probabilities can never guarantee us success, they act as a very important guide in everyday life.

A considerable part of this book will be devoted to problems of estimation, prediction, and testing of hypotheses, and it will therefore be of interest to see how probabilities are used to discuss the accuracy of results. Let us consider, for example, the problem of predicting the outcome of a certain election. If we ask a limited number of people how they plan to vote, this provides us with partial information about the opinions of all the voters. If we then estimate on the basis of this partial knowledge, and perhaps some fancy statistical techniques, that candidate X will receive from 57 to 59 per cent of the votes, *we cannot be absolutely certain that this estimate is correct.* This leaves us open to the question as to how sure we really are that the candidate will receive from 57 to 59 per cent of the total vote. Studying our data and our methods, we might say that we are 95 per cent sure, which means that *we assign our estimate a probability of .95 of being correct.* As we are interested in one particular election and one particular prediction, this could not possibly mean that candidate X would receive from 57 to 59 per cent of the vote about 95 per cent of the time if he ran for office a great number of times. No, if we assign to an estimate a probability of .95 (or some other value) this means that *we are using a method of estimation which we can expect to be successful about 95 per cent of the time.* In other words, *we discuss the accuracy of our results by giving the success ratio of the methods which we have employed.*

In the same fashion we shall express the goodness of decisions which are based on partial information (samples) in terms of the success ratio of the statistical techniques which we have employed. For example, if we decide that one student is better than another on the basis of certain grades, and if we say that we are 80 per cent sure that this decision is correct, *we again imply that we are using a statistical method which promises to provide us with the correct decision about 80 per cent of the time.*

The probabilities which we shall from now on assign to the results of predictions and estimations will therefore always express the goodness of the methods which we have employed, i.e., they will stand for the proportion of the time that we can expect these methods to present us with the correct results if they (the methods) are used a great number of times.

7.3 Some Rules of Probability

Many of the probabilities which we shall study in later chapters will refer to relatively complex situations. It is for this reason that we must now devote a few pages to some of the rules of probability which will be needed for the calculation of the probabilities of more complicated events. If we denote the probability of the occurrence of an event A by the symbol $P(A)$, we can write the first basic rule as

$$0 \leqslant P(A) \leqslant 1 \qquad (7.3.1)$$

which simply expresses the fact that, as we said before, probabilities must always lie between 0 and 1.

Another rule of probability, which follows immediately from the definition, states that the probability that the event A will *not* occur is given by the difference

$$1 - P(A) \qquad (7.3.2)^*$$

which means that the probability that A *will happen* plus the probability that A *will not happen* is equal to 1. For instance, if the probability that it will rain is .35, the probability that it will *not* rain is $1 - .35 = .65$; if our chances of winning a game are .73, our chances of losing it are $1 - .73 = .27$; if we are 95 per cent sure that we are right, we are 5 per cent sure that we are wrong.

The two rules of probability which we shall discuss next deal with the probabilities of the simultaneous occurrence of several events and the occurrence of one of a selection of alternative events. In order to clarify the terminology which we shall use, let us first define what we mean when we say that certain events are *mutually exclusive*. Two or more events are said to be mutually exclusive if they cannot possibly happen at the same time. Heads and tails, for example, are mutually exclusive since we can get heads, we can get tails, but we cannot get both at the same time. Similarly, a man is either born in Chicago or he is not, and an answer to a true-false test is either true or false but never both. On the other hand, if we are trying to make up our mind whether to have apple pie or ice cream for dessert, these two alternatives are *not* mutually exclusive since we could conceivably have both.

If two events A and B are mutually exclusive, the probability that *either* will occur is written as $P(A \text{ or } B)$, and it can be calculated by the formula

$$P(A \text{ or } B) = P(A) + P(B) \qquad (7.3.3)^*$$

To illustrate this formula let us consider the following example. If the probability that any one person drinks tea at a banquet is .45, and the probability that he drinks coffee is .30, the probability that a person drinks *either tea or coffee* is $.45 + .30 = .75$. We were able to use formula (7.3.3) in this example because we have never heard of anybody who drinks both tea *and* coffee (at the same time) at a banquet. The two events are therefore mutually exclusive.

Similarly, if we roll a pair of dice, the probability of getting a 7 is $\frac{6}{36}$, the probability of getting an 11 is $\frac{2}{36}$, and the probability of rolling a 7 or 11 is $\frac{6}{36} + \frac{2}{36} = \frac{8}{36}$. The two events were again mutually exclusive, which enabled us to use formula (7.3.3).

The treatment of events which are *not mutually exclusive* like, for example, sunshine and rain, which could both happen at the same time, is somewhat more complicated. We will be able to understand this problem better if we first examine what is meant by the *dependence* or *independence* of different events. An event B is said to be *independent* of another event A if the probability of the occurrence of B is the same regardless of whether A has previously occurred or is occurring at the same time. If, on the other hand, the probability of B is in any way affected by the result of what happened in A, the two events are said to be *dependent*.

The probability that a driver will wreck his car is *dependent*, for example, on the amount of snow or ice which is on the road; the probability that it will rain tomorrow *depends* to some extent on how the weather is today; and the probability that a student will pass an examination *depends* usually on how much he has studied. On the other hand, if we toss a coin, the result of each toss is *independent* of what might have happened in previous tosses, and the probability that a student will pass an examination should be *independent* of the color of his socks or the size of his shoes.

It is difficult to find illustrations of events which are independent of everything, and, to save ourselves the time which we might spend looking for such events, we should add that *all probabilities assume some unstated conditions on which an event A must depend.* Most of the time these conditions are so evident that they are not even mentioned. When we said that the probability of heads was .50, we assumed all along that the coin would be given a fair spin, and if we now say that the probability that it will rain on the Fourth of July is .35, we must, of course, assume that the world will not have come to an end before that date. If an insurance company claims that the probability of an individual being hit by a car is .002, it is taken for granted that this is true only if the individual exposes himself to the normal risks. If he were to fool us by moving, for example, to the Sahara desert, the probability of his getting hit by an automobile would no longer be the same.

The problem of the sandwiches and the picnic baskets which we gave as an illustration of the dangers of considering events as equally likely is also a good example of *dependent* probabilities. Evidently, the probability that the second sandwich is a ham sandwich *depends* on what kind of a sandwich was selected first.

Now that we have defined what we mean by dependent and independent events we are prepared to study the probability that 2 or more events will happen at the same time. If we write the probability that two events A and B will *both* take place as $P(A$ and $B)$, and if we add that the two events are *independent* of one another, the probability of their joint occurrence is given by the formula

$$P(A \text{ and } B) = P(A) \cdot P(B) \qquad (7.3.4)^*$$

This tells us that we must multiply the respective probabilities of the two events in order to find the probability that both will happen at the same time. This formula can be used, for example, to calculate the probability of getting heads in 2 successive flips of a coin. Since the two events are independent and since the probability is $\frac{1}{2}$ in each case, we find that the probability of getting two heads in a row is $\frac{1}{2} \cdot \frac{1}{2} = \frac{1}{4}$. Similarly, if the probability that it will rain on Joe's birthday is .20, and if the probability that somebody will give him a watch is .01, the probability that it will rain *and* that he will get a watch is $(.20) \cdot (.01) = .002$, since the two events are obviously independent.

It can easily be seen that formula (7.3.4) leads to very unreasonable results if we apply it to events which are not independent. Let us assume, for example, that A stands for the event that Mr. X will rob a certain bank, and that B stands for the event that he will go to jail. If he robs the bank (if A takes place) the probability of B is very large, if he does *not* rob the bank (if A does not take place) the probability of B should be much smaller. Consequently, the probability $P(B)$ assumes different values depending on what has happened in A. It is for this reason that we shall now introduce the concept of a *conditional probability*. The probability that B will happen provided that A has taken place is called the *conditional probability of B relative to A* and it will be written as $P_A(B)$. We can then write for *dependent* events

$$P(A \text{ and } B) = P(A) \cdot P_A(B) \qquad (7.3.5)^*$$

instead of formula (7.3.4). If the event B is independent of A, we can write

$$P(B) = P_A(B)$$

and formula (7.3.5) will reduce to formula (7.3.4), since by assumption the event A has no longer any effect upon the outcome of event B.

To illustrate the use of formula (7.3.5) let us suppose that A stands for a student's passing an examination in mathematics, and that B stands for his passing an examination in physics. The two probabilities $P(B)$ and $P_A(B)$ stand, respectively, for the student's passing in physics and for his passing in physics *provided that he has already passed in mathematics.* It is easy to see that these two probabilities are not the same, as it is a well-known fact that there exists a pronounced relationship between a student's ability in these two subjects. A student who does poorly in mathematics is likely to fail also in physics, while a student who is a genius in mathematics is likely to get high marks in physics. This implies that the probability $P_A(B)$ should be considerably higher than the probability $P(B)$, since the latter makes no reference to the student's performance in mathematics.

Let us suppose now that the probability that a certain student passes mathematics is .70, while the corresponding probability for physics is .80. It follows from what we have just said that the probability that he will pass *both* examinations is *not* equal to the product $(.70) \cdot (.80) = .56$. If we want to evaluate the probability that this student will pass both examinations, we will first have to inquire about the probability $P_A(B)$, which is the probability that he will pass physics if he has already passed in mathematics. Assuming that $P_A(B) = .90$, which could not have been derived from our other information, we find with the use of formula (7.3.5) that $P(A \text{ and } B)$ is equal to $(.70) \cdot (.90) = .63$.

Before we close this brief discussion of the basic rules of probability, let us give one more formula for the probability $P(A \text{ or } B)$ for the case where the two events A and B are *not mutually exclusive.* This probability is given as

$$P(A \text{ or } B) = P(A) + P(B) - P(A \text{ and} B) \qquad (7.3.6)^*$$

and we can use it to calculate the probability that *event A or event B or both* will take place.

Let us ask, for example, for the probability that it will either rain or snow on a given day in December. If the probability that it will rain is .75 and the probability that it will snow is .40, we find that we cannot simply add these two probabilities, as we might have done had we used formula (7.3.3). This would have given us .75 + .40 = 1.15, which is obviously incorrect, since no probability can ever be greater than 1. The mistake which we would thus have made would have been due to our forgetting that formula (7.3.3) applies only to mutually exclusive events. As it can most certainly rain *and* snow on the same day, we would first have to ask for the probability $P(A \text{ and } B)$, the probability that it will rain *and* snow on the same day, and then substitute the various probabilities into formula (7.3.6). Adding the information that $P(A \text{ and } B) = .25$, we can now calculate the desired probability, and we will find that the correct answer is $.75 + .40 - .25 = .90$.

EXERCISES

1. If A stands for a man's being honest and B stands for his being intelligent, write each of the following probabilities in a symbolic form:

(a) The probability that a man is not honest.
(b) The probability that an honest man is intelligent.
(c) The probability that a man is honest and intelligent.
(d) The probability that an intelligent man is honest.

2. If A stands for a man's being a politician and B stands for his being married, write each of the following probabilities in full:

(a) $P_B(A)$ (c) $P(A \text{ and } B)$
(b) $1 - P(B)$ (d) $P_A(B)$

3. Is it true that $P(A)P_A(B) = P(B)P_B(A)$? If A stands for a man's being fat and B for his having a weak heart, what probability is expressed by either side of this equation?

4. Which of the following are dependent and which are independent?

(a) Weight and age.
(b) The outcomes of two successive rolls of a die.
(c) The age and value of automobiles.
(d) The number of aces held in two successive hands in bridge?

5. If K stands for the drawing of a king out of an ordinary deck of cards, while A stands for the drawing of an ace, interpret and evaluate each of the following probabilities:

(a) $P(K)$ (c) $P(K \text{ and } A)$
(b) $P(K \text{ or } A)$ (d) $1 - P(A)$

6. If the probability that any one tooth will decay is .15, while the probability that two adjacent teeth will decay is .08, use formula (7.3.6) to determine the probability that either of two adjacent teeth will decay.

7. The probability that a 50-year-old man will be alive at 60 is .83, and the probability that a 45-year-old woman will be alive at 55 is .87. What is the probability that a man who is 50 and his wife who is 45 will *both* be alive 10 years hence? What assumption must we make?

8. If Jones can hit a target with a probability of .60, what is the probability that he will hit the target three times in succession?

9. If the probability that any one boy will become a criminal is .01, what additional probability must we know in order to be able to calculate the probability that two brothers will become criminals?

10. If three events A, B, and C are mutually exclusive, derive a formula for the probability $P(A$ or B or $C)$.

7.4 The Binomial Distribution and Applications

We are now in the position to get a better understanding of the *binomial distribution* which we used in Chapter 3 as an example of a theoretical distribution. This distribution, which we shall now call a *probability distribution*, was defined by the formula

$$p(x;n) = \binom{n}{x}p^x(1 - p)^{n-x} \qquad (3.3.1)^*$$

which gives us the probability of getting x successes in n trials. This formula, which is used to solve problems dealing with *repeated trials*, is a *distribution* inasmuch as it tells us how the chances of our obtaining 0 successes, 1 success, 2 successes, 3 successes, etc. are distributed. It is called a *probability distribution* because it gives us the distribution of the probabilities which are associated with the various eventualities.

Having defined the concept of probability in the beginning of this chapter, we can now substitute the word *probability* for *proportion* and look upon the normal curve as well as other theoretical distribution as *probability distributions*. This means, for example, that instead of saying that in a normal curve 68 per cent of the values fall within 1 standard deviation on either side of the mean, we say that the *probability* that any one of the values will fall inside of the one-sigma range is .68. Similarly, if the area between two z values is equal to .1500, we shall say that the probability that a value will fall into the corresponding interval is .15.

The words *success* and *trials* were used somewhat loosely in connection with formula (3.3.1). A trial can be any event whatsoever which is subsequently called a success if it fits a certain arbitrary description. If, for example, we want to know the probability that exactly 1 of 12 people who have malaria will die, we might say that we are interested in the probability of 1 success in 12 trials, even though a death is far from what is ordinarily called a success. This odd terminology is due mainly to the fact that the formula for repeated trials, i.e., the binomial distribution, was developed first with reference to certain games of chance. Since then it has assumed an important role in many statistical problems, while its terminology has remained the same.

To illustrate the binomial distribution let us consider the problem of evaluating the probabilities of 0, 1, 2, . . . , 10 successes in 10 trials, assuming that the trials are independent (which is always a necessary prerequisite for the use of the binomial distribution) and that the probability for a success in each separate trial is $\frac{1}{3}$. Substituting $p = \frac{1}{3}$ and $n = 10$ into formula (3.3.1), and letting x equal 0, 1, 2, etc., we can calculate the various probabilities which are shown in the distribution of Fig. 7.a.

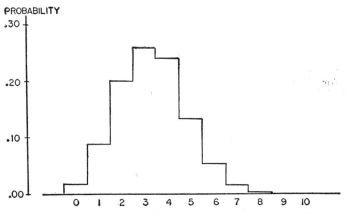

Figure 7.a.   The Binomial Distribution for $p = \frac{1}{3}$ and $n = 10$.

It is interesting to note from this illustration as well as directly from formula (3.3.1) that *the binomial distribution is completely determined, i.e., we are in the position to calculate all probabilities, if we know the two quantities n and p.*   Just as $\bar{x}$ and s were sufficient to determine a unique normal curve, n and p are sufficient to provide one and only one binomial distribution.   Since we have more or less grown accustomed to describe our distributions in terms of measures of central tendencies, measures of variation, etc., let us now see whether we can express the mean and standard deviation of the binomial distribution in terms of n and p.

The formula for the mean of the binomial distribution can easily be found (though not rigorously proven) by means of the following considerations.   If we toss a coin 100 times and if the coin is honest, we expect to get on the average 50 heads.   Similarly, if we perform n trials and if the probability of a success is equal to p in each case, we can then expect on the average n *times* p successes.   This seems to indicate that this average of the binomial distribution is given by the formula

$$m = np \qquad (7.4.1)^*$$

although it remains to be shown that this average agrees with our previous definition of the mean. We shall omit the proof of this formula in our introductory study of statistics, and we shall similarly omit the proof that the standard deviation of the binomial distribution is given by the formula

$$\sigma = \sqrt{np(1 - p)} \qquad (7.4.2)^*$$

If we are now given any arbitrary values for n and p, we can use formulas (7.4.1) and (7.4.2) to find the mean and standard deviation of the binomial distribution which is determined by these values. For example, the mean of the distribution which is shown in Fig. 7.a is $m = 10 \cdot \frac{1}{3} = 3\frac{1}{3}$ and $\sigma = \sqrt{10 \cdot \frac{1}{3} \cdot \frac{2}{3}} = 1.49$.

We pointed out in Chapter 3 that the binomial distribution rapidly approaches the shape of a normal curve when n becomes sufficiently large. As a matter of fact, we tried to picture this approximation by means of the normal curve machine which is illustrated in Fig. 3.j. Although it is true that the binomial distribution approaches a normal curve only when n is large, this approximation is fairly close even when n is as small as 10, provided that p is not far from $\frac{1}{2}$. To illustrate the closeness of this *normal curve approximation of the binomial distribution*, let us investigate the probability of getting 5 heads in 12 tosses of an honest coin, using (1) formula (3.3.1), and (2) the areas of Table I. Putting $n = 12$ and $p = .50$ in formula (3.3.1) we have

$$p(5;12) = \binom{12}{5} \cdot (.50)^5 (.50)^{12-5} = .1933$$

which means that the probability of getting 5 heads in 12 flips of a coin is slightly more than .19.

Now let us see what will happen if we approximate the binomial distribution by means of a normal curve and then calculate the same probability with the use of the areas of Table I. First, we must find the mean of the binomial distribution. Putting $n = 12$ and $p = .50$ into formulas (7.4.1) and (7.4.2) we get

$$m = 12(.50) = 6 \quad \text{and} \quad \sigma = \sqrt{12(.50)(.50)} = 1.732$$

which provides us with the mean and the standard deviation; these will, as we know, determine a unique normal curve to fit our binomial distribution.

Since the binomial distribution is a *discrete* distribution, i.e., we can get only an integral number of successes, we interpret 5 heads as representing the interval from 4.5 to 5.5. This is the customary procedure of spreading a discrete variable over a continuous scale. The two z values which correspond to the end points of the interval which goes from 4.5 to 5.5 are

$$z_1 = \frac{4.5 - 6}{1.732} = -.87 \quad \text{and} \quad z_2 = \frac{5.5 - 6}{1.732} = -.29$$

Their normal curve areas are .3078 and .1141, respectively. Since we are interested in the area between 4.5 and 5.5 (see Fig. 7.b), our

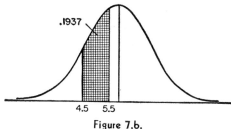

.1937

4.5   5.5

Figure 7.b.

result is given by the difference .3078 − .1141 = .1937, and according to our new interpretation of the normal curve areas, we can say that the probability which is associated with the given interval is .1937. Comparing this result with the value which we obtained earlier by use of (3.3.1), we find that the difference between the two results is for all practical purposes negligible.

This example should help to convince the reader that the binomial distribution can be approximated fairly closely (at times very closely) by means of a normal curve. This fact is of a great importance in problems in which the use of formula (3.3.1) would involve a prohibitive amount of work. Let us suppose, for instance, that we are asked to find the probability that fewer than 25 tulips will bloom among the 40 which have been planted, assuming that the probability that any one tulip will bloom is .75. This is a binomial problem in which $n = 40$, $p = .75$, and in which we must let x take on all values from 0 to 24. If we use formula (3.3.1), we must use it 25 times, once for each possible value of x, and we then must add (see formula 7.3.3) these results to get the total area under the curve which represents the required probability. Granting that this might conceivably take hours, we shall use the normal curve approximation, in which case the problem can be solved in a few minutes.   The mean and standard deviation of the binomial distribution with which we are now dealing are according to (7.4.1) and (7.4.2) equal, respectively, to

$$m = 40(.75) = 30 \quad \text{and} \quad \sigma = \sqrt{40(.75)(.25)} = 2.739$$

Since the number of successes is a discrete variable, 25 must stand for the interval from 24.5 to 25.5, and we shall therefore look for the area which lies below (to the left of) 24.5 (see Fig. 7.c).   The z value

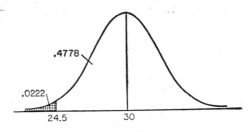

Figure 7.c.

of 24.5 is $z = (24.5 - 30)/2.739 = -2.01$, and the corresponding normal curve area is .4778.   Our result is then given by the difference .5000 − .4778 = .0222, and we can say that the probability that fewer than 25 of the tulips will bloom is a little more than .02.

As a further illustration let us consider the problem of determining the probability that anywhere from 25 to 40 people will pass a given test out of a group of 100 who take it, if it is known that, on the average, only 30 per cent can be expected to pass.   Putting $n = 100$ and $p = .30$, the mean and standard deviation of the corresponding binomial distribution are, respectively,

$$m = 100(.30) = 30 \quad \text{and} \quad \sigma = \sqrt{100(.30)(.70)} = 4.58$$

Since we are interested in the area under the normal curve which lies between 24.5 and 40.5, we first find the z values of these two points. It can easily be seen that this gives us $z_1 = -1.20$ and $z_2 = 2.29$, and that the corresponding normal curve areas are .3849 and .4890. The desired area under the normal curve is then given by the sum of these two areas, and it is equal to .8739.   This means that the probability that from 25 to 40 of the 100 people will pass is about .87. Since many problems which arise in scientific work deal with the estimation of rates, i.e., with the problem of determining *how often we can expect certain things to happen* or *what percentage of the time people will do this or that,* it is extremely important for the beginner to make sure that he understands the meaning of the binomial distribution and its approximation by means of the normal curve.

EXERCISES

1. Find the probability of getting 4 heads in 10 tosses of a coin using both formula (3.3.1) and the normal curve approximation.

2. If a true-false test consists of 50 questions, what is the probability that a student who answers the test by flipping a coin will get 32 or more questions correct? Use the normal curve method.

3. If we know that on the average 20 per cent of a certain kind of seed germinates, what is the probability that out of 200 seeds fewer than 35 will germinate? Use the normal curve method.

4. A manufacturer knows that on the average 2 per cent of his product is defective. What is the probability that a lot of 100 pieces will contain exactly 4 defective pieces? Use the normal curve method.

5. The probability that a poker hand will contain exactly one pair on the deal is about .42. If somebody plays 100 poker hands, what is the probability that he will hold exactly one pair on the deal more than 50 times? Use the normal curve approximation.

6. If we know that 30 per cent of the voters favor candidate X, what is the probability that if we ask any 20 of them, 3 or less will favor this candidate? Use the normal curve method.

7. If Quiz Kids are stumped on the average in 1 out of 4 questions, what is the probability that they will miss exactly 4 out of 20 questions? Use the normal curve approximation.

8. The favorite color of about 65 per cent of the people is red. If we take a sample of 1000 persons, what is the probability that less than 620 of them claim red as their favorite color? Use the normal curve method.

7.5 The Law of Large Numbers

A law of probability which is often completely misunderstood is the *law of large numbers,* which in everyday language is commonly referred to as the *law of averages.* This law states that if we increase the number of trials, i.e., if we repeat whatever we are doing a great number of times, it is practically certain or at least highly probable that the relative frequency of successes will come close to the actual probability of a success. This does *not* mean that we can guarantee that the relative frequency must necessarily come arbitrarily close to the probability, but that our chances of getting close become better and better as we increase the number of trials.

Many people are under the impression that the law which they call the *law of averages* must compensate for the discrepancies which they may find in the outcome of relatively short series of events.   They are inclined to bet on tails after they have observed a long run of heads, claiming that "tails is due to come up, thanks to the law of averages." This common interpretation of the *law of large numbers*, as it is called in statistics, is far from being correct.   Let us suppose, for example, that we have tossed a coin 100 times and that we have observed only 30 heads, which is considerably less than the 50 which we might have expected.   It would be ridiculous to argue at this point that the so-called *law of averages* will induce our coin to behave properly and give us more heads than tails until we have caught up.   As the well-known expression goes, *"a coin has neither a memory nor a conscience to which such a law could possibly appeal."*

For the sake of argument, let us suppose that we then flipped the coin an additional 100 times and obtained 44 more heads.   Does this mean that we can accuse the *law of averages* of having let us down? If we investigate our results more closely, we will discover, to our surprise, that this law has actually been behaving as it should.   After the first series of 100 tosses the relative frequency of heads was $\frac{30}{100} = .30$; after the second series the combined relative frequency was $(30 + 44)/200 = .37$.   This shows that in spite of the fact that the discrepancy between the actual number of heads and the number of heads which we expected had become *worse*, the relative frequency is already coming closer to the probability of .50.   It is important to remember, therefore, that the *law of large numbers* refers to the relative frequency and not necessarily to the actual number of successes.   It is the relative frequency which according to the law of large numbers will *in the long run* come close to the actual probability. More precisely, if n is large we can assert with a probability *close to one* that the difference between the relative frequency and p is very small.

This completes our study of the concept of probability and of some of its fundamental rules.   Although our treatment has not been rigorous, it should enable the reader to understand how probabilities are used in modern science.

REFERENCES

H. C. Levinson, *The Science of Chance*, Rinehart, New York, 1950, Chaps. 5, 6.

R. von Mises, *Probability, Statistics and Truth*, W. Hodge, London, 1939.

E. B. Mode, *The Elements of Statistics*, Prentice-Hall, New York, 1941, Chap. 13.

H. Reichenbach, *The Theory of Probability*, University of California Press, Berkeley, 1949, Chap. 1.

C. H. Richardson, *An Introduction to Statistical Analysis*, Harcourt, Brace, New York, 1935, Chaps. 11, 12.

H. L. Searles, *Logic and Scientific Methods*, Ronald Press, New York, 1948, Chap. 13.

A. E. Waugh, *Elements of Statistical Method*, McGraw-Hill, New York, 1943, Chap. 7.

S. S. Wilks, *Elementary Statistical Analysis*, Princeton University Press, Princeton, 1949, Chaps. 6, 8.

8. SAMPLING AND SAMPLING DISTRIBUTIONS

8.1 Fundamentals of Sampling

We have now a sufficient background to study some of the most basic ideas of inductive statistics, namely, those of *sampling, sampling distributions*, and *populations*. These concepts can be understood most readily if they are illustrated by means of artificial models which use objects such as marbles, dice, and other gambling devices. It should therefore not surprise the reader if he were asked to think, for example, of the opinion of a voter as given by the color of a marble, the salary of a teacher as represented by the number on a slip of paper, and the charge of an electron as given by the numbered top of a milk bottle. Although it must, of course, be understood that these models are only idealizations, it should not be difficult to see why problems relating to samples taken from such models are similar to those which scientists must face in real-life situations.

A set of measurements which constitutes part of the totality of all possible measurements of the same quantity (or quantities) is called a sample of the latter set. If we draw, for example, 5 marbles out of a box into which we placed 200, these 5 form a sample of all of the marbles which were placed into the box. Similarly, if we measure the length of the wings of 25 bees, these measurements form a sample of the length of the wings of *all* the bees from which the 25 were selected. Generally speaking, the technical use of the word *sample* coincides with its everyday connotation.

We sample chocolate fudge which is being prepared on the stove by tasting a small amount, *not the entire batch*, and we consider the information which we have thus obtained as indicative of the quality of the entire product. This illustration makes it plain why we must

144

generally be satisfied with partial information which is based on a sample rather than examine the entire product, i.e., make all possible measurements or observations. If we measure every object (quantity) that we want to describe, we say that our sampling is *exhaustive*. Had we used exhaustive sampling to determine the goodness of our fudge, we might have had a very enjoyable time taking the sample, but none of the product would have remained after we completed our investigation. Another illustration which emphasizes the undesirability of exhaustive sampling pertains to the inspection of lamp bulbs and radio tubes. Manufacturers of such products are usually interested to know the number of hours that their tubes will last in continuous use. It is obvious that they would have no tubes left to sell if they were to test the lifetime of every tube which they produce. Sampling procedures, which damage the product or object which they are supposed to measure, are referred to as *destructive sampling*. It is clear that exhaustive sampling can never be used if the sampling is destructive. Even if it is not destructive, however, it is seldom necessary or advisable to resort to exhaustive sampling techniques. The cost of sampling is usually so high that it does not warrant investigation of large samples, and furthermore, *it is often completely unnecessary to consider large samples, because we can get sufficiently accurate information from samples that are small.* A sample of 500 opinions might well enable us to make a sufficiently accurate prediction of the outcome of an election, and it would be a complete waste of time and money to take, for example, a sample of 10,000 voters. Considerations of this type are particularly important because, as we shall see, the increase in accuracy is usually not proportional to the increase in the size of our samples.

Our last illustration can be used also to explain what a statistician means by a *population* or a *universe*. The very fact that these two terms are synonymous to a statistician makes it evident that they are not used in their colloquial sense. We defined a *sample* in the previous paragraph as a set of measurements which constitutes part of a usually much larger set of measurements. Because it is this larger set of all possible measurements or observations—in our example the opinion of *every* voter—which we want to describe, this set is called the *population* or *universe* from which the sample was selected. Such a population is said to be *finite* if it contains a fixed number of elements, and it is said to be *infinite* if there is, logically speaking, no limit to the number of measurements which we could possibly take.

The population which consists of the opinions of all voters is necessarily a *finite* population because there is only a finite number of people who are able or eligible to vote. Similarly, an urn which contains 20 blue marbles and 30 red ones is also a finite population, although we could, by replacing each marble immediately after it is drawn, treat it as if it were an *infinite* population. If we do this we can, logically speaking, draw an infinite, unlimited number of marbles.

Other illustrations of infinite populations are those consisting of all possible measurements of the velocity of light, all possible measurements of a person's intelligence, or all possible observations of the color of roses. In each case there is no limit to the number of measurements or observations which can be made, except, perhaps, the limitations which are imposed by the shortness of human life.

Infinite populations are really more or less abstract constructions which are used with the understanding that they can only be approximated in actual problems. Evidently, no human being can ever make an unlimited number of observations or perform an infinite number of measurements. Nevertheless, the idea of an infinite population is very helpful because *the composition of such a population is not changed if we remove a few of its items.* If we replace the marbles of our earlier illustration after each drawing, the percentage of red and blue marbles in the urn will never change. On the other hand, if we are working with a finite population, the composition is likely to change each time we select a sample. Had we been interested, for instance, in determining the percentage of blue marbles in the given urn, we would have had to allow for the fact that this percentage would have changed each time we took out a marble.

For this reason most sampling procedures and most inductive methods are based on the assumption that we are dealing with infinite populations. If the population from which we are sampling is reasonably *large*, or if we sample with replacement as we did in the case of the marbles, this assumption is most of the time quite reasonable and should not introduce any appreciable errors into our calculations. However, if a population is small and we cannot sample with replacement, we must use special techniques, most of which are too complicated to be discussed in this text.

The totality of measurements which make up a population will describe a certain distribution which is appropriately called the distribution of the population or, simply, the *population distribution*. If we describe such a population distribution we shall call its descriptive measures (its mean, its standard deviation, and the like) the *parameters* of the population. Considering again the illustration of the 50 marbles, the distribution of this population is

Color	Frequency
red	30
blue	20

Similarly, if we study the weights of the inhabitants of a certain town, the actual distribution of all of their weights constitutes the population distribution. The mean of this population, i.e., the mean of all of the actual weights, is called the *population mean*, and its standard deviation is called the *population standard deviation*. Both of these descriptive measures are *parameters* of the distribution.

In general, the *parameters* are the descriptive measures of the population distribution, *and the parameters are what we are usually interested in estimating on the basis of a sample which has been selected from the population.* If we want to predict an election, for instance, the totality of opinions form the population from which we must take our sample, and the actual percentage of the voters who favor candidate X is the population parameter which we hope to estimate.

Since it is evidently quite important to distinguish between the mean of a sample and the mean of a population, or the standard deviation of a sample and the standard deviation of a population, we must distinguish between the population parameters and the corresponding sample values by denoting them with different symbols. Following the customary procedure we shall write the sample mean and standard deviation as $\bar{x}$ and s, and the corresponding parameters of the population as m and σ. This agrees with our earlier symbolism, according to which we wrote the mean and standard deviation of a theoretical or *expected* distribution as m and σ, respectively.

8.2 The Basic Problems of Inductive Statistics

The primary objective of inductive statistics is to generalize whatever knowledge is given in a sample to the point where we can arrive at conclusions concerning the parameter or parameters of a population. It has been the custom to divide the problems of inductive statistics into two groups. Into the first we classify *all problems in which we try to infer the value of a population parameter on the basis of some descriptive statistic which has been calculated from a sample.* These are the so-called problems of *estimation*. We might, for example, use a sample mean $\bar{x}$ as an *estimate* of the mean m of the population from which we took the sample, or we might use the percentage of red marbles which we obtained in a sample in order to estimate the *actual* percentage of red marbles which were put into the proverbial urn.

The second group of problems deals with the *decisions* which we try to make concerning the parameters of a distribution. We may want to decide, for instance, on the basis of two samples, whether the students of one school are really superior to the students of another. This means that we shall have to *decide* whether the population mean of the actual abilities of the students of the first school is really higher than that of the abilities of the students of the second. Similarly, we may want to *decide* whether candidate X can be expected to win an election. We must *decide* whether the actual percentage of the votes which he will receive will be 50 or more. If we want to test the effectiveness of a new serum, to mention one more example, we shall have to *decide* on the basis of some observations whether the *actual* percentage of cures, namely, the percentage of cures in all possible cases, is higher if the patients are injected with the new serum. As we must decide, in all problems of this type, whether to accept or reject certain hypotheses pertaining to the parameters of the population (or populations), we shall classify these problems under the heading of *the testing of hypotheses*. Chapter 9 will be devoted exclusively to problems of estimation, while Chapter 10 will contain a brief discussion of some of the basic principles which are involved in the testing of hypotheses.

Whenever we use samples as the basis of inductive generalizations such as estimations, predictions, or decisions about hypotheses, we must always insist that our samples be *random*. It would be nice and easy if we could present the reader with a clear-cut definition of what is meant by a random sample, but unfortunately this is not as simple as it may sound. In everyday language the idea of randomness is usually understood to imply a certain *lack of orderliness*. Although the scientific usage of the word *random* is not much different from its everyday use, it is extremely difficult to translate this intuitive and negative definition into precise and scientific terms.

If we sample from a finite population we can say that *a sample is random if every element of the population has an equal chance of being selected for our sample*. In spite of the fact that it is difficult to see how we can ever make sure that this is actually the case, we shall, for the time being, have to be satisfied with this more or less intuitive concept of randomness. As the general problem of randomness is of considerable importance in statistical theory, we shall treat it in more detail in Chapter 11.

8.3 Sampling Distributions

We shall now investigate some of the most basic problems of sampling with the use of a concrete, though somewhat artificial, illustration. Let us suppose that we want to *estimate* the average (mean) height of the men of a certain community and that we must base this estimate on a sample of their heights, selected at random. Before actually collecting the necessary data let us, first, try to get a bird's-eye view of the entire problem, assuming that we have the supernatural powers of Superman and that we can measure, at a glance, the height of every individual male inhabitant of this town.

With the aid of these supernatural powers we can easily discover that the *population distribution*, i.e., the distribution of the heights from which we must take our sample, is

Height (in inches)	Frequency
55–57	7
58–60	116
61–63	761
64–66	2379
67–69	3472
70–72	2379
73–75	761
76–78	116
79–81	7

From this distribution we can immediately calculate the *population* mean as $m = 68$ inches, and the *population standard deviation* as $\sigma = 3.33$ inches. Furthermore, it can easily be seen that the above distribution is extremely close to a normal curve.

If we really had all this information, our problem would be solved. We asked for the mean of the heights, and the answer is 68. Unfortunately, all this knowledge was acquired under the assumption that we were Superman, and since no human being can claim such a distinction we shall have to repeat this problem with the tools and methods which ordinary human beings have at their disposal. It would, of course, be possible to duplicate Superman's work by making an exhaustive study of the entire population, i.e., we could go to the trouble of measuring every height which belongs to our chosen population. However, this would be neither necessary nor practical because, as we shall see, we will be able to obtain a sufficiently accurate estimate from a relatively small and inexpensive sample.

Let us assume, therefore, that we have decided to base our estimate on a sample of 5 measurements, although it is ordinarily advisable to use a few more, particularly if they are not difficult to obtain. We shall limit ourselves to such a small number *only* because it will simplify our calculations. On the other hand, it will not interfere with our purpose of illustrating the fundamental problems of sampling. Let us finally assume that the 5 measurements which we obtained were

$$66, \quad 61, \quad 66, \quad 70, \quad 68$$

from which we can calculate the sample mean as

$$\bar{x} = \frac{66 + 61 + 66 + 70 + 68}{5} = 66.2 \text{ inches}$$

Once we have calculated this mean, we must decide what we can do with it, i.e., how we will be able to use it. As this sample mean is the only information which we actually have about the heights of this population, it seems quite reasonable for us to say that *we shall estimate the average height of the male inhabitants of this town as 66.2 inches.* It is important to realize that this last statement involves a considerable jump, since we are saying something about the average height of thousands of people in spite of the fact that we have measured as few as five. It is obvious that this must give rise to a great number of questions. To mention just a few, we might ask:

1. What right have we to make a statement about the average height of the entire population on the basis of as few as 5 measurements?

2. If we were to repeat this investigation several times, how closely could we expect the various sample means to cluster around the actual mean of the population?

3. How close can we expect a sample mean to be to the true mean (the population mean), say, 95 per cent of the time?

4. What is worst error that we might reasonably expect?

These are all fair questions, but before we can even try to answer them we must conduct an additional experiment. It must be obvious to the reader that it would be silly to expect every sample mean to coincide with the mean of the population. Furthermore, it would be as silly to expect that if we take several samples, their respective means would all be exactly alike. The differences which we expect to find—and which we actually will find—between the results of the various samples are generally attributed to what we might call *chance variation*. It is fortunate, indeed, that this chance fluctuation behaves, as we shall see, in a pretty orderly and predictable fashion.

The experiment which we must now conduct might well be called *a study of the behavior of sample means*. To begin with, we shall take 60 samples of 5 measurements each from the heights of the given population. These samples are shown in the following table:

Sample 1: 66, 61, 66, 70, 68	Sample 31: 66, 73, 70, 70, 73
Sample 2: 58, 73, 66, 65, 65	Sample 32: 73, 68, 63, 74, 71
Sample 3: 66, 73, 66, 65, 65	Sample 33: 75, 64, 70, 69, 71
Sample 4: 68, 65, 66, 70, 68	Sample 34: 68, 67, 70, 67, 69
Sample 5: 67, 64, 70, 69, 63	Sample 35: 71, 68, 65, 68, 69
Sample 6: 62, 72, 67, 67, 71	Sample 36: 73, 70, 65, 69, 67
Sample 7: 66, 69, 67, 65, 69	Sample 37: 64, 72, 66, 70, 69
Sample 8: 64, 64, 64, 70, 64	Sample 38: 67, 66, 69, 69, 67
Sample 9: 72, 69, 67, 64, 64	Sample 39: 62, 61, 66, 68, 69
Sample 10: 68, 66, 67, 71, 72	Sample 40: 64, 70, 69, 72, 68
Sample 11: 65, 68, 63, 65, 76	Sample 41: 66, 74, 68, 74, 69
Sample 12: 65, 70, 70, 63, 73	Sample 42: 64, 74, 66, 66, 69
Sample 13: 72, 64, 70, 63, 66	Sample 43: 68, 70, 69, 67, 73
Sample 14: 64, 72, 68, 70, 68	Sample 44: 66, 66, 66, 70, 68
Sample 15: 70, 63, 71, 65, 59	Sample 45: 72, 70, 63, 69, 70
Sample 16: 71, 70, 68, 62, 68	Sample 46: 60, 67, 71, 67, 67
Sample 17: 72, 64, 72, 66, 65	Sample 47: 68, 63, 61, 67, 61
Sample 18: 68, 67, 66, 65, 66	Sample 48: 66, 68, 68, 61, 63
Sample 19: 62, 71, 73, 62, 68	Sample 49: 65, 68, 63, 65, 65
Sample 20: 72, 68, 71, 65, 67	Sample 50: 67, 69, 64, 66, 68
Sample 21: 67, 65, 64, 61, 66	Sample 51: 65, 68, 68, 63, 72
Sample 22: 73, 66, 68, 66, 69	Sample 52: 65, 66, 69, 72, 64
Sample 23: 64, 68, 67, 70, 67	Sample 53: 71, 68, 69, 68, 70
Sample 24: 70, 65, 62, 71, 68	Sample 54: 71, 65, 66, 64, 67
Sample 25: 66, 70, 69, 71, 64	Sample 55: 68, 74, 63, 70, 64
Sample 26: 63, 66, 70, 69, 68	Sample 56: 70, 71, 58, 61, 66
Sample 27: 74, 66, 68, 71, 70	Sample 57: 65, 70, 72, 71, 67
Sample 28: 61, 67, 67, 67, 67	Sample 58: 69, 66, 65, 68, 68
Sample 29: 71, 74, 65, 62, 72	Sample 59: 73, 70, 64, 69, 66
Sample 30: 67, 69, 73, 69, 62	Sample 60: 67, 71, 64, 66, 61

Now that we have collected all this information we are in the position to compute the mean of each of the 60 samples. If we do this and group our results, we will get the following distribution of the sample means:

Sample means	Frequency
63.5–64.5	1
64.5–65.5	8
65.5–66.5	6
66.5–67.5	17
67.5–68.5	14
68.5–69.5	9
69.5–70.5	5

Since this distribution consists of the $\bar{x}$'s of the various samples, it is appropriately called an (experimental) *sampling distribution of* $\bar{x}$.

We could similarly construct the sampling distribution of any other statistic which we may choose to calculate from the given samples. If we take a large number of samples from a given population and calculate, in each case, the value of some chosen statistic (description), we can always group these values into a distribution which will be called the *sampling distribution* of the respective statistic. This means that we can also speak of the sampling distribution of the standard deviations which are obtained from repeated samples, the sampling distribution of the sample medians, the sampling distribution of the sample ranges, and the like.

As a matter of convenience we shall limit our discussion for the time being to the sampling distribution of the means, although it must be understood that all our considerations apply to all other sampling distributions as well.

If we now study some of the usual characteristics of the above distribution of the means and their histogram, which is given in Fig. 8.a, we will find, among other things, that the *mean* of this sampling distribution is 66.9 and its standard deviation 1.49. Whether or not this information will prove to be of any value will depend on whether it will enable us to answer the questions which were asked on page 150. After all, this was the purpose of our taking the additional 60 samples.

A casual inspection of Fig. 8.a makes it quite evident that all the sample means are clustered fairly closely about the true mean of 68 in a distribution which, with a little imagination, might be described as having the shape of a normal curve. The smallest value of $\bar{x}$ was 64 and the largest value was 70.4, neither of which deviate much from the actual mean of the population. Furthermore, only two sample means differed from 68 by more than two standard deviations (2 times 1.49), which is about 3 per cent of all of the sample means.

FREQUENCY

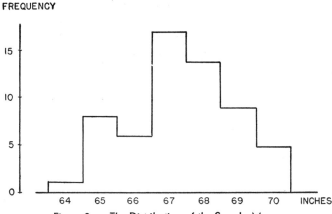

Figure 8.a. The Distribution of the Sample Means.

If this distribution were really a normal curve, we could then say that 95 per cent of the means should fall inside of the two-sigma range. It is interesting to note, therefore, that in our sampling distribution of the means 58 out of 60, or 97 per cent of the $\bar{x}$'s fell within two standard deviations on either side of the mean. This is, indeed, very close to the percentage which we would have expected *if* this sampling distribution were actually a normal curve.

If it were really true that the sampling distribution of the means can be expected to be close to a normal curve, we could then say that *the probability that a sample mean will differ from the true mean (the population mean) by more than two standard deviations is slightly less than .05.* This means that we could expect an *error* which is as large as two standard deviations only about 5 per cent of the time. It must be remembered, of course, that the standard deviation which we have been talking about is *the standard deviation of the sampling distribution of the means*, which, in our example, was equal to 1.49. We can therefore say that for sample means which consist of five measurements from the given population, the probability that the interval from $\bar{x} - 2.98$ (which is 2 standard deviations *below* the mean) to $\bar{x} + 2.98$ (which is 2 standard deviations *above* the mean) will contain the mean of the population, *is approximately .95*. It was advisable to add the word *approximately* because we really do not know whether our sampling distribution can be treated as if it were a normal curve, nor do we know whether the standard deviation, namely, 1.49, was really accurate.

These considerations seem to imply that if we want to evaluate the accuracy of an estimate which is based on a statistic (in our case the mean) we must refer to the sampling distribution of the respective statistic. If we take samples from a population which is normally distributed, or at least reasonably close to a normal curve, we are in the fortunate position of having at our disposal some very useful theorems concerning the sampling distributions of various statistics. Without giving a proof, let us take, for example, the following theorem dealing with the sampling distribution of the means:

THEOREM A: *If we take random samples of size n (a sample is said to be of size n if it contains n measurements) from a normal population which has the mean m and the standard deviation σ, the sampling distribution of the sample means is also a normal curve with the mean m and the standard deviation $\sigma/\sqrt{n}$.*

Since the distribution with which we began our experiment on page 149 had its mean m equal to 68 and its standard deviation σ equal to 3.33, and since it was, by construction, very close to a normal curve, we could expect, according to *Theorem A*, that the sampling distribution of the means should be a normal curve with the mean $m = 68$ and a standard deviation of $3.33/\sqrt{5} = 1.49$. It is very interesting to note that although we took as few as 60 samples, the distribution of their means was surprisingly close to what we might have expected according to Theorem A.

It is customary to denote the standard deviation of the sampling distribution of the means by the symbol $\sigma_{\bar{x}}$. We can therefore write that according to Theorem A,

$$\sigma_{\bar{x}} = \frac{\sigma}{\sqrt{n}} \qquad (8.3.1)^*$$

This quantity is usually called the *standard error of the mean*. Since we have learned from our experiment that the accuracy of an estimate is best discussed in terms of the sampling distribution of the statistic on which the estimate is based, *and* since the standard deviations of such sampling distributions tell us the amount of variation (error) which we may expect, *the standard errors of the various statistics are of fundamental importance in the analysis of the accuracy of our results.*

It can be seen directly from formula (8.3.1) that the *standard error of the mean* becomes smaller and smaller if we increase the size of our samples. This means that when n becomes large, our estimates will become more reliable, i.e., the sample means will, on the average, differ by less and less from the actual mean of the population. This last remark is really nothing but a precise mathematical formulation of the intuitive idea that our results (estimates) should be more accurate if they are based on larger samples or, in other words, on more information.

The discussion of the last two pages makes it possible for us to explain what is meant by the comparative reliability of two or more different statistical measures. *If the sampling distribution of one statistic has a smaller variation, a smaller standard error, than the sampling distribution of another statistic, we can then say that the first statistic is more reliable than the second.* (It should be added, however, that this comparison is valid only if the two sampling distributions have more or less the same shape, e.g., if they are both normal curves.)

To illustrate the comparison of the reliability or accuracy of two statistics, let us return briefly to our original experiment. Let us take the same 60 samples for which we have already calculated the means, and let us now calculate their respective sample medians. If we do this, we will obtain the following *sampling distribution of the medians.*

Sample medians	Frequency
63	1
64	1
65	4
66	14
67	9
68	13
69	10
70	6
71	2

The mean and standard deviation of this sampling distribution, which is also represented as a histogram in Fig. 8.b, are equal to 67.5 and 1.74, respectively. This tells us that the sampling distribution of the median has a *wider spread*, a *greater variation*, than the sampling distribution of the mean. Therefore we say that the sample mean is a more reliable estimate of the mean of a normal population than the sample median, or that *the mean is subject to less chance variation than the median.* If we sample from a normal population, we can state the following theorem concerning a sampling distribution of the median.

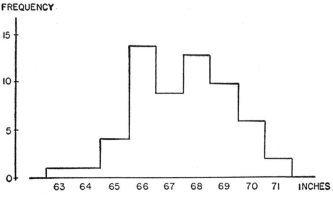

Figure 8.b.   The Distribution of the Sample Medians.

THEOREM B: *If we take random samples of size n from a normal population which has the mean m and the standard deviation σ, then if n is large, the sampling distribution of the median is closely approximated by a normal curve with the mean m and the standard deviation* $(1.2533)(\sigma/\sqrt{n})$.

We can thus write the *standard error of the median* as

$$\sigma_M = (1.2533)\frac{\sigma}{\sqrt{n}} \qquad (8.3.2)^*$$

which tells us that the standard error of the median is about 25 per cent larger than the standard error of the mean.

The following is another important theorem concerning the sampling distribution of the mean.   It refers to the sampling distribution of the mean for samples taken from populations which are not necessarily normally distributed.

THEOREM C: (*Central Limit Theorem*) *If we take random samples of size n from a population which has the mean m and the standard deviation σ, then if n is large, the sampling distribution of the mean is very closely approximated by a normal curve whose mean and standard deviation are equal to m and* $\sigma/\sqrt{n}$, *respectively.*

This theorem is extremely important because it enables us to apply normal curve methods in the discussion of the accuracy of sample means *regardless of whether the samples were taken from normal populations.*

It would be entirely erroneous to jump to the conclusion that the sampling distribution of every statistic must necessarily be a normal curve. As we shall see in the next few chapters, this is indeed not the case. Fortunately, it is usually quite reasonable to approximate most sampling distributions by means of normal curves *if* (and only if) we are dealing with very large samples.

REFERENCES

M. M. Blair, *Elementary Statistics*, Holt, New York, 1944, Chap. 14.

W. E. Deming, *Some Theory of Sampling*, Wiley, New York, 1950, Chap. 4A.

W. J. Dixon and F. J. Massey, *Introduction to Statistical Analysis*, McGraw-Hill, New York, 1951, Chap. 4.

J. P. Guilford, *Fundamental Statistics in Psychology and Education*, McGraw-Hill, New York, 1950, Chap. 9.

W. A. Neiswanger, *Elementary Statistical Methods*, Macmillan, New York, 1948, Chap. 4.

S. S. Wilks, *Elementary Statistical Analysis*, Princeton University Press, Princeton, 1949, Chap. 9.

EXERCISES

1. If we measure the length of a table 3 times, do these measurements form a sample? If so, what is the population from which we are sampling?

2. If we take the college indexes of 50 individuals, selected at random among the students of a certain university, what is the population from which we are sampling?

3. What happens to the standard error of the mean if we quadruple the size of our sample?

4. What happens to the standard error of the mean if we increase the size of our sample from 10 to 1000 observations? What does this tell us about the accuracy of the means of the two samples?

5. Combine the 60 samples which are given on page 151 into 30 samples of size 10. Calculate the mean of each of these 30 samples, group the sample means, and calculate the mean and standard deviation of this experimental sampling distribution of the mean. How does this standard deviation of the means compare with the value which we should have expected according to formula (8.3.1)?

6. Combine the 60 samples which are given on page 151 into 15 samples of size 20, combining the first four, the next four, etc. Find the mean of each of these 15 samples and calculate the standard deviation of these means without grouping them first. How does this result compare with the value which we should have expected according to formula (8.3.1)?

7. Calculate the range of each of the 60 samples which are given on page 151. Group the resulting 60 sample ranges and calculate the mean and standard deviation of this sampling distribution.

8. Take 100 milk-bottle tops, metal-rim tags, or other small symmetrical

cardboard objects, and record on them the following numbers with the given frequencies, i.e., write the number 1 on *one* tag, the number 2 on *three* tags, the number 3 on *seven* tags, etc.

Number to be written on tag	Frequency
1	1
2	3
3	7
4	12
5	17
6	20
7	17
8	12
9	7
10	3
11	1

This provides us with a population for which $m = 6$ and $\sigma = 2$, and which is closely approximated by a normal curve. Take 50 random samples of size 3, replacing the tags after each sample is drawn, and compute the mean and median of each of these 50 samples. Then construct a distribution of the sample means and calculate its mean and standard deviation. How does this standard deviation compare with the value which we should have expected according to formula (8.3.1)? Repeat this work with the 50 sample medians and compare the resulting standard deviation of the sample medians with the value which we should have expected according to formula (8.3.2).

9. PROBLEMS
OF ESTIMATION

9.1 Introduction

Many statistical problems deal with the figuring out, or more correctly, with the estimating of the unknown parameters of a population. The experiment of the previous chapter, namely, the problem of determining the true mean of the heights of the given individuals, was a problem of estimation. Similarly, the problem of finding a coefficient of friction or a molecular weight, the problem of finding the true standard deviation of a set of I.Q.'s, and the problem of determining the percentage of cures which a new drug will produce— all are problems of estimation.

Estimates of population parameters are practically always based on statistics (descriptive measures of samples) which are chosen either because of their inherent accuracy and reliability, or because they can be found with minimum effort. We can estimate a population mean m using, for instance, the mean of a sample, or we can estimate it on the basis of a sample median or mode; similarly, we can estimate a population standard deviation σ in terms of a sample standard deviation s or in terms of a sample range. Since the choice of the statistic which is to be used in a given problem must evidently be based on practical considerations, let us investigate first what approach we should use so that our estimates will impart a maximum amount of information with a minimum risk of ambiguity or misinterpretation. Oddly enough, the question of *how to state the results of a problem of estimation* will lead us to one of the most fundamental problems of statistics. The difficulties which we shall encounter in discussing the accuracy of an estimate, i.e., the difficulties of explaining the relationship between an estimate and the parameter which it is supposed to estimate, are brought out clearly in the following illustration. Let us suppose that we are again trying to estimate the average height which we experimented with in the last chapter, and that we are now going to base our estimate on the following 20 observations which constitute a random sample from the population which was given on page 149.

| 73, | 66, | 68, | 66, | 69, | 66, | 73, | 70, | 70, | 73 |
| 66, | 61, | 66, | 70, | 68, | 58, | 73, | 66, | 65, | 65 |

It can easily be seen that the mean and standard deviation of this sample are 67.6 and 3.78 inches, respectively.

If we now want to *estimate* the true average height (the population parameter m) on the basis of this sample mean, there is practically no limit to the variety of methods which we can use to state our result. To mention just a few of the many possible ways of stating our result, let us consider the following four alternatives.

Alternative 1. The mean of the population is estimated to be equal to 67.6 inches.

Alternative 2. The mean of the population is estimated to be equal to 67.6 inches. This estimate is based on the mean of a sample of 20 measurements.

Alternative 3. The mean of the population is estimated as 67.6 inches, which is the mean of a sample of 20 measurements which had a standard deviation of 3.78 inches. (Instead of using all these words, we could simply have stated that $\bar{x} = 67.6$, $n = 20$, and $s = 3.78$.)

Alternative 4. We are 95 per cent sure (certain, or confident) that the interval from 65.74 to 69.46 inches contains the actual mean of the population.

It should be apparent that whereas the first three alternatives are, in principle, much alike, the fourth is of an entirely different nature. The first alternative is not a particularly good way to report an estimate because it not only fails to mention the size of the sample and the fact that we used $\bar{x}$ but it also puts us in a spot where we cannot draw any conclusions whatsoever about the accuracy of our result.

Although the second alternative does present a slight improvement, it still has the unfortunate shortcoming that it tells us nothing about the variation of the measurements which made up the sample. It is true that we can use the fact that large samples are usually more reliable than small ones, but we are still in no position to get a real appraisal of the accuracy of the estimate.

The third alternative provides us with all information which we might need in order to discuss the reliability of our estimate, but it has the serious disadvantage that a considerable knowledge of statistics is required to translate the given values of s and n into an evaluation of the accuracy of the estimate. This criticism of the third alternative is quite important because it must be remembered that most statistical results are addressed to nonstatisticians. Consequently, it would be desirable to have a method of presenting an estimate which has not only the advantages of alternative 3, but which also tells us the whole story in a language which can be understood by a person who has had no statistical training.

Offhand it seems that alternative 4 might fill the prescription, although we must see whether the intuitive expression that we are *95 per cent sure* does have a precise scientific meaning. If we remember our discussion of the *meaning of probability* in Chapter 7, it is immediately obvious that *if we assign an estimate a probability of .95, i.e., if we say that we are 95 per cent sure, this means that we have used a method of estimation which is successful about 95 per cent of the time.* The statement which was made in alternative 4 implies, therefore, that it would be a fair bet to give 19 to 1 odds (95 to 5) that the interval from 65.74 to 69.46 inches contains the mean of the population. Had we wanted to be more certain, had we wanted to be able to give better odds, we could, for instance, have stated with a degree of confidence of .99 that the interval from 65.06 to 70.14 inches contains the true average height. It is interesting to note that in the fourth alternative we did not have to bother giving details about $\bar{x}$, s, and n, substituting instead an interval which supposedly contains the mean which we wanted to estimate. Alternative 4 presents us, therefore, with a method of stating our results in a form which is easily understood by the layman, which does not require any further calculations, and which informs us directly of the reliability of our method of estimation.

9.2 Point Estimates and Confidence Intervals

An estimate is said to be a *point estimate* if it is presented as a single number. Alternatives 1, 2, and 3 are all point estimates, since the mean of the population is given as 67.6, regardless of the additional information which might have been supplied. An obvious disadvantage of point estimates is that it would be silly to claim that the population parameters which we want to estimate must actually be equal to our estimates. For example, the population mean of our illustration was equal to 68, while our estimate was only 67.6. Consequently, if we want to discuss the accuracy of a point estimate we cannot ask whether the estimate is *equal* to the population mean, but only whether it is close. This means that in order to discuss the significance of this kind of estimate we must bring in sampling distributions, standard errors, etc., all of which are Greek to the average layman.

In contrast to these difficulties, alternative 4 provided us with an estimate by claiming that a certain interval contains the true value of *m*. Such estimates are appropriately called *interval estimates.* Since we assert with a certain degree of confidence (with a certain probability) that the interval will do its job, we shall call it a *confidence interval.* Furthermore, since it is not very scientific to say that we are 95 per cent sure or 95 per cent certain, we shall say instead that we have a *95 per cent confidence interval.* If we want to be more certain, we can similarly speak of *98 per cent confidence intervals* and *99 per cent confidence intervals*, which means that we can assert with probabilities of .98 and .99, respectively, that the interval will cover the population mean.

Whereas it was senseless to ask whether a point estimate was right or wrong, we now find that *interval estimates are always either true or false, depending on whether the population parameter which we are trying to estimate is actually covered by the interval or not.* This makes it easy to express and explain the accuracy of our estimates without having to refer to advanced statistical techniques.

If a confidence interval is wide, our estimate is either very inaccurate or we are asking for too high a degree of confidence. Had we wanted to be 99 per cent confident, for example, of the interval which we used in our illustration, the resulting interval would have been *wider* than the one which we were able to assert with a confidence of .95. Had we wanted to be 100 per cent sure, we could have given the interval from 0 to infinity, but this would no longer have told us anything about the mean of the population. *For all practical purposes we can, therefore, be as sure as we want, but the surer we are, the less we have to be sure of.* In other words, if we ask for an unreasonably high degree of confidence, we will get an interval which is so wide that it will tell us very little about the actual value of the mean of the population (or whatever parameter we are trying to estimate).

It has generally been accepted that a degree of confidence of .95 is quite suitable for most problems of estimation. A success ratio of .95, or odds of 19 to 1, express more or less what a scientist means when he says that he is reasonably certain. If a higher degree of confidence appears to be more desirable, we can, of course, construct confidence intervals for any arbitrary degree of confidence. It is needless to say that the method of interval estimation is not limited to the estimation of population means, but applies to the estimation of other population parameters as well. It is used, for instance, in the estimation of percentages, standard deviations, and for that matter, for estimation of any arbitrary population parameter.

Until now we have, so to speak, pulled out of a hat the confidence intervals which we have used as illustrations. The question of *how* confidence intervals are constructed is something which we have not yet discussed but, as we shall see in the next few sections, this will not prove to be difficult once we have fully grasped the meaning and significance of the sampling distribution of a statistical measure.

9.3 Confidence Intervals for Population Means (Large Samples)

Let us now turn to the problem of actually constructing confidence intervals for the mean of a population. We have already pointed out in the last chapter (Theorem C) that *for large samples* the sampling distribution of the mean is closely approximated by a normal curve whose mean and standard deviation are respectively equal to m and $\sigma/\sqrt{n}$, where m and σ are, respectively, the mean and standard deviation of the population from which we are taking the sample. Before we can continue with our problem, we must be somewhat more precise, however, as to what we understand by a large sample. It is difficult to draw an arbitrary line and to say that if n is less than a given number the sample is small, while otherwise the sample is large. However, as a matter of convenience (and also for some fairly important theoretical reasons) we shall agree that a sample is *small* if it contains less than 30 measurements. A sample which consists of 30 measurements or more will accordingly be called *large*.

Let us now continue our discussion of the construction of confidence intervals for m which are to be based on large samples. To do this let us suppose that Fig. 9.a represents the sampling distribution of the mean for samples of size n. This distribution has the mean m and the standard deviation (standard error) $\sigma_{\bar{x}} = \sigma/\sqrt{n}$, and assuming that it is a normal curve we can now ask for two values z_1 and z_2 (see Fig. 9.a) which are such that 95 per cent of the sample means can be expected to fall between these two points. As we shall

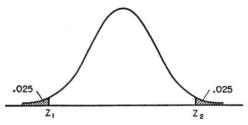

Figure 9.a.

see, the selection of these two points is not unique because we can distribute the remaining 5 per cent of the area arbitrarily between the two tails of the distribution.   In Fig. 9.a, we arbitrarily distributed this 5 per cent of the area *evenly* between the two tails, but in Fig. 9.b we put 4 per cent to the left of z_1 and 1 per cent to the right of z_2.   *Most of the time it is advantageous to put half of the area into each of the two tails, since this will tend to make the resulting confidence interval as short as possible.*   This is true, at least, for symmetrical distributions.

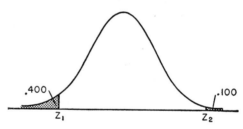

Figure 9.b.

Putting the sampling distribution of the mean which is given in Fig. 9.a into the *standard form*, we can then say that the probability that a z which corresponds to an arbitrary sample mean will fall between z_1 and z_2 is given by the normal curve area which lies between z_1 and z_2.   This means that we can say with a certain probability (usually .95) that

$$z_1 < z < z_2 \qquad (9.3.1)$$

Since by definition z is always equal to the deviation from the mean divided by the standard deviation, we can now put

$$z = \frac{\bar{x} - m}{\sigma_{\bar{x}}} \qquad (9.3.2)$$

It must be understood, of course, that we have taken the deviation of the sample mean $\bar{x}$ from the mean m of its sampling distribution and divided it by the standard deviation of the sampling distribution. Substituting (9.3.2) into (9.3.1) we obtain

$$z_1 < \frac{\bar{x} - m}{\sigma_{\bar{x}}} < z_2 \qquad (9.3.3)$$

which can also be written

$$\bar{x} - z_2\sigma_{\bar{x}} < m < \bar{x} - z_1\sigma_{\bar{x}} \qquad (9.3.4)$$

Since we know from Theorem A of Chapter 8 that $\sigma_{\bar{x}} = \sigma/\sqrt{n}$, we can finally write this expression as

$$\bar{x} - z_2\frac{\sigma}{\sqrt{n}} < m < \bar{x} - z_1\frac{\sigma}{\sqrt{n}} \qquad (9.3.5)$$

which gives us the desired confidence interval for m. The degree of confidence with which we can assert such an interval will, of course, depend on the values which we select for z_1 and z_2.

If we were to try calculating *confidence limits* (end points of the confidence interval) by use of (9.3.5), we would notice that we must know $\bar{x}$, n, and σ, and some suitably chosen values of z_1 and z_2. The disadvantage of formula (9.3.5) is that we can *practically never* know the true value of the standard deviation σ. This means that we must approximate it, perhaps with the sample standard deviation s. Unfortunately, this approximation is reasonable *only* if we are dealing with large samples, and it follows that the confidence intervals which are given in expression (9.3.6) cannot be used if n is small. Substituting s for σ, we can now rewrite formula (9.3.5) as

$$\bar{x} - z_2\frac{s}{\sqrt{n}} < m < \bar{x} - z_1\frac{s}{\sqrt{n}} \qquad (9.3.6)$$

and we will have a formula which gives us *confidence intervals for m for large samples.* If we want to assert these intervals with a confidence of .95, we must find the corresponding values of z_1 and z_2 from Table I. Putting 2.5 per cent of the area into each tail of the normal curve, we must thus locate the z which corresponds to an area of $.5000 - .0250 = .4750$. It can be found without difficulty that this will give us $z_1 = -1.96$ and $z_2 = 1.96$. (It is usually sufficiently accurate to approximate these two values as -2 and $+2$.)

Formula (9.3.6) cannot be used in the problem which we have used as an illustration earlier in this chapter because the size of the sample (n was equal to 20) does not permit us to use large sample techniques. Let us therefore add 10 more measurements and consider the following sample:

73,	66,	68,	69,	66,	66,	73,	70,	70,	73
66,	61,	66,	70,	68,	58,	73,	66,	65,	65
66,	73,	66,	65,	65,	68,	65,	66,	70,	68

This sample has a mean of 67.47 and a standard deviation of 3.42 which, incidentally, is quite close to the population standard deviation, which was 3.33. Substituting these values into (9.3.6), the 95 per cent confidence interval of m is

$$67.47 - 1.96 \frac{3.42}{\sqrt{30}} < m < 67.47 + 1.96 \frac{3.42}{\sqrt{30}}$$

or $\qquad\qquad 66.25 < m < 68.69$

and we can claim that we are 95 per cent sure that this interval contains the true mean of the population. The fact that this interval *does* cover the mean of the population is known to us only because Superman informed us that the population mean is 68.

If we had wanted to construct the 95 per cent confidence interval which was described in Fig. 9.b, we would first find the two z values which correspond to the normal curve areas of .4900 and .4600. This will give us $z_1 = -1.75$ and $z_2 = 2.33$, and the resulting 95 per cent confidence interval is

$$67.47 - 2.33 \frac{3.42}{\sqrt{30}} < m < 67.47 + 1.75 \frac{3.42}{\sqrt{30}}$$

or $\qquad\qquad 66.02 < m < 68.56$

It is interesting to observe that the confidence interval which divided the 5 per cent evenly between the two tails had a width of $68.69 - 66.25 = 2.44$, while the second confidence interval had the greater width of $68.56 - 66.02 = 2.54$. Since it is obviously desirable to make the interval as short as possible (for a fixed degree of confidence), this demonstrates the fact which we have pointed out before, namely, that it is desirable to put equal areas into the two tails of the sampling distribution.

A frequent mistake in the interpretation of a confidence interval is repeated in the statement: "If we assign an interval a degree of confidence of .95, this means that the probability that the population mean will fall into the interval is .95." This interpretation of the confidence interval is *incorrect* because the interval either does or does not contain the population mean. Consequently, the probability does not refer to the location of the mean of the population, but to the methods which we have used in this process of estimation. It cannot be repeated too often that *the degree of confidence, i.e., the probability of .95, .99, etc., refers to the success ratio of our method, in this case to the method of interval estimation which we have used.*

In general, if a population mean is estimated on the basis of a large sample, the 95 per cent confidence interval is given by the expression

$$\bar{x} - 1.96 \frac{s}{\sqrt{n}} < m < \bar{x} + 1.96 \frac{s}{\sqrt{n}} \qquad (9.3.7)^*$$

and the reader can easily check for himself that the corresponding 98 and 99 per cent confidence intervals are

$$\bar{x} - 2.33 \frac{s}{\sqrt{n}} < m < \bar{x} + 2.33 \frac{s}{\sqrt{n}} \qquad (9.3.8)^*$$

$$\bar{x} - 2.58 \frac{s}{\sqrt{n}} < m < \bar{x} + 2.58 \frac{s}{\sqrt{n}} \qquad (9.3.9)^*$$

The techniques which we used so far can also be used to solve questions of similar type. Let us consider, for example, the following:

Example 1. If the intelligence quotients of a sample of 100 students have a mean of 108 and a standard deviation of 12.4, with what degree of confidence can we assert that this sample mean differs from the average intelligence quotient of all the students from which the sample was taken *by less than 3?*

Since this sample is large, it is reasonable to treat the sampling distribution of $\bar{x}$ as if it were a normal curve which has the standard deviation $12.4/\sqrt{100} = 1.24$ (see formula 8.3.1). The probability of getting a sample mean which differs from the population mean by 3 or more is found with the z value which corresponds to this deviation from the mean. We have, therefore, $z = 3/1.24 = 2.42$, and the corresponding normal curve area is .4922. As we are interested in the area which lies between $z = -2.42$ and $z = 2.42$, the probability which we were asked to find is twice .4922, or .9844. It follows that we can say that we are about *98.5 per cent confident* that the sample mean of 108 does not differ from the population mean by 3 or more. In other words, the interval from 105 to 111 is a 98.5 per cent confidence interval of the mean. The distinction between this problem and the ones which we discussed before is that we are now given the interval and asked to find its degree of confidence, while previously it was the other way around.

> *Example 2.* Let us suppose that a biologist wants to estimate the mean diameter of the human ovum and that he knows from past experience that measurements of this type have a standard deviation of .02 mm. How large a sample must he take in order to be able to state with a confidence of .95 that his estimate will not differ from the true mean diameter by more than .005 mm?

If the biologist is going to base his estimate on the mean of his sample, we know from formula (9.3.7) that for 95 per cent confidence intervals the difference between the unknown mean of the population and the mean of the sample is at most

$$1.96 \frac{s}{\sqrt{n}}$$

Since we are asked to make this quantity equal to .005, we can write

$$1.96 \frac{.02}{\sqrt{n}} = .005$$

where .02 is the known standard deviation. Solving this equation for n, we have $\sqrt{n} = 7.84$ or $n = 61.5$. A sample of *size 62* would thus be sufficient to enable the biologist to assert with a degree of confidence of .95 that his error will not exceed .005 mm (see also Fig. 9.c).

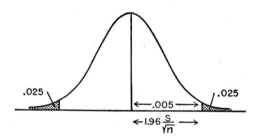

Figure 9.c.

In most problems of this type it is advisable to begin by drawing a picture of the sampling distribution, indicate whatever information we might have, and decide on the basis of this diagram what z values or areas we must find in order to solve the problem. The method which was illustrated in Example 2 is particularly important, because it enables us to determine the *minimum sample size* which is needed to guarantee a desired degree of accuracy (for a given degree of confidence).

9.4 Confidence Intervals for Population Means (Small Samples)

As we have pointed out in the previous section, formulas (9.3.7), (9.3.8), and (9.3.9) cannot be used for small samples because the sample standard deviation s can then not be expected to be sufficiently close to the true value of σ. This means that if we are dealing with small samples we cannot substitute s for σ in (9.3.5). To eliminate this difficulty we shall consider instead of the sampling distribution of $\bar{x}$ the sampling distribution of the statistic

$$\frac{\bar{x} - m}{s} \sqrt{n - 1}$$

which is a theoretical distribution that goes by the name of the *Student-t distribution*, and was originally developed by W. S. Gosset who published his work under the pen name of Student.

If we take samples of size n from a normal population which has the mean m and the standard deviation σ, the statistic

$$t = \frac{\bar{x} - m}{s} \sqrt{n - 1} \qquad (9.4.1)$$

has a sampling distribution which differs slightly from the normal curve (see Fig. 9.d), but which approaches the normal curve when n

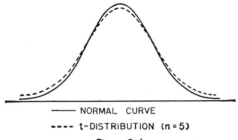

——— NORMAL CURVE

- - - - t-DISTRIBUTION (n = 5)

Figure 9.d.

is large. Since this t distribution is, like the normal curve, a symmetrical distribution, it will again suffice to tabulate its areas only for positive values of t. It would not be practical, however, to tabulate this distribution as we have tabulated the normal curve, since this would make it necessary to give a separate table for each value of n. As we are interested primarily in knowing the t's (which in most respects are very similar to the z values of the normal curve) above or below which we can expect to find 5, 2.5, 1, and .5 per cent of the area under the curve, these particular values of t are given in Table II for values of n from 2 to 30. It will simplify our symbolism considerably if we denote the value of t above which we can find the highest 5 per cent of the area under the curve as $t_{.05}$, the value above which we can find the highest 1 per cent as $t_{.01}$, etc. (Table II is on page 390.)

Applying now the identical reasoning which we used in the derivation of the confidence intervals of m for large samples, we can say that the probability of our getting a sample value of t which lies between $-t_{.025}$ and $t_{.025}$ is .95. This means that 95 per cent of the t's which we might compute from our samples by use of (9.4.1) can be expected to satisfy the inequality

$$-t_{.025} < t < t_{.025} \qquad (9.4.2)$$

Substituting (9.4.1) in place of t, we have

$$-t_{.025} < \frac{\bar{x} - m}{s} \sqrt{n - 1} < t_{.025}$$

which can also be written as

$$\bar{x} - t_{.025} \frac{s}{\sqrt{n - 1}} < m < \bar{x} + t_{.025} \frac{s}{\sqrt{n - 1}} \qquad (9.4.3)*$$

This last formula provides us with the necessary 95 per cent confidence interval of m for small samples.

Comparing this result with formula (9.3.7), which we used to calculate the corresponding confidence interval for large values of n, we will note that although the two formulas look much alike, they exhibit the following differences: instead of the square root of n we now have the square root of $(n - 1)$, and instead of the normal curve z value of 1.96 we are now using the t value, which is written as $t_{.025}$ and depends on the sample size n. When n is large (30 or more) there is practically no difference between 1.96 and $t_{.025}$ (see Table II), and the difference in the confidence limits is even smaller because we are using $n - 1$ instead of n.

If it is preferable to use confidence intervals which can be asserted with a confidence of .98 or .99, we simply replace $t_{.025}$ by $t_{.01}$ or $t_{.005}$ in formula (9.4.3). These values can also be found in Table II.

To illustrate the calculation of the confidence limits of a mean on the basis of a small sample, let us consider the 20 observations which we used as an example in the beginning of this chapter. We took a sample of 20 measurements of the heights of certain individuals and obtained a mean of 67.6 and a standard deviation of 3.78. For $n = 20$ we find from Table II that $t_{.025} = 2.093$. Substituting all this information into (9.4.3) we finally get

$$67.6 - 2.093 \frac{3.78}{\sqrt{19}} < m < 67.6 + 2.093 \frac{3.78}{\sqrt{19}}$$

or
$$65.74 < m < 69.46$$

and we have found the 95 per cent confidence interval of the true average height. Had we wanted to use a 99 per cent confidence interval instead, we would have found that $t_{.005} = 2.861$ (for $n = 20$) and that the corresponding interval would have gone from 65.06 to 70.14.

This illustration shows that it is not difficult to calculate confidence intervals of m for small samples. It is needless to say that there is absolutely no excuse for the common mistake of applying large-sample techniques to small samples.

EXERCISES

1. Calculate a 95 per cent confidence interval for the mean of the population from which each of the following samples was selected:

   (a) $n = 100$, $\bar{x} = 65.40$, $s = 3.21$
   (b) $n = 400$, $\bar{x} = 38.60$, $s = 1.48$
   (c) $n = 12$, $\bar{x} = 52.10$, $s = 5.61$
   (d) $n = 17$, $\bar{x} = 13.60$, $s = 1.54$

2. Calculate a 98 per cent confidence interval of the mean on the basis of each of the four samples of Exercise 1.

3. Use each of the four samples of Exercise 1 to calculate a 99 per cent confidence interval of the mean of the population from which the sample was chosen.

4. An analyst who took 17 measurements of the manganese in ferro-manganese, an alloy of manganese and iron, obtained a mean of 82.90 per cent and a standard deviation of $\frac{1}{4}$ of 1 per cent. Estimate the average manganese content of this alloy.

5. If 100 measurements of one and the same object had a mean of 32.50 inches and a standard deviation of 1 inch, calculate 90 per cent confidence limits for the true length of the object.

6. Use any one of the 60 samples which are given on page 151 to construct a 90 per cent confidence interval of the mean of the population.

7. Use the first sample of Exercise 1, page 70, to determine a 98 per cent confidence interval of the mean length of the fish from which the sample was taken.

8. If 50 measurements of the specific gravity of aluminum had a mean of 2.695 and a standard deviation of .045, with what degree of confidence can we assert that we are not off by more than .010 by estimating the specific gravity as 2.695?

9. If 200 measurements of the reaction time to an auditory stimulus had a mean of .143 and a standard deviation of .020, with what degree of confidence can we claim that we are not off by more than .003 if we give the true mean reaction time as .143?

10. If we want to estimate the average mechanical aptitude of a large group of people, how large a sample should we take in order to be 95 per cent confident that our estimate will not differ from the true mean by more than 2.5 points? We know from previous work with similar types of measurements that the standard deviation of the scores may be taken as $\sigma = 12$.

11. What results would we have obtained in Exercise 10 if we had wanted to be 98 per cent confident? What if we had wanted to be 99 per cent confident?

9.5 Confidence Intervals for Proportions

Many scientific problems deal with the estimation of percentages, rates, and probabilities. Therefore, our next task will be to investigate how we can construct confidence intervals for these important population parameters. To simplify our presentation we shall write all three quantities as decimal fractions, giving 75 *per cent* as .75, the mortality *rate* of a disease as .12, and the *probability* that it will rain on a certain day as .24. This again brings out the fact that these three types of quantities are really the same. After all, a mortality rate is only the proportion of patients who can be expected to die. Such a proportion, in turn, stands for the probability that any one patient will die from the disease.

The information which is ordinarily available for the estimation of a percentage is the relative frequency with which a certain event has taken place. If an event has happened x *times out of* n, we shall write the relative frequency of its occurrence as $f_n = x/n$, while the true proportion, namely, the proportion which we want to estimate, will be given by the letter p. *Therefore we can now ask how we can estimate the parameter p on the basis of a sample value of the relative frequency f_n.* (Percentage is then 100 p.)

To investigate the relationship between a sample value of f_n and the parameter p of the population from which the sample has been selected we must, as before, look at the sampling distribution of our statistic. In other words, we must ask how the quantities f_n can be expected to be distributed if we are to take repeated samples of size n from the same population. Since the statistic f_n is simply the fraction of successes which we have obtained in n trials, it follows immediately that the sampling distribution of f_n is the *binomial distribution* which we discussed in Chapters 3 and 8.

We saw in Chapter 8 that the mean and standard deviation of the *number* of successes in n trials were

$$m = np \quad \text{and} \quad \sigma = \sqrt{np(1 - p)}$$

but since we are interested in the proportion of successes (their relative frequency) and not in their actual number, we will have to divide both of these quantities by n. After all, in order to convert the *number* of successes into a *proportion*, we divide x by n. The sampling distribution of f_n is therefore given by the binomial distribution which has

$$m = p \quad \text{and} \quad \sigma_{f_n} = \sqrt{\frac{p(1 - p)}{n}} \qquad (9.5.1)^*$$

If we flip a coin 100 times, the mean and standard deviation of the *number of heads* which we can expect if we repeat this experiment a large number of times are, according to formulas (7.4.1) and (7.4.2)

$$m = 100(\tfrac{1}{2}) = 50 \quad \text{and} \quad \sigma = \sqrt{100(\tfrac{1}{2})(\tfrac{1}{2})} = 5$$

respectively, while the corresponding mean and standard deviation of the *proportion of heads* obtained in 100 tosses are

$$m = .50 \quad \text{and} \quad \sigma_{f_n} = .05$$

These last two values can be obtained *either* by dividing the first two values by n, i.e., by 100, or by directly substituting $n = 100$ and $p = \tfrac{1}{2}$ into formula (9.5.1). The reader should always be careful in distinguishing between the *number of successes* and their *relative frequency*. It is true that we can use either of the two sets of formulas in most problems which deal with the estimation of p's, but it would lead to serious confusion if we were to evaluate the accuracy of an estimate of the *proportion* of successes, referring to the standard error of their actual *number*.

As we have demonstrated in Chapter 7, it is usually quite reasonable to approximate binomial distributions by means of normal curves. Since this will simplify our work to a considerable extent, we shall from now on treat the sampling distribution of f_n as if it were a *normal curve* which has the mean p and the standard deviation $\sqrt{p(1-p)}/\sqrt{n}$. Subsequently we can study the sampling distribution of f_n by use of Table I after we have found the z values which correspond to the f_n's. By definition, z values are always given by the *deviation from the mean divided by the standard deviation*, and since we are now concerned with the sampling distribution of f_n, we have

$$z = \frac{f_n - m}{\sigma_{f_n}} = \frac{f_n - p}{\sqrt{\dfrac{p(1-p)}{n}}} \tag{9.5.2}$$

This completes the preliminaries, and we are now in the position to construct confidence intervals for population proportions, probabilities, or rates.

Whenever the sampling distribution of a statistic is approximated by a normal curve, we can say that we are 95 per cent sure that the z value which corresponds to the sample value of our statistic will lie between -1.96 and 1.96 (see Fig. 9.e). In other words, we are 95

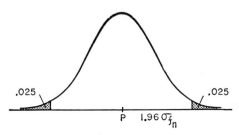

Figure 9.e.

per cent confident, or it should happen about 95 per cent of the time that

$$-1.96 < z < 1.96 \tag{9.5.3}$$

Substituting (9.5.2) for z into this inequality we obtain

$$-1.96 < \frac{f_n - p}{\sqrt{\dfrac{p(1-p)}{n}}} < 1.96 \tag{9.5.4}$$

and since we are 95 per cent sure that this inequality will be satisfied by a sample value of f_n, we could solve it for p and construct, in this fashion, the desired 95 per cent confidence interval of p. We shall not do this, however, because the necessary mathematical detail is much too involved. Instead of doing all this work ourselves, we shall leave it to others and use tables which have been constructed specially for this purpose. Such a table is given in Table III on page 391. It provides us directly with 95 per cent confidence limits of p for samples of size 10, 15, 20, 30, 50, 100, 250, and 1000. For other values of n the reader will literally have to read between the lines of this table.

To illustrate the use of Table III, let us suppose that in a random sample of 100 smokers, 24 claimed that they preferred brand A to all other brands of cigarettes. We are asked to find 95 per cent confidence limits of the actual percentage of all smokers who prefer this brand.

First we shall calculate the relative frequency f_n, which in this example is simply equal to $\frac{24}{100} = .24$. Then we mark this value on the *horizontal f_n scale* of Table III (see Fig. 9.f) and go up vertically

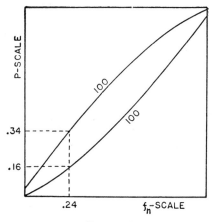

Figure 9.f.

from this point until we hit the two lines of the diagram which correspond to samples for which $n = 100$. The two values of the *vertical p scale* which correspond to these two points finally give us the desired 95 per cent confidence limits for the true value of p. It is easily seen that these numbers are approximately .16 and .34, and we can therefore say that the 95 per cent confidence interval for p is .16 − .34. This means that we are 95 per cent sure that from 16 to 34 per cent of all smokers prefer the cigarettes of brand A.

It should be noted that the lines of the diagram of Table III which correspond to the different values of n are numbered as follows: the sample size is given *below* the lines representing the lower limits of the confidence intervals, while it is written *above* the lines which give us the upper limits. Similar tables for 98 and 99 per cent confidence intervals can be found in *Biometrika* which is mentioned among the references at the end of this chapter.

If we have large samples, and if either Table III is not available or we want to use a degree of confidence for which the corresponding tables have not been made, we can approximate the p's of formulas (9.5.1) and (9.5.2) by means of the observed relative frequency f_n. The standard error of f_n can then be written as

$$\sigma_{f_n} = \sqrt{\frac{f_n(1 - f_n)}{n}} \qquad (9.5.5)^*$$

and the resulting *95 per cent confidence interval of p* becomes

$$f_n - 1.96\sqrt{\frac{f_n(1 - f_n)}{n}} < p < f_n + 1.96\sqrt{\frac{f_n(1 - f_n)}{n}} \qquad (9.5.6)^*$$

Had we wanted to be 98 or 99 per cent confident, we could simply have replaced 1.96 by 2.33 or 2.58, respectively. *It must be remembered, of course, that formulas (9.5.5) and (9.5.6) can be used only for large samples.*

Using the last formula to solve the problem in which we were asked to estimate the percentage of all smokers who prefer brand A to all other brands of cigarettes, we would find that by substituting $n = 100$ and $f_n = .24$ into formula (9.5.6), the resulting confidence interval goes from .156 to .324. This result does *not* differ by much from the interval which we previously obtained from Table III.

Since the probability p must, by definition, always lie between 0 and 1 (including 0 and 1), the quantity $p(1 - p)$ which appears in the formula for the standard error of f_n has a *maximum value* of $\frac{1}{4}$. (This can easily be verified by either completing the square or by using elementary differential calculus.) Applying this knowledge to formula (9.5.1), we can rewrite it as the inequality

$$\sigma_{f_n} \leqslant \frac{1}{2\sqrt{n}} \qquad (9.5.7)^*$$

This tells us that the standard error of f_n is always less or equal to $1/2\sqrt{n}$. If we now substitute the quantity $1/2\sqrt{n}$ in place of σ_{f_n} in formula (9.5.6), we can expect to get a confidence interval for p which is *wider*, or at least *never narrower* than the one which is based on the correct value of σ_{f_n}. We can say, therefore, that we are *at least 95 per cent confident* that this new confidence interval will cover the true value of p. It can very well happen that this will make the interval *unnecessarily wide*, particularly if p is not close to .50, but as we shall see from the following illustrations, this approximation has some useful applications.

Example 1. How large a sample must we take to be at least 95 per cent confident that our prediction of the percentage of votes which candidate X will receive is not off by more than 2 per cent?

Since we are interested in being at least 95 per cent sure that our estimate will not differ from p by more than .02, we shall put this value equal to $1.96\sigma_{f_n}$ (see Fig. 9.g), using the approximation of formula (9.5.7). This gives us

$$1.96 \frac{1}{2\sqrt{n}} = .02$$

which, solved for n, provides the desired answer that the required minimum sample size is $n = 2401$. This implies that if we base our

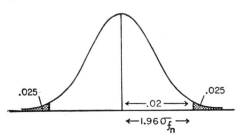

Figure 9.g.

estimate on a sample of size 2401, we can say that we are at least 95 per cent sure that our error will not exceed 2 per cent *regardless of the true value of p.*

Example 2. If, in the previous example, we had wanted to be at least 95 per cent confident that our error will not exceed .10, how large a sample must we take?

Using the same argument as before, we have

$$1.96 \frac{1}{2\sqrt{n}} = .10 \quad \text{and} \quad n = 97$$

It is interesting that a sample consisting of as few as 97 observations will provide us with the desired degree of accuracy.

Example 3. If we suspect (on the basis of collateral information) that a candidate will receive in the neighborhood of 80 per cent of the vote, how large a sample must we take to be 99 per cent sure that our error will not exceed 5 per cent?

In contrast to Examples 1 and 2 in which we had no idea of the actual value of p, we are now told that it is somewhere near .80, and we can therefore use formula (9.5.1), putting $p = .80$. This tells us that the standard error of f_n is

$$\sigma_{f_n} = \sqrt{\frac{(.20)(.80)}{n}} = \frac{.40}{\sqrt{n}}$$

and choosing the proper z value for a degree of confidence of .99 we finally have

$$2.58 \frac{.40}{\sqrt{n}} = .05 \quad \text{and} \quad n = 426$$

A sample of 426 random opinions would, thus, suffice to enable us to give 99 to 1 odds that our sample value of f_n will not differ from the true value of p by more than 5 per cent.

It becomes apparent from these three examples that the minimum size of sample which is needed in any one problem depends not only on the degree of confidence with which we want to assert our results, but also on the maximum error which we are willing to commit.

EXERCISES

1. If a random sample of 100 teacups contained 18 that were slightly defective, use Table III to find a 95 per cent confidence interval for the true percentage of defective teacups.

2. If 12 out of 25 people died from a certain fever, find 95 per cent confidence limits for the mortality rate of this disease.

3. A random sample of 250 Parisians showed that only 14 owned cars. Use Table III to find 95 per cent confidence limits for the actual percentage of Parisians who own cars.

4. A study of 400 random opinions disclosed that 310 of the 400 people prefer to live in a medium-sized town. Use Table III to find a 95 per cent confidence interval of the true percentage.

5. If a straw poll showed that 28 per cent of the people reacted favorably to a certain policy, use the method of Example 3 (page 178) to find the minimum sample needed if we want to be 95 per cent sure that we are not off by more than .03.

6. If 80 out of a random sample of 240 listeners were tuned in to a certain radio program, use Table III to construct 95 per cent confidence limits of the true percentage. Assuming that the actual percentage was very close to 25, construct the corresponding interval with the use of formula (9.5.1) putting $p = .25$. Compare the two results.

7. Use formula (9.5.7) to determine the minimum sample which is needed to be 95 per cent sure that we will not be off by more than .01.

8. Suppose that we want to estimate the proportion of children who fail to reach emotional maturity. How large a sample must we take so that we can be 98 per cent sure that our error will not exceed .04? Use formula (9.5.7).

9. If we want to estimate the proportion of people who prefer a certain kind of candy, what is the smallest sample for which we could assert with a degree of confidence of .95 that we are not off by more than .05? Use formula (9.5.7).

10. What is the smallest sample which a public opinion poll must take to be able to assert with a degree of confidence of .99 that the error of the estimated proportion will not exceed .02? Use formula (9.5.7).

9.6 Confidence Intervals for Standard Deviations (Large Samples)

We have shown in our discussion of the standard deviation in Chapter 5 how important it can be to know the standard deviation or some other measure of the variability of a population. Since the variation, spread, or dispersion of a population is most frequently expressed in terms of its standard deviation, let us now see how we can construct confidence intervals for the parameter σ. Following the customary procedure, we shall base our estimate of σ on the sample standard deviation s, although there is no reason why we could not have based it, for example, on the sample range.

As in all previous cases, we must discuss the accuracy of an estimate of σ by referring to the sampling distribution of the statistic on which the estimate is based. If we are dealing with *large samples*, we can base the confidence interval of σ on the following theorem concerning the sampling distribution of s (this sampling distribution stands for the distribution which we could expect if we were to group the s's which are calculated from repeated samples from the same population).

THEOREM D: *If we sample from a normal population which has the mean m and the standard deviation σ, the sampling distribution of s is (for large samples) closely approximated by a normal curve which has the mean σ and the standard deviation (standard error) $\sigma/\sqrt{2n}$.*

Since the true value of σ is always unknown in problems of this type (there would otherwise be no need to estimate it from the sample), we approximate the σ which appears in the standard error of s by means of the sample value of s. According to Theorem D we can write, therefore, that

$$\sigma_s - \frac{s}{\sqrt{2n}} \qquad (9.6.1)^*$$

is an approximation of the standard error of s, appropriately written as σ_s. Due to the approximation which is involved in this formula, the confidence intervals which we shall discuss next can be used *only* if we are dealing with very large samples.

It is quite understandable that the beginner may be confused when we speak of the *standard deviation of a standard deviation*, but if he remembers that we are concerned with the *standard deviation of the sampling distribution of* s, it should not be difficult to keep the meanings of the various standard deviations apart.

Using Theorem D and formula (9.6.1) we can now write the *95 per cent confidence interval of* σ as

$$s - 1.96 \frac{s}{\sqrt{2n}} < \sigma < s + 1.96 \frac{s}{\sqrt{2n}} \qquad (9.6.2)^*$$

which is analogous to our previous confidence interval of m except that we now have s in place of $\bar{x}$ and σ_s instead of $\sigma_{\bar{x}}$.

To illustrate the use of the confidence interval which is given in (9.6.2), let us return to the problem which we discussed earlier in this chapter on page 166, where we took a sample of 30 measurements of the heights of a certain group of individuals. We had a mean of 67.47 and a standard deviation of 3.42, and substituting these results into (9.6.2) we obtain

$$3.42 - 1.96 \frac{3.42}{\sqrt{60}} < \sigma < 3.42 + 1.96 \frac{3.42}{\sqrt{60}}$$

or $$2.55 < \sigma < 4.29$$

This interval *does* contain the mean of the population which, as we know, thanks to Superman, was 3.33.

It is quite evident that the interval which we have obtained is *very wide* which goes to show that it is almost impossible to get accurate estimates of σ unless we have very large samples. We might even add that it is somewhat doubtful whether we should have used formula (9.6.2), since a sample of size 30 can hardly be described as *very* large.

9.7 Confidence Intervals for Standard Deviations (Small Samples)

If a standard deviation is to be estimated on the basis of a *small sample* we can no longer replace σ by s in formula (9.6.1). What we shall do instead involves a new theoretical distribution which is called the *chi-square distribution* and which can also be written as the χ^2 *distribution*. Since the development and the theory of this new theoretical distribution is far beyond the scope of this book, we shall simply use the table of its areas (Table IV on page 392) and accept without question the most important of its theoretical results. As far as we are concerned, at least in this chapter, *the most important fact is that the sampling distribution of the statistic*

$$\frac{ns^2}{\sigma^2}$$

is the chi-square distribution (*a picture of which is given in Fig. 9.h*) *if we are sampling from a normal population.*

Treating this distribution like all the other theoretical distributions which we have discussed, we can now ask for two numbers χ_1^2 and χ_2^2 (see Fig. 9.h) which are such that 95, 96, 98, 99, or any arbitrary

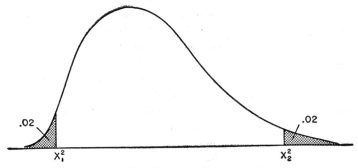

Figure 9.h. The Chi-Square Distribution (n = 6).

percentage of the total area under the curve must fall between them. Arbitrarily selecting 96 per cent, we can then distribute the remaining 4 per cent evenly between the two tails of the distribution with a suitable choice of χ_1^2 and χ_2^2. If the two points χ_1^2 and χ_2^2 are chosen in this manner we can say that *96 per cent of the sample values of a statistic which has the chi-square distribution as its sampling distribution must satisfy the inequality*

$$\chi_1^2 < \chi^2 < \chi_2^2 \qquad \qquad (9.7.1)$$

Substituting for χ^2 the quantity ns^2/σ^2 which, as we have said before, has the chi-square distribution as its sampling distribution, we get

$$\chi_1^2 < \frac{ns^2}{\sigma^2} < \chi_2^2 \qquad (9.7.2)$$

Finally, solving this inequality for σ we obtain

$$\sqrt{\frac{ns^2}{\chi_2^2}} < \sigma < \sqrt{\frac{ns^2}{\chi_1^2}} \qquad (9.7.3)*$$

and *we now have a 96 per cent confidence interval of σ which can be used whenever we are dealing with small samples which are taken from a population which is reasonably close to a normal curve.* If, instead of a degree of confidence of .96, we had wanted to assert our interval with a degree of confidence of .98, we could have found the corresponding values of χ_1^2 and χ_2^2 also in Table IV.

If we want to use formula (9.7.3) in a practical problem, we must know the sample values of s and n *and* the two tabular values of χ^2, which can be found on page 392. If we put 2 per cent of the area *to the left of* χ_1^2 and 98 per cent of the area *to its right*, we shall write this value of χ^2 as $\chi^2_{.98}$. Using the identical reason we shall, similarly, write χ_2^2 as $\chi^2_{.02}$, and this is how these values of χ^2 are denoted in the second and fifth columns of Table IV. Had we desired a degree of confidence of .98 (instead of .96) we could have used the values of $\chi^2_{.99}$ and $\chi^2_{.01}$, which are also given in Table IV.

In the illustration in which we studied the sample of the 20 measurements of the heights of certain people we had a sample standard deviation of $s = 3.78$. If we now want to use this information to construct a 96 per cent confidence interval of the actual value of the population standard deviation, we first must determine the necessary values of $\chi^2_{.98}$ and $\chi^2_{.02}$. Checking $n = 20$ in the left-hand column of Table IV, we find that the required values of *chi-square* are $\chi^2_{.98} = 8.567$ and $\chi^2_{.02} = 33.687$. Substituting all this information into formula (9.7.3), we get

$$\sqrt{\frac{20(3.78)^2}{33.687}} < \sigma < \sqrt{\frac{20(3.78)^2}{8.576}}$$

or $2.91 < \sigma < 5.78$

which gives us the desired 96 per cent confidence interval for σ. It is important that the only assumption which we have made in the development of our formula is that the sample was taken from a close to normally distributed population.

EXERCISES

1. Given $n = 128$ and $s = 33.4$, find 95 per cent confidence limits for the standard deviation of the population from which this sample was taken.

2. Given $n = 14$ and $s = 7.3$, find a 96 per cent confidence interval of σ.

3. The intelligence scores of a sample of 200 students showed a standard deviation of 14. Find 99 per cent confidence limits for the standard deviation of the population from which this sample was taken. What is the population in this case?

4. A sample of 100 measurements of the lifetime of electronic tubes had a standard deviation of 6 hours. Construct a 98 per cent confidence interval for σ.

5. If 10 measurements of the density of glass had a standard deviation of .02, determine a 96 per cent confidence interval for the true variability (σ) of the density of glass.

6. If 7 measurements of the weight of rats that are used in a certain experiment had a standard deviation of 4.3 grams, find a 98 per cent confidence interval for the true value of σ of the population from which the sample was selected.

9.8 Probable Errors

Although we have limited our discussion to the construction of confidence intervals for m, p, and σ, the identical approach can be used in general to estimate any population parameter whatsoever. We can speak, for example, of confidence intervals of quartiles, confidence intervals for coefficients of variation, and as we shall see later on, also of confidence intervals of coefficients of correlation and other measures of association. It is true that the general method is, logically speaking, the same, but there exist obstacles which are caused by the sampling distributions of some of these further statistics. Many of the sampling distributions which we can thus expect to meet are of an extremely complicated nature. *It is, therefore, fortunate that it can be shown that a great number of the sampling distributions approach a normal curve when the size of the sample on which the statistic is based becomes very large.*

This implies that if we have some arbitrary statistic S which has the standard error σ_S, we can very often say that the 95 per cent confidence interval of the true value of S is given by the interval

$$S - 1.96\sigma_S < \text{population value} < S + 1.96\sigma_S \qquad (9.8.1)$$

provided, of course, that the sample value of S was originally based on a *very large sample*. Had the sample been small, we would have had no right to assume that the sampling distribution of the statistic S is a normal curve.

It has been customary in the past to indicate the accuracy of an estimate by giving the error (deviation from the true population value) which we do not expect to exceed more than 50 per cent of the time. In other words, it has been the custom to give a certain number, called the *probable error*, of which we can be *50 per cent sure* that it will not be exceeded by the error of our estimates.

If the sampling distribution of the statistic which is being used for estimating the corresponding population parameter is a normal curve, we can easily find by use of Table I that the z value which corresponds to an area of .2500 is equal to .6745. The middle 50 per cent of the area under the normal curve is thus contained between $z_1 = -.6745$ and $z_2 = .6745$, *and we can define the probable error of a given statistic as .6745 times its standard error.*

Given any arbitrary statistic S, we can write its probable error $P.E._S$ as

$$P.E._S = .6745\sigma_S \tag{9.8.2}$$

and we have, for example,

$$P.E._{\bar{x}} = .6745 \frac{s}{\sqrt{n}} \tag{9.8.3}$$

$$P.E._s = .6745 \frac{s}{\sqrt{2n}} \tag{9.8.4}$$

$$P.E._{f_n} = .6745 \sqrt{\frac{f_n(1 - f_n)}{n}} \tag{9.8.5}$$

These formulas can be used *if and only if* we are dealing with large samples.

The actual use of the probable error is somewhat outdated because it is difficult to see why we should care about an interval of which we can be only *50 per cent certain* that it will accomplish its purpose. It seems to be of little value to know that it is *an even bet* that the error of an estimate will not exceed the quantity which is called the probable error. A further disadvantage of the probable error is that it obviously can be used only if the sampling distribution of a statistic is reasonably close to a normal curve. This last fact is often overlooked in the actual application of the probable error.

The definition of the probable error has been given in this chapter only because it has played a fairly important role in the past and is still mentioned in quite a few books, research papers, and articles. We are not suggesting, however, that it should actually be used for the discussion of the accuracy of statistical results.

9.9 Sampling from Finite Populations

The methods of confidence estimation which we have discussed in the last few sections were based on several assumptions. First, it was assumed that our samples were *random*; second, it was assumed that we were sampling from *infinite* (or at least very large) populations. This last assumption was necessary because, as we shall see from the following illustration, our methods simply do not apply if we are sampling from a finite population, unless, of course, such a finite population is reasonably large.

Let us suppose, for instance, that we are asked to determine the percentage of the doctors who live in a given town and who smoke cigars. A thorough investigation tells us that there are 10 doctors in this town. Three smoke cigars, six do not. The tenth doctor was away on his vacation and could not be reached. We have therefore a *sample* which does not give us the complete information which we were after. Using our so-called standard technique of Section 9.5, we find that since $n = 9$ and $f_n = 3/9$, the 95 per cent confidence interval for the proportion of cigar smoking doctors in this town is $.07 - .69$. This result, which was obtained directly from Table III, is obviously *incorrect* because if the tenth doctor does happen to smoke cigars the final proportion will be $\frac{4}{10} = .40$ and if he does not, the proportion will be $\frac{3}{10} = .30$. In either case it would be nonsensical to say that we are 95 per cent confident that the true proportion lies between .07 and .69. After all, we know that it must be either .30 or .40, both of which fall into the interval which we have calculated above.

The mistake which we made by using Table III is that we took a very small finite population consisting of as few as 10 elements and treated it as if it were an infinite population. Because it *does* happen quite often that we have to deal with small finite populations, techniques have been developed which apply especially in that case. It can be shown that the mistake which we have made can be avoided if we make a suitable adjustment in the formula for the standard error of the statistic on which our estimate is based. This adjustment consists of multiplying the standard error by the factor

$$\sqrt{\frac{N-n}{N}}$$

and *the standard error of an arbitrary statistic S adjusted for samples from finite populations* can be written as

$$\sigma_S' = \sqrt{\frac{N-n}{N}}\, \sigma_S \tag{9.9.1}$$

In this formula N stands for the size of the population (in our example it was 10) while n stands, as always, for the size of our sample.

If we were to take a sample of size 100 from a population which is of size 10,000, the factor $\sqrt{N-n}/\sqrt{N}$ would become equal to $\sqrt{10{,}000 - 100}/\sqrt{10{,}000} = .995$, and it would hardly be worth while to even consider this adjustment in most practical problems. If, on the other hand, our sample consists of a sizable portion of the total population, it is essential to make the necessary adjustment with the use of formula (9.9.1). Let us consider, for example, the problem of estimating the average intelligence of a group of 400 farmers on the basis of a sample of size 200. The adjusted standard error of the mean is according to (9.9.1) given by the expression

$$\sigma_{\bar{x}}' = \frac{s}{\sqrt{n}} \sqrt{\frac{N-n}{N}} \tag{9.9.2}$$

which, in this example, would be equal to

$$\sigma_{\bar{x}}' = \frac{s}{\sqrt{n}} \sqrt{\frac{400-200}{400}} = \frac{s}{\sqrt{n}}\,(.707)$$

This makes a difference of almost 30 per cent in the width of the resulting confidence interval. It is worthwhile noting that *the adjusted standard error is actually smaller than the corresponding standard error for samples from an infinite population*. This implies that it will always be safe to assume that we are dealing with an infinite population, since this assumption will tend to *increase* the degree of confidence with which we can assert our results, i.e., the confidence intervals will be unnecessarily wide. It would therefore have been correct to say in our first illustration that we were *at least 95 per cent sure* that the proportion of cigar smoking doctors in that town was between .07 and .69.

9.10 A Word of Caution

We mentioned very briefly in Chapter 1 that most statistical methods are only a *refinement* of the procedures which we are accustomed to use in everyday life. Since it must be evident that different kinds of problems will require different kinds of refinement, we must apply the more or less standard techniques which we have studied in this chapter with a good deal of discretion.

In spite of the fancy mathematical formulas it will still be necessary to use common sense and sound judgment in deciding whether or not a certain technique is applicable to a given situation, whether it utilizes all relevant information, and whether we can satisfy all necessary assumptions.

As a word of caution we therefore relate the following little story.[1]

> Let us assume that you are a naturalist of some note and have made trips through all of North and South America, Europe, Asia, and Africa, and have made a specialty of the study of deer. In all of these travels you have noticed the one general fact that all of the deer of the various areas were tan colored brown. There was, however, one outstanding exception. On a visit to the Bronx Zoo, you saw one albino deer and, in discussing that animal with fellow naturalists, you heard of several other such rare cases. You and I are now taking a trip to Australia for the first time and shortly after landing we go out into the bush and we see our first Australian deer. It is tan colored brown and I ask you, just as a sporting proposition, what odds you would give me that most of the deer in Australia are tan colored brown. I am sure that you would give me at least in the neighborhood of ten to one. Having later found that practically all of the deer in Australia are tan colored brown, we continue our travels and go to New Zealand. When we get into the wooded area, we finally meet our first New Zealand deer and, lo!—it is a white one. Again, I ask you to name your odds; but now I propose that most of the deer in New Zealand are white. I doubt very much whether you would even consider giving me even money on that one.

The moral of this story is that we must often use past experience, relevant collateral facts, as well as direct observations in evaluating the probabilities (and other parameters) which we need in order to make wise decisions.

---

[1] This story is a favorite of Mr. Arthur L. Bailey, Chief Actuary (Casualty) of the Insurance Department of the State of New York.

REFERENCES

C. J. Clopper and E. S. Pearson, "The Use of Confidence or Fiducial Limits Illustrated in the Case of the Binomial," *Biometrika*, Vol. 26 (1934), p. 404.

W. J. Dixon and F. J. Massey, *Introduction to Statistical Analysis*, McGraw-Hill, New York, 1951, Chaps. 8, 9.

A. L. Edwards, *Statistical Analysis for Students in Psychology and Education*, Rinehart, New York, 1946, Chap. 8.

M. J. Hagood, *Statistics for Sociologists*, Holt, New York, 1941, Chaps. 14, 15.

M. G. Kendall, *The Advanced Theory of Statistics*, Charles Griffin, London, 1946, Vol. II, Chap. 19.

S. S. Wilks, *Elementary Statistical Analysis*, Princeton University Press, Princeton, 1949, Chaps. 9, 10.

10. THE TESTING
OF HYPOTHESES

10.1 Introduction

It is hardly an exaggeration to say that the mere job of living compels us to make decisions in practically everything we do. True enough, many of these decisions involve only an expression of taste or a personal preference, yet many decisions are such that whatever alternative we may pick we must always face the risk of having made the wrong choice.

The decisions which we make in everyday life are usually based on past experience, on authoritative demands, on popular fads and momentary impulses, and, of course, also on scientific evidence. In spite of this evident diversity of the criteria which we can use as the basis for our decisions, it is possible to study and analyze the merits and disadvantages of the various *methods of decision* by evaluating the risks which they force us to assume. The only types of decisions which are excluded from this last statement are those which are merely a matter of taste, as there is no question in that case whether our decision is right or wrong, or true or false.

To illustrate the *type of decision* which must be made almost always in scientific work let us suppose, for example, that we are traveling along a highway and, having come to a fork in the road at which there are no signs, we have to decide whether we should turn to the left or to the right. *It is obvious that whatever we may decide to do in such a situation, we cannot avoid the risk of making a mistake.* If we choose the road which goes to the left, we are gambling that the town which we hope to reach does not lie to the right and, similarly, if we select the road which leads to the right, we would be making a mistake if our destination is actually to the left. This example is typical of the kind of situation which we can expect to meet in problems in which we want to test a hypothesis. As we shall see later, it will be possible to evaluate the merits of the methods on which we can base such decisions by comparing the risks to which we are exposed by the various methods of decision. The task of evaluating these risks becomes very complicated if we permit situations in which we have to choose between more than two different courses of action. In principle, there is really no difference between the methods which pertain to *two* alternatives and those which must be used if we consider *three or more*, but for reasons of simplicity we shall limit our discussion to problems in which we have to consider only two.

It is not always easy to find a suitable or most suitable method of deciding any given question. In our illustration we could, for example, have based our decision to turn to the left or to the right on a vague recollection of having passed the same fork in the road before; possibly we might improve our chances of making the correct decision by asking a farmer who is working in a nearby field; or if nobody is around we might even be forced to resort to flipping a coin: "Heads we turn left and tails we turn right."

In order to choose between these three methods of decision (and conceivably more) we will have to ask ourselves *which is least likely to send us in the wrong direction.* Strangely enough, only the third method of decision, namely, the one which bases the decision on the flip of a coin, lends itself to an immediate evaluation of the chances of our making the wrong decision. If we trust our fate to the coin, we can expect to make the correct decision 50 per cent of the time regardless of whether our destination lies to the left or to the right. It must be understood, of course, that if we assign a probability to a method of decision, in this case the probability .50, we are referring to the success ratio of the given method of decision *if this method is used a great number of times.* If we based all decisions on the flip of a coin, we could expect to come up with the right choice about 50 per cent of the time.

The errors which are entailed in the other two methods of decision which we mentioned in the previous paragraph cannot easily be evaluated because they depend on the reliability of our memory, the honesty and knowledge of the farmer, etc., which are all factors that cannot easily be determined.

The problem of deciding whether to accept or reject a scientific hypothesis on the basis of experimental data is, logically speaking, identical with the problem of deciding whether to turn to the left or to the right in the preceding example. Naturally, the methods that must be used are usually a good deal more refined and at times also much more complicated, but *in principle they are all more or less the same.*

To get a clear picture of some of the difficulties with which we can expect to come face to face when we are asked to accept or reject a scientific hypothesis, let us consider a *fictional case.* The example which we shall use is not particularly important in itself, but it should serve the purpose of emphasizing the main features of the most common methods of decision which utilize statistical information.

Let us suppose, therefore, that the QRS Bulb Co. has advertised a special sale of bulbs in large packages, each of which is claimed to contain 50 per cent daffodils and 50 per cent narcissus bulbs. For some reason or other the Better Business Bureau decides to investigate this claim and it assigns one of its agents *to test the hypothesis that 50 per cent of these bulbs are actually daffodils.* To simplify our notation we shall denote this hypothesis, namely, the hypothesis that 50 per cent of the bulbs are daffodils, by the letter H.

The director of the Better Business Bureau instructs his agent to take a sample of 100 bulbs and base his final decision on the following criterion:

> He should *accept the hypothesis H* if the sample of 100 bulbs contains anywhere from 41 to 59 daffodils.
> He should *reject the hypothesis H* if the number of daffodils in his sample is either less than 41 or more than 59.

In other words, the investigator must base his decision on the number of daffodils which he finds in a random sample of size 100. If there are from 41 to 59 daffodils in his sample he will accept the hypothesis that the true proportion is .50; if not, he will reject the hypothesis, and the QRS Bulb Co. will be accused of making false advertising claims.

The manager of the QRS Bulb Co., who is not a trained statistician, agrees reluctantly that the criterion seems fair, but he is worried that bad luck might play tricks on him and that the experiment might produce unusual and to him unfortunate results, as he puts it, purely due to chance. *He is worried, therefore, about the possibility that the hypothesis H might be rejected even though there are actually 50 per cent daffodils among his bulbs.*

On the basis of what we have already learned about statistics we are forced to agree with him that it is certainly possible that the investigation might produce less than 41 or more than 59 daffodils in spite of the fact that the true proportion is .50.   On the other hand, we also know enough statistics to assure him that such an occurrence would be extremely unlikely, and to make him feel better, we might even go as far as *to calculate the probability that the given criterion will reject the hypothesis H even though it should really have been accepted.*

The number of daffodils contained in a random sample of 100 bulbs follows the *binomial distribution* (*x* successes in *n* trials), which for reasons of simplicity will be approximated by a normal curve.   Because the normal curve is a continuous distribution we must restate our criterion for accepting or rejecting the hypothesis H as follows.

Accept the hypothesis H if the number of daffodils lies between 40.5 and 59.5.

Reject the hypothesis H if the number of daffodils is less than 40.5 or greater than 59.5.

This change in the criterion is nothing but the customary procedure of spreading a discrete variable over a continuous scale, and since we obviously cannot get 40.5 or 59.5 daffodils the criterion is, for all practical purposes, exactly the same as before.

To appease the manager of the QRS Bulb Co. we must now ask ourselves the following question: *If the true proportion of daffodils is .50, what is the probability of our getting a sample which contains either less than 41 or more than 59 daffodils?*   In other words, what is the probability of our rejecting the hypothesis H while it actually should not have been rejected?   This probability is given by the shaded area of Fig. 10.a, and it can easily be evaluated with the use of the normal

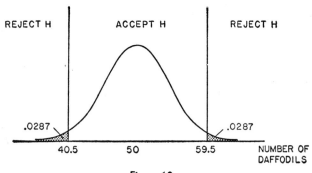

Figure 10.a.

curve areas of Table I. Since we have by assumption (the hypothesis H) $p = .50$ and since $n = 100$, the mean and standard deviation of the sampling distribution of the number of daffodils in a sample of size 100 are, according to formulas (7.4.1) and (7.4.2),

$$m = 100(\tfrac{1}{2}) = 50 \quad \text{and} \quad \sigma = \sqrt{100(\tfrac{1}{2})(\tfrac{1}{2})} = 5$$

The z values which correspond to the dividing lines of our criterion, i.e., to 40.5 and 59.5, are $z_1 = (40.5 - 50)/5 = -1.90$ and $z_2 = (59.5 - 50)/5 = 1.90$. The normal curve area which corresponds to a z value of 1.90 is .4713 (see Table I), and the shaded area either to the left of 40.5 or to the right of 59.5 in Fig. 10.a is thus equal to $.5000 - .4713 = .0287$. The total probability of our getting a sample for which the observed number of daffodils falls into either tail of the distribution, i.e., into the region where the hypothesis H is rejected, is $2(.0287) = .0574$. Consequently, *the probability of our rejecting the hypothesis H on the basis of this criterion is approximately .057 if the true proportion is actually .50, i.e., if the hypothesis H is actually true.* If, by chance, we were to reject a hypothesis which should really have been accepted we are committing an error which is usually called a *type I error.* It is this type I error which the manager of the QRS Bulb Co. is worried about.

It is understandable that the manager of the QRS Bulb Co. may feel that a probability of .057 is too high a risk for him to take, and he therefore suggests to the investigator to use a criterion which has a smaller type I error. *Logically speaking, we can make the type I error as small as we want. As a matter of fact we can make sure that a type I error is never committed by accepting the hypothesis H regardless of what values we might get in our samples.* Surely, this would be perfect as far as the manager of the QRS Bulb Co. is concerned, but it must be evident to the reader that although we have eliminated the risk of a type I error, we have left ourselves wide open to another kind of error, namely, *the error of accepting the hypothesis H while it should actually have been rejected.* This type of error which is committed whenever we accept a hypothesis which should really have been rejected is called a *type II error.*

Leaving this type II error aside for the moment, let us see whether we cannot compromise and reduce the type I error to, say, less than .01 by modifying our criterion for the acceptance and rejection of the hypothesis H. We could, for example, change the criterion to read

Accept the hypothesis H if there are from 36 to 64 daffodils in the sample containing 100 bulbs.

Reject the hypothesis H if the sample contains less than 36 or more than 64 daffodils.

Duplicating the calculations which we used for the evaluation of the type I error of the previous criterion, we can easily see that the probability of our rejecting the hypothesis H with the new criterion is about .004 (see Fig. 10.b). This new criterion is thus much more

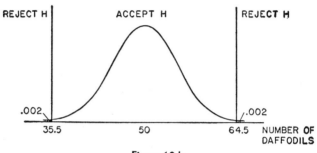

Figure 10.b.

favorable to the QRS Bulb Co., but, and this is important, *at the same time it puts the Better Business Bureau at a decided disadvantage.* It makes it much more difficult for them to prove that the advertising claims are false if the actual proportion of daffodils is *not* .50.

As we have pointed out before, methods of decision must be described in terms of the probabilities with which they are liable to give us a wrong decision. Usually it is not difficult to find the type I error, but it is far from easy to evaluate the type II error, which normally depends on additional factors that are usually unknown.

To explain this last statement let us now return to our illustration and let us investigate the risk which the Better Business Bureau is assuming by basing its decision on the first criterion. It is evident that a risk exists, because it could happen, for example, that the true proportion of daffodils is only .10 while the sample contains between 41 and 59. If this were to happen, the Better Business Bureau would be making a mistake by accepting the hypothesis H.

The probability of such a mistake, i.e., the probability of a type II error, can be calculated also by means of the normal curve approximation of the binomial distribution. If, for example, the true proportion of daffodils is .10, the mean and standard deviation of the sampling distribution of the *number* of daffodils in samples of size 100 are, respectively,

$$m = 100(.10) = 10 \quad \text{and} \quad \sigma = \sqrt{(.10)(.90)100} = 3$$

The probability of our committing the error of accepting H while the true proportion is actually .10 is represented by the shaded area of

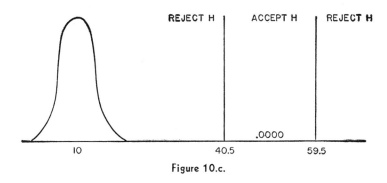

Figure 10.c.

Fig. 10.c, which covers the interval from 40.5 to 59.5. The z values which correspond to 40.5 and 59.5 are

$$z_1 = \frac{40.5 - 10}{3} = 10.17 \quad \text{and} \quad z_2 = \frac{59.5 - 10}{3} = 16.50$$

which are both so large (larger than any value given in Table I) that the probability of our getting from 41 to 59 daffodils is *practically zero*. *The probability of a type II error is therefore for all practical purposes zero if the true percentage of daffodils is 10.*

The mistake of accepting H under these circumstances is consequently unlikely. However, we are immediately led to ask for the probabilities of committing type II errors if the true proportion of daffodils happens to be .20, .30, .40, .45, and, for that matter, any value but .50. It is evident that we must be making a mistake whenever we accept H while the true proportion of daffodils is equal to some value other than .50. It follows that to get a complete picture of the situation we shall have to investigate the probabilities of type II errors for various alternative values of p.

Let us begin with the case in which the true proportion of daffodils

is .20.   The mean and standard deviation of the sampling distribution
of the number of daffodils in samples of size 100 are now, respectively,

$$m = 100(.20) = 20 \quad \text{and} \quad \sigma = \sqrt{(.80)(.20)100} = 4$$

and we can see from Fig. 10.d that the probability of our getting 41

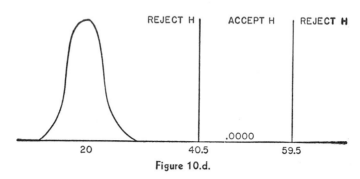

Figure 10.d.

to 59 daffodils is still extremely small.   The z value of 40.5, for instance, is equal to $(40.5 - 20)/4 = 5.12$, and we can check in normal
curve tables which are more complete than the one given at the end
of this book that our chances of getting a z value which is greater
than 5 are less than .0000006.

Next, if we put p equal to .30, the mean and standard deviation of
the sampling distribution of the number of daffodils are equal to 30
and 4.6, respectively.   The probability of H being accepted under
these conditions is given by the shaded area of Fig. 10.e, and it is
approximately .01.

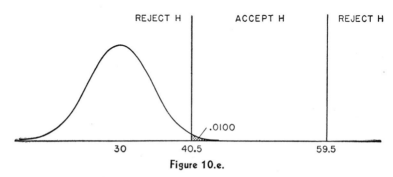

Figure 10.e.

If the true proportion of daffodils is .40, the probability of getting
41 to 59 is given by the shaded area of Fig. 10.f, which lies between

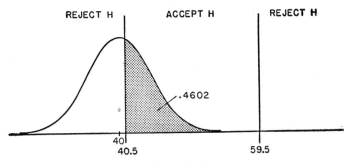

Figure 10.f.

40.5 to 59.5. Since the mean and standard deviation of the number of daffodils are now, respectively,

$$m = 100(.40) = 40 \quad \text{and} \quad \sigma = \sqrt{(.40)(.60)100} = 4.9$$

the two z values corresponding to 40.5 and 59.5 are

$$z_1 = \frac{40.5 - 40}{4.9} = .10 \quad \text{and} \quad z_2 = \frac{59.5 - 40}{4.9} = 4.0$$

Checking these two values in Table I, we find that the probability of a type II error is approximately .46.

This situation gets worse and worse, the closer the true percentage comes to .50. To mention just one more case, let us put $p = .45$. The mean and the standard deviation of the sampling distribution of the number of daffodils are then,

$$m = 100(.45) = 45 \quad \text{and} \quad \sigma = \sqrt{(.45)(.55)100} = 5$$

and the two z values corresponding to 40.5 and 59.5 are $-.90$ and 2.90, respectively. The corresponding normal curve areas are .3159 and .4981, and the total shaded area of Fig. 10.g is equal to .3159 + .4981

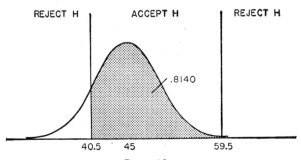

Figure 10.g.

= .8140. This means that if the true percentage of daffodils is .45, the probability of our committing a type II error by accepting the hypothesis H is .814. The odds are, therefore, better than 4 to 1 that the first criterion will give us the wrong decision if the true proportion of daffodils happens to be .45.

Obviously, such a tremendous proportion of incorrect decisions is not desirable unless we were to consider .45 as sufficiently close to .50 not to worry about the difference between the two. Otherwise, we might improve the situation by changing the criterion to read as follows.

> *Accept the hypothesis H* if the sample contains from 49 to 51 daffodils.
> *Reject the hypothesis H* if it contains less than 49 or more than 51.

As before, H is the hypothesis that the true proportion of daffodils is .50. If we let the true value of p again be equal to .45, the probability of our committing a type II error is now given by the shaded area of Fig. 10.h, and it can easily be seen that it is equal to .1452.

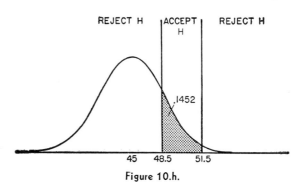

Figure 10.h.

This represents a considerable improvement as far as the type II error is concerned, since the probability of our committing such an error has been reduced from .8140 to .1452. On the other hand, it is very doubtful whether this changed criterion would be acceptable to the manager of the QRS Bulb Co. The reader can easily check for himself that the probability of committing a type I error (see Fig. 10.i) has now become .7642. This means that although the advertising claims of the bulb company are correct, the probability that the Better Business Bureau will say that they are not is as large as .76.

The primary objective of this discussion has been to demonstrate

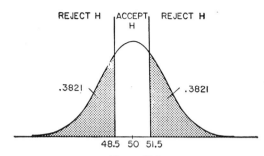

Figure 10.i.

how we can calculate the probabilities of the two types of errors which are associated with a given method of decision, and how these two probabilities are related. We have seen that if we make one error *small*, the other one will become correspondingly *large*. This can be avoided only if we are willing to increase the size of our samples to such an extent that both errors can be made reasonably small. However, this is usually not very practical because of the expense and other factors which make it undesirable to take very large samples.

The basic difference between the type I and type II errors is also illustrated very nicely by means of the statistical methods which are employed in the inspection of manufactured products. Let us suppose, for example, that a lot of machine parts is considered as good if at most 2 per cent of the pieces fall below certain minimum specifications. Before a lot is shipped out it is customary to subject it to some sort of sampling inspection on the basis of which the lot is classified as good or bad. This means that it is necessary to test the hypothesis that at most 2 per cent of the pieces fall below minimum specification and that we must, therefore, run the risk of (a) rejecting a good lot as bad; (b) accepting a bad lot as good. It is evident that the rejection of a good lot represents a very definite disadvantage to the *producer*, and since we would thus be committing a type I error, this kind of error, or better, the probability of committing this kind of error is also called the *producer's risk*. Similarly, the consumer will take a beating if bad lots are accepted as good, and the probability of the occurrence of a type II error is consequently called the *consumer's risk*. The goodness of an industrial inspection plan depends, therefore, on the risks to which it exposes both the producer and the consumer.

The merits of a given criterion (method of decision) which is used for the testing of a certain hypothesis can be understood most easily with the use of a table which might very well be called the *performance chart of the criterion.* Our first criterion specified that we had to:

> *Accept the hypothesis H* if our sample contains from 41 to 59 daffodils.
> *Reject the hypothesis H* if it contains less than 41 or more than 59.

We can now plot a graph showing the probabilities of our committing a type II error for various different values of *p.* Such a *performance chart* is given in Fig. 10.j, in which the proportion *p* is plotted on the horizontal scale, while the *probability of rejecting H* (with the given criterion) is given by the vertical scale. Using the symmetry of the normal curve, it was easy to *complete* this figure for values of *p* greater than .50.

The over-all picture which is presented by the *performance chart* of Fig. 10.j makes it easy to visualize how the method of decision

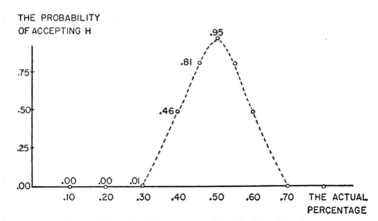

Figure 10.j. The "Performance Chart" of the Criterion.

behaves under various conditions. As we should have expected, the type II error is very large when the true percentage is close to .50. Of course, if *p* is actually equal to .50, we are *not* committing an error and the probability which is expressed by the graph must, *for that particular point,* be interpreted as the probability of our making the correct decision.

A thorough study of the performance charts of test criteria would go far beyond the scope of this text. We shall be satisfied, therefore, having given a more or less intuitive idea of how we can study and evaluate the advantages and disadvantages of criteria which are used for the testing of hypotheses.

10.2 Significance Tests and the Null Hypothesis

Our study of the case of the Better Business Bureau *vs.* the QRS Bulb Co. has made it clear that although it is relatively easy to evaluate type I errors, it is much more difficult to calculate the type II errors which, as we have seen, depend on the actual value of the parameter p. Generalizing from this experience we can safely say that *it is, in general, much easier to calculate the error which may be committed by rejecting a hypothesis than it is to calculate the error which may be committed by accepting it.* This statement is really nothing but a more precise formulation of the age-old rule that *it is much easier to prove things wrong than it is to prove things right.* If somebody were to ask us to prove, for example, that all sheep are white, we would have to investigate the color of every single sheep. *On the other hand, it would take only one black sheep to show that the hypothesis is false.* This goes to show that it is much easier to prove that a general statement is *false* than it is to prove it *correct.*

One possible escape from the difficulties which we must face whenever we examine a hypothesis is to avoid committing type II errors altogether. This can be done in the following manner: if we use again the example of the daffodils, we can change our criterion for testing the hypothesis that the true proportion of daffodils is .50 to read as follows.

> We must *reject the hypothesis H* if the sample contains less than 41 or more than 59 daffodils.

> We do not commit ourselves, i.e., *we reserve our judgment,* if the sample contains from 41 to 59 daffodils.

Comparing this new criterion with the earlier one, we find that the rule for the rejection of the hypothesis H has remained the same, and we are therefore exposed to the identical type I error. However, as far as the acceptance of the hypothesis H is concerned, *we are now playing it safe by never accepting H at all.* Instead, we report that we were unable to reject the hypothesis H, *which does not necessarily mean that we accept it.* The fact that we were unable to reject H, and had thus to reserve judgment merely tells us that our sample did not accomplish a certain purpose.

It is easy to understand that what we have done in the last paragraph may look to the reader as if we were imitating an ostrich which is burying its head in the sand. Actually, the technique of avoiding the type II error is of fundamental importance in all so-called *tests of significance.*

The indirect approach of either rejecting a hypothesis or not committing ourselves at all demands extreme care in the *formulation* of the hypothesis which we want to test. If we want to prove, for example, that the advertising claims of the QRS Bulb Co. are *false,* we must assume the converse, namely, that they are *true,* with the hope that we will be able to reject this latter hypothesis. If we are able to reject the hypothesis that the advertising claims were true, we have then succeeded in showing that they were false *without having had to expose ourselves to the risk of a type II error.* If, on the other hand, our sample fails to reject the hypothesis, we *cannot* conclude that the advertising claims of the QRS Bulb Co. were true; we can only shrug our shoulders, saying that we were unable to prove that they were wrong.

A hypothesis which is formulated for the express purpose of being rejected is called a *null hypothesis.* The investigator who set out to prove that the QRS Bulb Co. was wrong, first formulated the *null hypothesis* that they were right. Similarly, if we hope to show that one student is more intelligent than another, we formulate the *null hypothesis* that they are equally intelligent. If we are subsequently able to reject the null hypothesis, we have shown that the two students are *not* equally intelligent, which is precisely what we had wanted to prove.

If we cannot reject a null hypothesis on the basis of a given experiment (sample), it is proper to report this fact by saying that we were simply unable to reject the hypothesis and are therefore *reserving judgment.* It does not follow by any means that we are necessarily forced to accept an alternative hypothesis. This procedure will limit our worries to the type I error, which is the error of rejecting a (null) hypothesis which should not have been rejected. If we never accept an alternative hypothesis, there is no danger of committing a type II error.

The logical structure of this approach makes it necessary to follow certain definite steps in the testing of a null hypothesis. These can be outlined as follows:

    1. The null hypothesis must be formulated in such a manner that it will be possible to construct a suitable criterion for testing it. (This step may seem somewhat trivial to the beginner, but we will soon learn from

experience that careless formulation of a hypothesis can easily put him in a position where it becomes exceedingly difficult to develop a suitable criterion.   For example, if the agent of the Better Business Bureau had carelessly formulated the hypothesis that the advertising claims were *false*, he would have been in a lot of trouble trying to formulate a criterion for testing this hypothesis.)

2. We must next specify the probability with which we are willing to risk a type I error.   This probability is usually referred to as the *level of significance* at which the test of the hypothesis is being conducted.   This level of significance should always be reported together with the decision that we may have reached concerning the hypothesis which we set out to test.   It tells us in a way how sure we are of our decision *if* we have rejected the null hypothesis.

3. The following step consists of selecting a statistic and a suitable sample size on which we shall base the criterion for testing the hypothesis.

4. Having chosen a level of significance in step 2 and a sample size and statistic in step 3, we can use the sampling distribution of the chosen statistic to construct the actual criterion on which we shall base our decision.

5. The final step consists of taking the actual measurements or observations and deciding on the basis of our results whether we can reject the null hypothesis at the given level of significance, or whether we have to reserve judgment.

To illustrate all the detail which is actually involved in this procedure, let us return to the original problem of checking the advertising claims of the QRS Bulb Co.   The agent of the Better Business Bureau decides to proceed as follows, numbering his steps according to our outline:

1. He formulates the null hypothesis H that the actual proportion of daffodils is .50.   This will make it possible for him to construct a testing criterion, as he knows that the sampling distribution of the number of daffodils in a sample of size n has a binomial distribution with a *known* mean and standard deviation.

2. He follows the customary rule of choosing the level of significance as .05.

3. His *statistic* will be the actual number of daffodils observed in a sample of size 400.

4. The sampling distribution of the number of daffodils in a sample of size 400 is the binomial distribution, which as before, will be approximated by means of a normal curve.   Putting, by hypothesis, $p = .50$, we find with the use of formulas (7.4.1) and (7.4.2) that

$$m = 400(.50) = 200$$

and
$$\sigma = \sqrt{400(.50)(.50)} = 10$$

Since we have chosen a level of significance, i.e., a type I error of .05, we can put half of this probability into each tail of the sampling distribution. This will give us the usual result that the z values of the dividing lines of our criterion are -1.96 and 1.96. If we then denote these dividing lines of our criterion as x_1 and x_2, we have

$$\frac{x_1 - 200}{10} = -1.96 \quad \text{and} \quad \frac{x_2 - 200}{10} = 1.96$$

which gives us $x_1 = 180.4$ and $x_2 = 219.6$. The criterion which we must therefore use to *reject the hypothesis H* is that the sample contains less than 181 or more than 219 daffodils, and *to reserve judgment* if the sample contains from 181 to 219.

5. If his sample contained, for instance, 235 daffodils, the agent of the Better Business Bureau can report that *he was able to reject the hypothesis H (that $p = .50$) at the level of significance of .05.* If, however, his sample had contained only 212 daffodils, he would be forced to report that *the experiment did not enable him to reject the hypothesis that the advertising claims were true at the level of significance of .05.*

This is the way in which the result of the test of a null hypothesis should always be reported. Since the purpose of such a test is to decide whether the difference between values which are assumed under the hypothesis and values which were obtained in the sample *can reasonably be ascribed to chance*, these tests are also called *tests of significance*. They enable us to decide whether the discrepancy between experience and expectation is significant (means anything at all) or whether it can be attributed to chance. In our example we *expected*, under the null hypothesis, to obtain 200 daffodils. According to the criterion which we developed in step 4 *the difference between the observed number and the expected number of daffodils is significant if it is 19 or more, but it may very well be attributed to chance if it is less than 19.*

Therefore, if a sample value falls into the interval for which we decided to reject the null hypothesis H, we can say that the sample value differs *significantly* from the value which was assumed under the hypothesis. Otherwise we say that the difference is *not significant* and that it may well be due purely to chance.

In our illustration we had to decide whether the difference between the observed number of daffodils, namely, 235, and the assumed number of daffodils, namely, 200, was large enough to be called significant. As we have shown above, this difference was significant, and the null hypothesis was rejected.

In actual practice it is usually not necessary to go through all the work of calculating the dividing lines of the criterion. What we could have done instead in our illustration would have been to calculate the z value which corresponds to the 235 daffodils that were observed in the sample. Knowing that $m = 200$ and $\sigma = 10$, we could immediately have found that

$$z = \frac{235 - 200}{10} = 3.5$$

As 95 per cent of the z values can be expected to lie between -1.96 and 1.96, *we can reject the null hypothesis at a level of significance of .05 if the z value which is calculated on the basis of the sample is either less than -1.96 or greater than 1.96.* Consequently, we can reject the null hypothesis in our example, because $z = 3.5$ exceeds the critical value of 1.96.

10.3 Testing the Significance of a Deviation from an Assumed Proportion

This test is, logically speaking, identical with the test which we have used as an illustration in the previous sections. We shall assume the null hypothesis that a certain proportion, rate, or probability is equal to a fixed value p, and we shall then decide on the basis of the relative frequency or the actual number of successes which we observe in a sample whether we can reject this hypothesis. It does not matter, in this kind of test, whether we use the relative frequency f_n or the actual number of successes, as long as we are consistent in this respect throughout our work. In the previous section we used the actual number of successes, and we shall now develop the general theory using instead the relative frequency f_n.

We know already from formulas (9.5.1) that the mean and standard deviation of the sampling distribution of the relative frequency are

$$m = p \quad \text{and} \quad \sigma = \sqrt{\frac{p(1 - p)}{n}}$$

and we also know that we can approximate this binomial sampling distribution by means of a normal curve if we are dealing with reasonably large samples.

This information is sufficient to enable us to find the z value corresponding to the relative frequency of any sample as

$$z = \frac{f_n - p}{\sqrt{p(1 - p)}/\sqrt{n}} \qquad (10.3.1)^*$$

and we can use this expression to evaluate the critical values of the testing criterion for any arbitrary level of significance.

Let us suppose, for instance, that somebody has claimed that the mortality rate of a certain disease is .15, and that we want to test this hypothesis (that $p = .15$) at a level of significance of .05 on the basis of a sample of size 500. We have according to (9.5.1)

$$m = .15 \quad \text{and} \quad \sigma_{f_n} = \sqrt{\frac{(.15)(.85)}{500}} = .016$$

and if we denote the dividing lines of the testing criterion as f_1 and f_2 we can write

$$\frac{f_1 - .15}{.016} = -1.96 \qquad \frac{f_2 - .15}{.016} = 1.96$$

and $\qquad\qquad f_1 = .1186 \qquad\qquad f_2 = .1814$

Consequently, we can reject the hypothesis that $p = .15$ (at the level of significance of .05) if the relative frequency which we observe in our sample is less than .1186 or greater than .1814 (see Fig. 10.k).

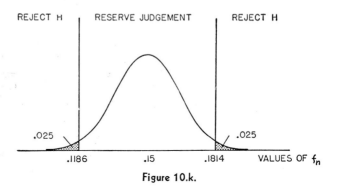

Figure 10.k.

Had our sample shown 68 deaths among the 500 patients who had the given disease, the relative frequency would have been 68/500 = .132 *and we would not have been able to reject the null hypothesis.*

Instead of calculating the critical values of the criterion, i.e., f_1 and f_2, we could have reached the same decision by computing the z value, which corresponds to the sample value of the relative frequency, according to formula (10.3.1). This would have given us

$$z = \frac{f_n - .15}{.016} = \frac{.132 - .15}{.016} = 1.12$$

Since this value falls *between* the critical values of z of -1.96 and 1.96 we were thus *not* able to reject the null hypothesis.

It will be necessary to modify this procedure to some extent if we want to test the hypothesis that the true proportion is equal to p *or less* (or p *or more*). If we are interested, for example, in testing the hypothesis that the percentage of the votes which a candidate will receive in a certain election is *.15 or less*, it is only the large values of the relative frequency which can be considered as contrary to the assumed hypothesis. Consequently we must limit our worries to the right-hand tail of the sampling distribution of f_n, and put the entire 5 per cent of the area (if the level of significance is .05) into that tail of the distribution (see Fig. 10.1). The z value of the dividing line

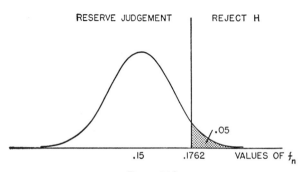

RESERVE JUDGEMENT   REJECT H

.05

.15   .1762   VALUES OF f_n

Figure 10.1.

(there is only one in this case) is 1.64, which corresponds to the normal curve area of .4500 in Table I. If f is the relative frequency at which we draw the line, we can write

$$\frac{f - .15}{.016} = 1.64 \quad \text{and} \quad f = .1762$$

provided, of course, that we are again using a sample of size 500. If 92 of the 500 voters asked expressed a preference for our candidate, the relative frequency is $92/500 = .184$ and we can *reject* the null hypothesis that the candidate will receive 15 per cent of the vote or less. The level of significance at which we have been able to reach this decision is *at most .05*, since the probability of our committing a type I error would have been even smaller if the true percentage had actually been less than .15.

This type of test has many important applications because it happens quite often that we are interested primarily in seeing whether a percentage is greater than (or less than) an assumed value of p. We could again have saved ourselves the trouble of calculating the critical value of f, which was .1762, by comparing the z value corresponding to the sample value of f_n with the critical z value of 1.64.

10.4 Testing the Significance of the Difference Between Two Proportions

A question which often arises in the study of experimental data is whether or not the difference between two observed percentages is significant or whether it can reasonably be ascribed to chance. For example, if 79 per cent of one kind of seed germinates, but only 74 per cent of another, it is important to know whether this difference (which was based on samples) can be interpreted as indicating an actual difference between the two kinds of seeds. Similarly, if 85 per cent of the students of one school pass the regents' examination, and only 73 per cent of another, it might be interesting to know whether we can conclude that the students of one school are actually superior to those of the other. (It must be understood, of course, that both of the above percentages must be considered as having been based on a sample.)

Problems of this type are usually treated in the following fashion: *if we have large samples of size n_1 and n_2 taken from two different populations for which the true proportions are p_1 and p_2, the sampling distribution of the difference between the observed relative frequencies, namely, the difference $f_{n_1} - f_{n_2}$, is closely approximated by a normal curve for which*

$$m = p_1 - p_2 \qquad (10.4.1)$$

$$\sigma_{f_{n_1} - f_{n_2}} = \sqrt{\frac{p_1(1 - p_1)}{n_1} + \frac{p_2(1 - p_2)}{n_2}} \qquad (10.4.2)$$

Since the two proportions (rates or probabilities) p_1 and p_2 are, of course, unknown and since we are interested mainly in determining whether one is larger than the other, we shall formulate in all problems of this type *the null hypothesis that there is no difference between the two proportions, i.e., that $p_1 = p_2$ ($= p$)*. Substituting these values into (10.4.1) and (10.4.2) we get

$$m = 0 \qquad (10.4.3)$$

$$\sigma_{f_{n_1} - f_{n_2}} = \sqrt{p(1 - p)\left(\frac{1}{n_1} + \frac{1}{n_2}\right)} \qquad (10.4.4)^*$$

in which the proportion p, which is unknown, is generally approximated by the relative frequency of successes of the two samples combined. This means that we must put

$$p = \frac{x_1 + x_2}{n_1 + n_2} \qquad (10.4.5)*$$

x_1 and x_2 being the number of successes which were observed in each of the two groups. Because of this approximation of p in formula (10.4.4) the testing criterion which we are discussing in this section can be used only if our samples are large.

It is important to note that we are concerned now with the sampling distribution of the statistic $f_{n_1} - f_{n_2}$. Repeated samples from the same two populations will usually give us different values for f_{n_1} and f_{n_2}, and consequently also different values for their difference. If we were to take a large number of samples from each of the two populations, the values of $f_{n_1} - f_{n_2}$ can be expected to fall into a distribution which is closely approximated by a normal curve whose mean and standard deviation are given by (10.4.1) and (10.4.2), respectively.

To illustrate how we can actually perform a test of the significance of the difference between two proportions (between two relative frequencies) let us consider a problem in which we have to decide whether there exists a difference between two machines which manufacture milk bottles. Among 400 bottles taken from the first machine, 16 were defective, while 24 out of 300 were defective among the bottles produced by the second machine. This poses the question whether we may conclude on the basis of this evidence that one machine actually produces a smaller percentage of defectives than the other.

The two relative frequencies are $f_{n_1} = 16/400 = .04$ and $f_{n_2} = .08$, and their difference is $.04 - .08 = -.04$. Before we can decide whether this difference is *significant* we must determine the mean and standard deviation of the sampling distribution of the statistic $f_{n_1} - f_{n_2}$ by use of (10.4.3) and (10.4.4) *under the null hypothesis that there is no difference between the actual proportions.* This will give us

$$m = 0$$

and $\qquad \sigma_{f_{n_1} - f_{n_2}} = \sqrt{(.057)(.943)(\tfrac{1}{400} + \tfrac{1}{300})} = .0177$

where the value of p, which is needed for (10.4.4), was calculated by use of (10.4.5) as

$$p = \frac{16 + 24}{400 + 300} = .057$$

Choosing a level of significance of .05, the two dividing lines of our criterion (d_1 and d_2) will have the customary z values of -1.96 and 1.96, and we can write

$$\frac{d_1 - 0}{.0177} = -1.96 \qquad \frac{d_2 - 0}{.0177} = 1.96$$

or $\qquad\qquad d_1 = -.0347 \qquad\qquad d_2 = .0347$

The resulting criterion for testing our null hypothesis is shown in Fig. 10.m. Since the observed value of the difference of the pro-

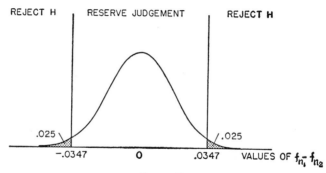

Figure 10.m.

portions (relative frequencies) was $-.04$, which falls to the left of $-.0347$, we can reject the hypothesis that there is no difference between the percentage of defective bottles produced by the two machines. Hence the difference is significant, and we have proof that one machine is definitely better than the other (subject only to a type I error of .05).

We could have arrived at the identical conclusion with much less work by considering the z value which corresponds to the observed difference of $-.04$. Using the same mean and standard deviation which we calculated in the previous paragraph by use of (10.4.3) and (10.4.4), we could have written

$$z = \frac{-.04 - 0}{.0177} = -2.26$$

and we could immediately have rejected the null hypothesis, because -2.26 is less than the critical z value of -1.96. *If there is no particular reason why we might want to know the actual dividing lines of the criterion, it is usually advisable to use this second method. We have only to find the z value corresponding to the observed value of the chosen statistic and compare it with the critical value of z which, for a given level of significance, can be found in Table I.*

The significance test which we have studied in this section has numerous important applications in every field of scientific inquiry. It can be used, for example, to test the significance between observed percentages of correct responses in an objective test; it can be used to test the significance of the difference between the percentage of cures which resulted from two drugs; the significance of differences in expressions of public opinion, etc. In each of these problems we begin by assuming the null hypothesis that there is *no difference*, with the hope that we shall be able to reject it on the basis of experiments or observations.

EXERCISES

1. Construct a criterion which can be used to test the honesty of a coin at a level of significance of .05 on the basis of a sample of size 400.

2. Candidate X claims that he will obtain 60 per cent of the vote. Construct a criterion which can be used to test the validity of his claims, using a level of significance of .02 and a sample of size 1000. (Reject his claim if he gets either too many or too few votes.)

3. If an outfit producing hair tonics claims to be able to cure baldness 80 per cent of the time, construct a criterion which will enable us to test this claim by use of samples of size 100 at a level of significance of .05. (Reject their claim only if there are too few cures.)

4. A student answered 72 questions correctly in a true-false test containing 100 questions. Test the hypothesis that he obtained his answers by flipping a coin (using a level of significance of .05).

5. If among 1000 automobiles made in 1940 only 308 were still running in 1950, test the hypothesis that 35 per cent of all cars made that year last at least 10 years. Use a level of significance of .02.

6. It is known that the mortality rate of a certain disease is .10 *or more*. If 98 out of 100 patients who had this disease survived after having been given a new drug, test whether this drug is really effective at a level of significance of .05.

7. A public opinion survey of 400 voters showed that 238 favored a certain piece of legislation. Test the hypothesis that this bill will receive *at least* 50 per cent of the vote at a level of significance of .05.

8. To test the hypothesis that 25 per cent of all smokers prefer brand A of cigarettes, we have decided to use a sample of size 300 and the following

criterion: we shall reject the hypothesis if less than 55 or more than 95 of the 300 smokers prefer brand A. What is the level of significance of this criterion?

9. It has been claimed that *at most* 50 per cent of the people have exactly two colds per year. If we decide to reject this claim if among 400 people 216 *or more* say that they had two colds in the previous year, what is our level of significance?

10. A test item in an objective test is really good if it discriminates between the poor and the good students. Is a test item good if it was answered correctly by 134 out of 250 good students and by 68 out of 180 poor students? Level of significance is .05.

11. In a poll taken at the preview of a new movie 23 out of 100 men said that they liked it, while 52 out of 200 women also reacted favorably. Was there really a difference of opinion between the two groups?

12. If one baseball player got 84 hits in 233 at bats while another player got 103 hits in 350 at bats, is there a significant difference between their batting averages? Use a level of significance of .02.

10.5 Testing the Significance of a Deviation from an Assumed Mean

Once the reader has understood the fundamental ideas which underlie a test of significance, the various new tests which we shall discuss in this and in later sections will not present further difficulties. In principle we always do the same. We assume a certain null hypothesis and we construct a criterion, basing it on the sampling distribution of a chosen statistic. Then if something happens which under the stated hypothesis is *very unlikely*, we reject the hypothesis. For example, if we assume that a coin is *honest*, it would happen very rarely that we obtain either a very small or a very large number of heads. If this *does* happen, however, we reject the null hypothesis in spite of the fact that such an unusual event could, of course, be due purely to chance even if the hypothesis were true. The risk which we must thus assume is expressed by the level of significance at which we have reached our decision.

The question as to what kind of a result should be considered as unusual or unlikely is something which must be decided *before* an experiment is conducted. Otherwise it might prove too much of a temptation to choose, for example, a level of significance which would permit us to prove what we had set out to show. *In general, we consider as unusual those situations in which an observed statistic differs from the value which we expected by more than we can reasonably ascribe to chance.*

The significance test which we shall discuss in this section refers to problems in which we have to decide whether the *mean* of a population is equal to a certain value m. We may be interested, for example, in testing the hypothesis that the melting point of lead is 327°; that the average hourly wage paid to workers in a certain industry is \$1.28; or that the average I.Q. of a given group of college students is 110.

To test any one of these hypotheses we must begin by formulating a hypothesis concerning the true value of the mean of the population. Then we must take a sample of size n, compute the sample mean $\bar{x}$ (or some other statistic), and finally we must decide whether the discrepancy between the assumed mean m and the observed sample mean $\bar{x}$ is sufficiently large to enable us to reject the hypothesis. If this is the case we can conclude that the sample mean differs *significantly* from the assumed value of m, and the hypothesis can therefore be rejected.

To illustrate this technique, let us test the hypothesis that the average weight of men who are from 25 to 29 years of age and 5 ft. 7 in. tall is 146 pounds. To do this we shall use a random sample of size n selected from the given population. Under the assumption that $m = 146$, the sampling distribution of the statistic $\bar{x}$ is (for large samples) closely approximated by a normal curve for which

$$m = 146 \quad \text{and} \quad \sigma_{\bar{x}} = \frac{s}{\sqrt{n}}$$

where s is, as always, the sample standard deviation which is used instead of the unknown population standard deviation σ. Selecting a level of significance of .05, we shall now consider a sample value of $\bar{x}$ as *sufficiently unreasonable* to reject the hypothesis that $m = 146$ if its corresponding z value is less than -1.96 or greater than 1.96 (see Fig. 10.n). The criterion which we shall use can, therefore, be stated as follows:

We shall *reject the hypothesis* (that $m = 146$) if the z value corresponding to our sample mean is less than -1.96 or greater than 1.96.

We shall *reserve judgment* if the z value lies between -1.96 and 1.96.

The z value which is needed for this criterion can easily be found with the customary formula

$$z = \frac{\bar{x} - m}{s/\sqrt{n}} \qquad\qquad (10.5.1)^*$$

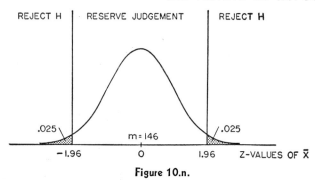

Figure 10.n.

in which $\bar{x}$ and s are the sample values, while m is the assumed mean of the population.

To show how this method works let us say, for instance, that we have taken a random sample of 100 measurements and that our results gave us

$$\bar{x} = 152 \quad \text{and} \quad s = 14$$

The z value corresponding to our sample mean is according to (10.5.1)

$$z = \frac{152 - 146}{14/\sqrt{100}} = 4.21$$

and since this value certainly exceeds the critical z value of 1.96, we can reject the hypothesis that $m = 146$ at the level of significance of .05. (We could actually have rejected this hypothesis at an even smaller level of significance because our observed z value was so much larger than 1.96.)

It is important to remember that the method which we have just developed can be used only if our samples are *large*. This is because σ cannot be approximated sufficiently by s if we are dealing with small samples. *If n is small, therefore, we will be forced to replace the statistic z by the Student-t and base our decision on the Student-t-distribution instead of the normal curve.*

In order to test the hypothesis that the mean of a population equals m (at the level of significance of .05) we can then use the following *small sample criterion*:

We shall *reject the hypothesis* (that the population mean is m) if the t which is computed on the basis of the sample is either less than $-t_{.025}$ or greater than $t_{.025}$.

We shall *reserve judgment* if t falls between these two critical values.

The statistic t on which this criterion is based can be found from formula (9.4.1) which gave us

$$t = \frac{\bar{x} - m}{s} \sqrt{n-1} \qquad (10.5.2)^*$$

It is interesting to note that this formula differs from (10.5.1) only in that n is replaced by $n - 1$. The required values of $t_{.025}$ can always be found very easily in Table II for any desired value of n. If it is preferable to use a different level of significance, we would simply have to replace $t_{.025}$ with the correspondingly different value of t. Had we wanted to use a level of significance of .02, for instance, the critical values of our criterion would be given by $-t_{.01}$ and $t_{.01}$.

To illustrate this *small sample technique* let us now test the hypothesis that the average hourly wage paid to workers in a certain factory is \$1.24, and let us suppose that a small random sample of 17 workers provided us with the following results:

$$\bar{x} = \$1.31 \quad \text{and} \quad s = \$.21$$

In spite of the fact that the average hourly wage which we obtained in this sample differs considerably from the assumed value of $m = \$1.24$, *it remains to be seen whether this difference is large enough to enable us to say that it is significant.* Using formula (10.5.2) we have

$$t = \frac{1.31 - 1.24}{.21} \sqrt{17 - 1} = 1.33$$

which is *less* than the $t_{.025}$, which according to Table II is equal to 2.120 for $n = 17$. Consequently we *cannot* reject the hypothesis that $m = \$1.24$ on the basis of this experiment, and we must report that the deviation which we have observed is not significant. *This does not mean that the average hourly wage must necessarily be \$1.24; it means only that we were not able to disprove it on the basis of our sample.*

10.6 Testing the Significance of the Difference Between Two Means

Another important test of significance is the one which is used to decide whether the observed difference between two sample means $\bar{x}_1$ and $\bar{x}_2$ (taken from two different populations) is large enough to permit us to say that there actually exists a difference between the corresponding population means m_1 and m_2.

We may want to know, for example, whether the students of one school are actually superior in intelligence to those of another if a sample of 50 students from school A averaged 78 in a certain test while a sample of 30 students of school B averaged only 73. Similarly, we may want to know whether it is true that western universities pay higher salaries to their professors than eastern universities if we have some partial information consisting of samples taken from both of these groups; and finally, a biologist may want to know whether there is really a difference between two kinds of eggs if a sample of 200 eggs of one kind had an average length of 54 mm while a sample of 150 eggs of another kind had an average length of 57 mm.

In all these problems we are interested in deciding whether the observed difference $\bar{x}_1 - \bar{x}_2$ is large enough to enable us to say that it is *significant*. The technique which is generally used to reach such a decision can be outlined as follows. *If we take samples of size* n_1 *and* n_2 *which are random and which are also independent of one another (the measurements of one sample are not affected in any respect by those of the other), the sampling distribution of the statistic* $\bar{x}_1 - \bar{x}_2$ *is for large samples closely approximated by a normal curve which has the mean and standard deviation*

$$m = m_1 - m_2 \qquad (10.6.1)$$

$$\sigma_{\bar{x}_1 - \bar{x}_2} = \sqrt{\frac{\sigma_1^2}{n_1} + \frac{\sigma_2^2}{n_2}} \qquad (10.6.2)$$

where m_1 and m_2 are the two population means and σ_1 and σ_2 the population standard deviations.

The sampling distribution which we are now talking about is the distribution which we can *expect* to obtain if we group the values of $\bar{x}_1 - \bar{x}_2$ which are calculated from a large number of repeated samples from the same two populations.

In most practical problems we know neither the actual values of m_1 and m_2 nor the standard deviations σ_1 and σ_2. *Consequently, we must formulate the null hypothesis that there is no difference between the means of the two populations, i.e., we must assume that* $m_1 - m_2 = 0$. Since the population standard deviations are also unknown we must approximate them by means of the sample standard deviations s_1 and s_2, and formulas (10.6.1) and (10.6.2) can then be rewritten as

$$m = 0 \qquad (10.6.3)^*$$

$$\sigma_{\bar{x}_1 - \bar{x}_2} = \sqrt{\frac{s_1^2}{n_1} + \frac{s_2^2}{n_2}} \qquad (10.6.4)^*$$

Formula (10.6.4) is generally known as *the standard error of the difference between two means.*

Let us now illustrate how these formulas are used to test the significance of the difference between two sample means, by use of an example dealing with the scores which two groups of students obtained in the same examination. A sample of 240 students of school A had scores which averaged 79 and which had a standard deviation of 12, while a sample of 180 students of school B averaged 74 with a standard deviation of 14. This information can be restated as follows:

$$n_1 = 240 \qquad n_2 = 180$$
$$\bar{x}_1 = 79 \qquad \bar{x}_2 = 74$$
$$s_1 = 12 \qquad s_2 = 14$$

Under the assumption that there is no difference between the means of these two populations, the mean and standard deviation of the sampling distribution of $\bar{x}_1 - \bar{x}_2$ are, according to (10.6.3) and (10.6.4),

$$m = 0$$

$$\sigma_{\bar{x}_1 - \bar{x}_2} = \sqrt{\frac{12^2}{240} + \frac{14^2}{180}} = 1.3$$

Selecting a level of significance of .05, we will then be able to reject the null hypothesis if the z value which corresponds to $\bar{x}_1 - \bar{x}_2$ falls

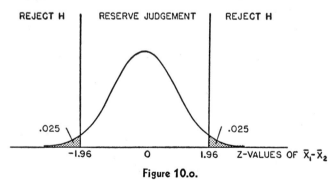

Figure 10.o.

outside of the interval from -1.96 to 1.96. Since the necessary z value is in this case given by the formula

$$z = \frac{\bar{x}_1 - \bar{x}_2}{\sigma_{\bar{x}_1 - \bar{x}_2}} \qquad (10.6.5)^*$$

we have $z = (79 - 74)/1.3 = 3.85$, and we are justified in saying that *the difference is significant*. We can therefore reject the null hypothesis and we have shown that there really exists a difference in the abilities of the students of the two schools.

As we have said before, this test can be used only if both n_1 and n_2 are large. If we have small samples we must again modify our technique, using the Student-t instead of the normal distribution. Although this small sample technique is not difficult, we shall omit it in this introductory study of statistical methods.

EXERCISES

1. Given $\bar{x} = 64$, $s = 15$, and $n = 100$, test the hypothesis that $m = 60$ at a level of significance of .05.

2. Given $\bar{x} = 17.4$, $s = .8$, and $n = 26$, test the hypothesis that $m = 17.5$ at a level of significance of .05.

3. Test the hypothesis that the average savings account is \$59.00 if a random sample of 400 such accounts showed an average deposit of \$61.23 and a standard deviation of \$18.24. Use a level of significance of .02.

4. An achievement test which was given to a sample of 250 students produced the following results: $\bar{x} = 79$ and $s = 15$. Use this information to test the hypothesis that the true average is 85 at a level of significance of .01.

5. A sample of 13 steel beams showed an average compressive strength of 54,275 psi, with a standard deviation of 583 psi. Test the hypothesis that the true average compressive strength of these beams is 56,000 psi at a level of significance of .05.

6. A sample of 8 measurements of the percentage of manganese in ferromanganese had a mean of 82.7 and a standard deviation of 1.2 per cent. Test the hypothesis that the true percentage is 80 at a level of significance of .02.

7. The identical test was given to samples of 50 students from two different communities. If the results which were observed are

$$n_1 = 50 \qquad \bar{x}_1 = 89 \qquad s_1 = 4$$
$$n_2 = 50 \qquad \bar{x}_2 = 93 \qquad s_2 = 3$$

test the hypothesis that there is no difference between the means of the two populations. Level of significance .05.

8. Measurements of the height of people belonging to two different nationalities produced the following results:

$$n_1 = 130 \qquad \bar{x}_1 = 67 \text{ in.} \qquad s_1 = 2 \text{ in.}$$
$$n_2 = 250 \qquad \bar{x}_2 = 66 \text{ in.} \qquad s_2 = 3 \text{ in.}$$

Use a level of significance of .05 to test the hypothesis that there is no difference in the average height of the two groups.

9. An investigation of the relative merits of two types of flashlight batteries showed that a sample of 100 batteries made by company A had an average lifetime of 24 hours with a standard deviation of 4 hours. If a

sample of 80 batteries made by company B had an average lifetime of 30 hours with a standard deviation of 5 hours, is the difference between these two means significant at a level of significance of .05?

10. If a sample of 400 fraternity men had an average college index of 1.40 with a standard deviation of .30, while a sample of 200 nonfraternity men averaged 1.35 with a standard deviation of .40, can we conclude that fraternity men have higher indexes than nonfraternity men at a level of significance of .01?

10.7 Further Tests of Significance

The systematic study and evaluation of tests of hypotheses, though still a relatively new subject, has assumed a very important role in modern statistical theory. Unfortunately, a thorough study of this subject would demand a much more advanced knowledge of mathematics than we assumed at the outset of this book, and we therefore had to limit ourselves to a relatively nontechnical discussion of some of the more elementary applications. There exist, of course, many applications other than those which we have discussed in this chapter. We will find, for example, a test of the significance of a coefficient of correlation in Chapter 14, a test which will enable us to decide whether a distribution differs significantly from a normal curve (Chapter 16), and a test of the hypothesis that a sample is really random in Chapter 11.

In principle, all these tests are much alike. We always decide whether the discrepancies between observed values and values which were expected under a certain hypothesis are large enough so that they cannot reasonably be ascribed to chance. Then the differences are said to be significant and the null hypothesis is rejected.

REFERENCES

W. J. Dixon and F. J. Massey, *Introduction to Statistical Analysis*, McGraw-Hill, New York, 1951, Chaps. 7, 9.

M. J. Hagood, *Statistics for Sociologists*, Holt, New York, 1941, Chaps. 16, 17.

P. G. Hoel, *Introduction to Mathematical Statistics*, Wiley, New York, 1947, Chaps. 4, 11.

M. G. Kendall, *The Advanced Theory of Statistics*, Charles Griffin, London, 1946, Chaps. 26, 27.

J. F. Kenney and E. S. Keeping, *Mathematics of Statistics*, 2d ed., Van Nostrand, New York, 1951, Chap. 6.

J. Neyman, *First Course in Probability and Statistics*, Holt, New York, 1950, Chap. 5.

S. S. Wilks, *Elementary Statistical Analysis*, Princeton University Press, Princeton, 1949, Chaps. 10, 11.

11. TESTS OF RANDOMNESS

11.1 Introduction

The most fundamental concept which underlies all the theory of estimation and the testing of hypotheses is that of the *randomness* of samples. Since this concept is far from easy to understand we have been treating it until now on a more intuitive basis, calling a sample *random* if every element of the population has supposedly an equal chance of being chosen.

In everyday language randomness is generally interpreted as a certain haphazardness or lack of bias which is supposed to imply that no single item or groups of items (elements) belonging to the population are preferred, avoided, or distorted during the process of sampling. *In this sense randomness really refers to the method which is being used in obtaining the sample, or better, it refers to the things which we should avoid so that we can rightfully say that our samples are random.* Since obviously there must exist many things which should be avoided, it is clear that it is quite difficult to establish criteria on the basis of which we can decide whether a given sample is random or, at least, whether our method of sampling is without bias. This negative approach of defining randomness as the *absence of bias* makes it complicated to decide whether samples are actually random except, perhaps, under certain ideal conditions which are seldom met in real problems.

Such ideal conditions can be found primarily in gambling devices like roulette wheels, slips of paper which are drawn out of a bowl, etc., but even then it is difficult to eliminate all possible sources of bias which might conceivably affect results. Sampling techniques which are based on gambling devices can, for practical reasons, be used only if we sample from relatively small populations. For example, if we want to select a sample of size 10 among a group of 120 farmers who live in a certain county, we could write the name of each farmer on a slip of paper, shake the slips up thoroughly, and then draw 10 slips out of the bowl in which they were mixed. If the slips are all identical in weight and shape, and if they are shaken up very carefully, we have come about as close to a random sample as we can ever hope to get.

Since it will evidently be impossible to develop sampling techniques which are random in every respect, it seems much more realistic to list the most common factors which might contribute to non-randomness of a sample, namely, those factors which might possibly introduce a bias, and to make sure that these potentially disturbing factors are under control. This will give us samples which are (as far as we know) random at least in respect to certain factors which otherwise could easily have ruined the validity of our results.

11.2 The Importance of the Choice of the Correct Population

One question which must always be studied carefully before a sample is actually taken is the question of whether we have planned to select our sample from the correct population. What we mean by the *correct population* can easily be understood from the following example. Let us suppose, for instance, that we want to predict an election of the governor of California. It would hardly seem reasonable, in that case, to limit our sample to the residents of Pasadena even though the method of sampling which we had intended to use might have been perfectly random *relative to the inhabitants of this particular community*. This means that although every voter of Pasadena may have an equal chance of being asked for whom he intends to vote, *we do not have a random sample from the total population which is relevant to our problem*. A good illustration of the disastrous consequences of the choice of the wrong population is the prediction which the now defunct *Literary Digest* made of the 1936 presidential election. The *Literary Digest* predicted a Republican victory on the basis of tremendously large samples taken at random from names listed in telephone directories and from lists of automobile registrations. Although the results may have been quite indicative of the group from which they took their sample, it was definitely *not* a random sample of the entire population of voters. It just so happened that President Roosevelt's support came mainly from the lower income groups which were not sufficiently represented among the owners of telephones and automobiles. Consequently, the *Literary Digest* poll was biased, and the effect of this error of sampling was disastrous to the magazine.

We must always remember, therefore, that *predictions or estimations which are made on the basis of a sample apply only to the particular population from which the sample was selected.* Any generalizations to populations which either contain or are part of the population from which the sample was obtained are either pure guesswork, or must be based on an extremely careful analysis.

Many important scientific studies have been subjected to the criticism that the population from which the sample was taken does not warrant generalizations to larger populations or to parts of the population which was the subject of the investigation. Several statisticians as well as non-statisticians have questioned the validity of the results of the recently published *Kinsey Report*, for example, on the grounds that the samples were not representative of the entire group of American males which the author of this study is claiming to describe.

Contrary to what we have said earlier in this chapter, it is at times advantageous to take samples which are not strictly random relative to the entire population. The accuracy of estimates and predictions can often be increased if we make sure that the various subgroups which make up our population are all represented in our sample. If we know, for instance, the percentage make-up of a population with respect to some characteristic such as income, nationality, education, etc., *we can actually improve the accuracy of our results by distributing our sample proportionally among the subgroups of the population.*

Let us assume, for instance, that income level is a factor which has an important bearing on public opinion concerning a certain election, and that 40 per cent of the voters have low incomes, 50 per cent have medium incomes, while 10 per cent have high incomes. If this were the case, we could improve the accuracy of our prediction if we were to allocate 40 per cent of the total sample to members of the low-income group, 50 per cent to the medium-income group, and the remaining 10 per cent of the sample to persons having high incomes.

This method of sampling is generally referred to as *stratified random sampling* provided, of course, that the sample which is taken from each subgroup is itself a random sample. This technique can be improved further if we break down the population with respect to some other relevant characteristic. Had we known, for instance, that nationality background is an additional factor which has an important bearing on public opinion concerning the same election, *and* had we known that 70 per cent of the voters belonged to nationality group A while the remaining 30 per cent belonged to group B, we could then have *cross-stratified* our sample as follows (assuming that the income distribution is the same for both groups).

$(.40)(.70) = .28$ of the sample from the low-income group of nationality A.
$(.40)(.30) = .12$ from the low-income group of nationality B.
$(.50)(.70) = .35$ from the medium-income group of nationality A.
$(.50)(.30) = .15$ from the medium-income group of nationality B.
$(.10)(.70) = .07$ from the high-income group of nationality A.
$(.10)(.03) = .03$ from the high-income group of nationality B.

Carrying this method even further, we could cross-stratify our sample with respect to as many factors as would be practically possible. Evidently, this can be done only if we know not only what factors will have a bearing on our results but also the proper breakdown of the population with respect to the various factors.

11.3 The Theory of Runs

The subject matter which might reasonably be included in a study of randomness covers such a vast territory that we must content ourselves here with a discussion of certain specific elements of bias (nonrandomness) which can be detected through an analysis of the *internal structure* of a sample. To do this we record the individual measurements which make up a sample in the precise order in which they were originally obtained.

To illustrate what we mean by the *internal structure* of a sample, let us consider the following example. The director of a public opinion poll instructs three of his investigators to take a sample of 30 voters each and to ask each voter whether he favors candidate A or candidate B, who are both running for the same office. The results turned in by the three investigators are

	For candidate A	For candidate B
Investigator 1	17	13
Investigator 2	15	15
Investigator 3	15	15

If we look at these figures as they are reported in the above table there is no obvious reason why we should suspect that any sample was not random. As a matter of fact, it would be useless even to consider questioning the randomness of these samples unless we could ask the three investigators for more information as to where and in what manner they had taken their samples.

As we shall learn in the remainder of this chapter, much can be learned about the randomness of a sample from the *order* in which the individual observations were made. Let us suppose that we ask the three investigators to specify the order in which they collected the opinions favoring either candidate A or candidate B, denoting a vote for candidate A by the letter *a* and a vote for candidate B by the letter *b*, and that their original worksheets showed the following raw data.

Investigator 1

$a, a, a, a, a, a, a, b, b, b, b, a, a, a, a, a, a, a, a, a, b, b, b, b, b, b, b, a, b, b$

Investigator 2

$b, a, b, a, b, a, b, a, b, a, b, a, b, a, b, a, b, a, b, a, b, a, b, a, b, a, b, a, b, a$

Investigator 3

$a, a, b, a, b, b, b, a, b, a, a, a, a, b, b, a, a, a, b, a, b, a, b, b, b, a, a, b, b, b$

We can now ask whether any features of these series of *a*'s and *b*'s might conceivably arouse our suspicion that the samples were not random.

It is apparent that the sample which was collected by Investigator 1 is distinguished by a considerable grouping of the *a*'s and *b*'s, i.e., there are relatively long sequences of consecutive *a*'s or *b*'s. This might arouse our suspicion that Investigator 1 had taken a group of voters from a district which was predominantly for candidate A, then moved to a district in which the voters favored candidate B, etc. Naturally, there could have been other reasons, but in any case it is difficult to accept as *random* the arrangement of the *a*'s and *b*'s obtained by Investigator 1.

The results of Investigator 2 are even more difficult to understand or explain. It would seem almost ridiculous to accept the definite alternation of the *a*'s and *b*'s as a *random sample* or a *random arrangement*.

Finally, the data which were collected by Investigator 3 appear to be quite random, or at least there is no obvious reason why we should suspect the randomness of this particular sample.

There exist several techniques which have been developed in the past ten years which enable us to test the hypothesis that a sample is random, on the basis of the order in which the individual items were originally obtained. The special method which we shall discuss in this chapter is based on the idea of studying the *number of runs* of a's and b's which we may find in a sample, but it is by no means the only technique which could be used to test the randomness of a sample on the basis of its internal structure.

A run is defined as a succession of identical letters which are followed and preceded by a different letter or by no letter at all. Taking the result of Investigator 3, for example, we find that he first had a run of two a's, then a run of one b, then a run of one a, then a run of three b's, etc. Combining the successive letters which jointly form the various runs we can easily see that the sample of Investigator 3 had the following 16 runs:

$$aa, \quad b, \quad a, \quad bbb, \quad a, \quad b, \quad aaaa, \quad bb, \quad aaa, \quad b, \quad a, \quad b, \quad a, \quad bbb, \quad aa, bbb$$
$$1 \quad 2 \quad 3 \quad 4 \quad 5 \quad 6 \quad 7 \quad 8 \quad 9 \quad 10 \quad 11 \quad 12 \quad 13 \quad 14 \quad 15 \quad 16$$

The total number of runs which we may find in a sample of this kind is often a good indication of a possible lack of randomness. If there are *too few* runs we might suspect a definite grouping, or possibly a trend within the sample (see Section 11.4), and *too many* runs might easily mean that there are other factors present which detract from the randomness of the sample.

To study the number of runs of a sample we shall use a criterion (which has been developed especially for this purpose) on the basis of which we can decide whether a sample has too many or too few runs. *Like all other tests of significance, it will enable us to decide whether we have more (or less) runs than we could reasonably expect if our sample were a random arrangement.* Selecting a level of significance of .05, we shall say that a sample has too few runs, i.e., *that it is not random,* if the total number of runs which is denoted by the letter u is less than or equal to the quantity $u_{.025}$. Similarly, a sample will be said to have too many runs, which is again a deviation from randomness, if the total number of runs u is greater than or equal to the quantity $u_{.975}$. If a sample value of u falls between these two critical values we cannot reject the null hypothesis that the sample is random, and we can say only that *the sample does not show a significant deviation from randomness as far as the total number of runs is concerned.*

The necessary values of $u_{.025}$ and $u_{.975}$ are given in Tables Va and Vb (pp. 393, 394). In these tables m stands for the number of elements (not runs) of one kind, while n stands for the number of elements of the other kind in the total arrangement which makes up the sample. Since both tables are symmetrical with respect to m and n, it does not matter which number is called m and which is called n.[1]

To illustrate the use of these tables, let us apply this criterion to the sample which was obtained by Investigator 1 in our previous illustration. Counting the number of a's and b's and the total number of runs we have

$$m = 17 \quad n = 13 \quad u = 6$$

According to Tables Va and Vb, the critical values of u are

$$u_{.025} = 10 \quad \text{and} \quad u_{.975} = 22$$

and since our sample value of u was *less than 10*, we can reject the null hypothesis that our sample was random. Hence we have shown that the sample of Investigator 1 differed significantly from what we would have expected it to be like if it were a random sample.

Another problem which can be solved with the use of the theory of runs is whether a certain plant disease attacks flowers at random or whether it attacks them in some sort of a pattern. Denoting healthy plants by the letter H and diseased plants by the letter D, let us assume that 28 plants which were planted in a row in a certain experiment showed the following arrangement of healthy and diseased plants.

$H, H, H, H, H, H, H, H, D, D, D, H, H, H, H, H, H, D, D, D, H, H, H, H, H, H, D, D$

In this arrangement of H's and D's the number of healthy plants is $m = 20$, the number of diseased plants is $n = 8$, and the total number of runs is $u = 6$. Since the critical values of u are according to Tables Va and Vb equal to $u_{.025} = 7$ and $u_{.975} = 17$, we are justified in saying that the disease did not attack these plants at random.

Finally, let us apply the theory of runs to check whether people choose theater seats in a random fashion. Denoting male theatergoers by the letter M and female theatergoers by the letter F, let us suppose that we observed the following seating arrangement in the front row of a theater.

$M,F,M,F,M,M,F,M,F,M,F,F,M,F,F,M,F,M,F,F,F,M,F,M,F,M,F,F,M,F,F$

[1] When m or n are very small it can happen that all large (or small) values of u can reasonably be expected for a given level of significance. This explains the blanks spaces which appear in Tables Va and Vb.

In this arrangement the number of males is $m = 13$, the number of females is $n = 18$, and the total number of runs is $u = 21$. The critical values of u corresponding to these particular values of m and n are $u_{.025} = 10$ and $u_{.975} = 22$, and we can conclude that the seating arrangement displays a significant deviation from what might reasonably be called a random order. This was, of course, to be expected.

The critical values of u which are given in Tables Va and Vb were calculated directly from the sampling distribution of u, which is, as always, the distribution of the various values of the statistic u which we can expect to obtain from repeated random samples. If either m or n is greater than 20 (in which case Tables Va and Vb can no longer be used), and if the other one is not too small (at least 10), it is quite reasonable to approximate the sampling distribution of u by means of a normal curve whose mean and standard deviation are, respectively,

$$m_u = \frac{2mn}{m+n} + 1 \qquad (11.3.1)^*$$

$$\sigma_u = \sqrt{\frac{2mn(2mn - m - n)}{(m+n)^2(m+n-1)}} \qquad (11.3.2)^*$$

The null hypothesis that our sample is random can then be tested by use of the following criterion.

Reject the hypothesis of randomness if the total number of runs in the sample is either less than $m_u - 1.96\sigma_u$ or if it is greater than $m_u + 1.96\sigma_u$.

Reserve judgment if the sample value of u falls between the above two limits. We can then also say that the sample does not show a significant deviation from randomness.

Instead of using this criterion we could also reject the null hypothesis if the z value which corresponds to our sample value of u is less than -1.96 or greater than 1.96. This z value of u can be found by means of the formula

$$z = \frac{u - m_u}{\sigma_u} \qquad (11.3.3)^*$$

where m_u and σ_u must be calculated first from formulas (11.3.1) and (11.3.2). Both criteria are designed for a level of significance of .05, but it would not be difficult to change either to fit any arbitrary level of significance.

To illustrate the use of this criterion let us now look at a series of 115 flips of a silver dollar of which 60 were heads, 55 were tails, and which produced altogether 52 runs. Substituting $m = 60$ and $n = 55$ into formulas (11.3.1) and (11.3.2), we find that

$$m_u = \frac{2(60)(55)}{60 + 55} + 1 = 58.4$$

$$\sigma_u = \sqrt{\frac{2(60)(55)[2(60)(55) - 60 - 55]}{(60 + 55)^2(60 + 55 - 1)}} = 5.32$$

and the critical values of u are $58.4 \pm 1.96(5.32)$ or approximately 48 and 69. Since our sample value of u falls between 48 and 69 we are unable to reject the null hypothesis, which means that our experiment did not show a significant deviation from what we could have expected if our tosses were really random.

11.4 Runs Above and Below the Median

It is fortunate that the easy and useful test of randomness which we have just discussed is not limited in its application to the study of the randomness of series of attributes like the a's and b's, H's and D's, of our previous illustrations. Any sample which consists of numerical measurements can be treated similarly if we use the simple trick of denoting measurements which fall *below the median of the sample* by the letter b and those which fall *above the median* by the letter a. Measurements which are actually equal to the median will be omitted, and the resulting series of a's and b's can then be studied for a possible deviation from randomness by the method of the last section.

This technique is illustrated by the following example dealing with the heights of certain animals given to the nearest inch in the order in which the measurements were performed:

$$3, \quad 8, \quad 5, \quad 6, \quad 4, \quad 2, \quad 6, \quad 5, \quad 3, \quad 7, \quad 5, \quad 6, \quad 4, \quad 7, \quad 9, \quad 6$$

The median of this sample being 5.5, we can now rewrite this sample as

$$b, \quad a, \quad b, \quad a, \quad b, \quad b, \quad a, \quad b, \quad b, \quad a, \quad b, \quad a, \quad b, \quad a, \quad a, \quad a$$

and since 8 of the measurements were below the median, and 8 were above, we have $m = 8$, $n = 8$, and (as the reader can easily check for himself) $u = 12$. The corresponding critical values of u are, according to Tables Va and Vb, equal to $u_{.025} = 4$ and $u_{.975} = 14$, and since our sample value of u falls between these two numbers we cannot reject the null hypothesis, i.e., we must report that *the sample does not show a significant deviation from randomness.*

The method of runs above and below the median is particularly useful in the detection of *trends* and *cyclic patterns*. Let us suppose, for instance, that the following data represent the number of defective pieces which were detected among successive samples taken from the products of two different machines:

Machine U: 4, 6, 5, 7, 5, 6, 7, 6, 4, 8, 9, 8, 7, 9, 9, 8, 10
Machine V: 3, 8, 4, 9, 2, 8, 4, 7, 5, 9, 6, 8, 7, 8, 4, 6

The median of the number of defective pieces found in the samples taken from machine U is 7, and the first series of numbers can be rewritten as

$$b, \quad b, \quad b, \quad b, \quad b, \quad b, \quad b, \quad a, \quad a, \quad a, \quad a, \quad a, \quad a, \quad a$$

which gives us $m = 7$, $n = 7$, and $u = 2$. It can easily be checked that $u = 2$ is sufficiently small to enable us to *reject* the null hypothesis that the arrangement of our sample values is random. A possible explanation of this deviation from randomness is that the machine might be wearing out, as there is an upward *trend* in the number of defectives. Perhaps the raw materials used are getting progressively worse, the operators of the machine are getting lazier, etc.

The median of the number of defectives which were observed in the samples of machine V is 6.5, and the second series of numbers can be rewritten as

$$b, \quad a, \quad b, \quad a, \quad b, \quad a, \quad b, \quad a, \quad b, \quad a, \quad b, \quad a, \quad a, \quad a, \quad b, \quad a$$

which gives us $m = 9$, $n = 7$, and $u = 14$. Since the observed number of runs equals the critical value $u_{.975} = 14$ (see Table Vb), we can again reject the null hypothesis that the arrangement is random. The surprising alternating of the a's and b's, i.e., values above and below the median, can be due to many different causes. It could have happened, for example, that the samples were taken at the rate of two a day, one in the morning and one in the late afternoon, and that the cyclic behavior might be due to the tiring of the machine (or of its operator) at the end of each day.

It is important to remember that none of these tests of randomness can be made unless we preserve the order in which the sample values were originally obtained. If this is done we have a handy and easily applied criterion for testing the randomness of a sample.

REFERENCES

P. G. Hoel, *Introduction to Mathematical Statistics*, Wiley, New York, 1947, Chap. 9.

F. Mosteller, "Note on the Application of Runs to Quality Control Charts," *Annals of Mathematical Statistics*, 1941, Vol. XII, pp. 228–232.

F. Swed and C. Eisenhart, "Tables for Testing Randomness of Grouping in a Sequence of Alternatives," *Annals of Mathematical Statistics*, 1943, Vol. XIV, pp. 66–87.

S. S. Wilks, *Elementary Statistical Analysis*, Princeton University Press, Princeton, 1949, Chap. 12.

EXERCISES

1. At a meeting of mathematicians and psychologists the members of the two societies seated themselves in the following arrangement:

$$M, M, M, P, P, P, P, P, P, P, M, M, M, M, M, M, P, P, M, M, M, M, M, M, P, P, M$$

Test whether this arrangement may be considered random (level of significance is .05).

2. Toss a coin 20 times, write down the corresponding H's and T's, and use the theory of runs to test whether the arrangement is random at a level of significance of .05.

3. The following is an arrangement of empty (E) and occupied (O) seats at a lunch counter:

$$E, E, O, O, E, E, E, E, E, O, E, E, E, O, O, E, E, E, E, E, E, O, O, E, E, E, O$$

Check whether it may be considered as random (level of significance is .05).

4. Write down a series of 15 a's and 15 b's which you feel is fairly random, and then test the randomness at a level of significance of .05.

5. The following is the arrangement of a number of men (m) and women (w) who were lined up at the box office of a theater:

$$m, w, m, w, m, m, m, w, m, w, m, m, m, w, m, m, w, w, m, m, m, m, w, w, m,$$
$$w, m, w, m, w, m, w, m, m, w, m, m, m, w, m, w, w, m, m, m, w, m, w, m, w$$

Test whether this arrangement is random at a level of significance of .05.

6. Roll a die 100 times and record the result of each throw as E or O depending on whether the number of points was even or odd. Test whether this arrangement of E's and O's is random at a level of significance of .02.

7. The following is the order in which red (R) and black (B) playing cards were dealt to a bridge player:

$$B, \ B, \ B, \ B, \ R, \ R, \ B, \ R, \ R, \ R, \ R, \ B, \ R$$

Is it reasonable to say that this deal is random? Use level of significance of .05.

8. Try as hard as you can to pick *at random* 30 numbers from 0 to 50, and record them in the order in which they were selected. Then use the

method of runs above and below the median to test whether the arrangement is random at a level of significance of .05.

9. The following numbers represent the number of items which a certain machine produced in 23 successive days:

735, 742, 739, 740, 738, 740, 742, 741, 742, 746, 750, 745, 747, 739, 740, 742, 745, 744, 748, 746, 741, 738, 736.

Use the method of runs above and below the median to check whether this arrangement is random (level of significance is .05).

10. Use the method of runs above and below the median to test the randomness of the arrangement of the 120 college indexes of Exercise 6, page 19 (level of significance is .01). Take successive columns.

PART THREE:

*PREDICTION
AND CORRELATION*

12. THE NATURE
OF SCIENTIFIC
PREDICTIONS

12.1 Perfect and Imperfect Predictions

Knowledge which is based on experimental or observed information and which generally goes by the name of *scientific* or *empirical knowledge* has the distinguishing feature that it is *predictive knowledge*. This means that the main value of scientific knowledge lies in the fact that, *due to its very nature*, it enables us to make predictions concerning the behavior of observable phenomena. To this we must add, of course, that when a scientist predicts the occurrence of a certain event, his prediction is quite different in nature from predictions made by fortune tellers, prophets of ancient oracles, and astrologers.

In classical mythology it was predicted, for example, that Oedipus, son of Laius, King of Thebes, and Jocasta would kill his father and marry his own mother. In spite of his father's precautionary measures of leaving him to die on Mount Cithaeron, he was found by a shepherd and adopted by the king of Corinth. Through an odd mixture of circumstances he finally did kill his own father and marry his mother, after having solved the famous riddle of the Sphinx, which put him on the throne of Thebes.

This illustration is typical of what a scientist cannot do. He cannot predict with absolute certainty that certain apparently totally unrelated events will take place at some time in the distant future. As a matter of fact, he cannot predict anything whatsoever with absolute certainty. Instead he asserts his predictions in terms of probabilities, implying that he is satisfied if his predictions come true a certain percentage of the time or, better, he aims in his predictions for a success ratio which is as high as possible.

It is known, for instance, that the probability that a child of 10 will live to the ripe old age of 80 is .15. An actuary who subsequently predicts for each child of 10 that it will *not* live to be 80 can expect to be called a prophet 85 per cent of the time, and a fool the remaining 15 per cent. This illustrates the *calculated risk* which a scientist must always assume if he ventures to make a prediction.

Taking the meaning of the word *prediction* in its classical sense, a prediction is good if the predicted event actually comes true, and is called bad if the event does not come to pass. Scientific predictions, on the other hand, are quite different inasmuch as *scientists are usually satisfied if their predictions come close even though they may, literally speaking, not have been correct.* To understand fully what is meant by a good scientific prediction, let us consider the following illustration.

A certain game or contest consists of guessing (predicting) a set of numbers which are written on seven little pieces of paper drawn at random out of a goldfish bowl. To make the problem more interesting each contestant is asked to predict the seven numbers in the precise order in which they will be drawn. The individual slips are not replaced after they are drawn, and each piece of paper will thus appear exactly once during the course of the game. The numbers which the judges wrote on the seven slips of paper are

$$3, \quad 5, \quad 7, \quad 9, \quad 20, \quad 20, \quad 20$$

and the five contestants who volunteered for this ordeal are told what these numbers are in order to make their task easier (although they are *not* compelled to use all of this information). Of course, they are *not* told in what order the numbers will be drawn; that is what they must predict.

The five contestants make the following predictions.

Contestant A consulted the psychic powers of one of his aunts and was advised by her to predict the order:

$$20, \quad 5, \quad 9, \quad 20, \quad 20, \quad 3, \quad 7$$

Contestant B, who believes in ESP, bases his prediction on his extrasensory powers and predicts the order:

$$20, \quad 7, \quad 5, \quad 20, \quad 9, \quad 20, \quad 3$$

Contestant C feels that one arrangement has as much chance as the next one. Leaving his arrangement to chance, he writes the same seven numbers on his own slips of paper and draws them out of a hat in the order:

$$5, \quad 3, \quad 20, \quad 9, \quad 20, \quad 7, \quad 20$$

Contestant D, who professionally guesses people's weights in an amusement park, predicts for each drawing the number 20. His entry blank therefore looks like this:

$$20, \quad 20, \quad 20, \quad 20, \quad 20, \quad 20, \quad 20$$

Contestant E, who is an insurance man, predicts for each drawing the number 9. Without giving an explanation he enters:

$$9, \quad 9, \quad 9, \quad 9, \quad 9, \quad 9, \quad 9$$

After all entries were submitted the judges conducted the actual drawing, and came up with the result:

$$7, \quad 20, \quad 20, \quad 9, \quad 3, \quad 20, \quad 5$$

Since no contestant seemed to have distinguished himself as a prophet, the judges are faced with the difficult question as to who is to receive the grand prize.

One judge immediately suggests that the first prize should go to the contestant who had *the most numbers correct*. Checking the five entries we find that A had none right, B had one correct, C had two, D had three, and E had one. It would seem, therefore, that the award should be given to contestant D.

This contestant, who is quite a clever man, was told by a friend who is a mathematician that the seven given numbers could be arranged in 840 different ways, and that therefore his chances of picking them all right were extremely slim. This made him decide to predict for each drawing the *mode* of the seven numbers. He knew that by doing this he had no chance of getting all correct, *but he also knew that he would get exactly three numbers correct regardless of the outcome of the drawing*. This, he reasoned, would give him a greater success ratio than he could reasonably expect if he had used any other method of prediction.

Everybody appears to be happy at this solution except E, who raises the following objection: It seems only fair to him, since the judges failed to specify what they would consider as the best set of predictions in case that no contestant was a perfect prophet, that the award be given to the contestant who, *on the average, came as close as possible to each of the seven numbers.*

Checking the errors which were made by each contestant, ignoring the + and − signs of the amounts by which the various predictions were off, we find that the *average error* made by A was

$$\frac{13 + 15 + 11 + 11 + 17 + 17 + 2}{7} = 12.3$$

The average error committed by B was

$$\frac{13 + 13 + 15 + 11 + 6 + 0 + 2}{7} = 8.6$$

The average error committed by C was

$$\frac{2 + 17 + 0 + 0 + 17 + 13 + 15}{7} = 9.1$$

The average error committed by D was

$$\frac{13 + 0 + 0 + 11 + 17 + 0 + 15}{7} = 8.0$$

and, finally, the average error committed by E was

$$\frac{2 + 11 + 11 + 0 + 6 + 11 + 4}{7} = 6.4$$

which shows that, on the average, E's predictions were much the closest.

It is true that the judges could easily solve this dilemma by splitting the award between D and E, but logically speaking, this does not solve our problem.

Just as D knew that by predicting for each drawing the *mode* of the seven numbers he would be right three times, E knew that by predicting for each drawing the *median* of the seven numbers, in this case 9, his error could be expected to be, on the average, as small as possible. This fact is fairly easy to prove, and we shall therefore leave it as an exercise for the reader to show that the median of a set of numbers has the property that the average of the absolute values of the deviations is minimum. Contestant E chose this method of prediction because in his field (insurance) it is much more important to have rates which are on the average as close as possible to claim costs and other expenses than to have rates which are precisely correct as often as possible yet which, at the same time, are seriously off for other risks.

Similarly, the carnival man, D, chose his method of prediction because it promised him three absolutely correct predictions regardless of what would happen in the actual drawing. This is more than he could have expected from any other method of prediction, and this is important to him because it does not help him in his profession if he comes close; he wins *only* if he guesses a person's weight precisely on the nose.

These considerations have brought out the important fact that *if we want to classify nonperfect predictions as good or bad, we must decide beforehand upon a criterion which will serve as a yardstick for such a classification.* What kind of yardstick should preferably be used in a given situation, i.e., whether we would rather be 100 per cent correct as often as possible, on the average as close as possible, etc., will depend mainly on the type of event which we want to predict and the risks which are involved.

We have shown, therefore, that predictions can still be described as good or bad even though they are not perfect, *if we specify a suitable criterion on which this description can be based.* For example, a doctor who diagnoses a disease is not interested merely in coming close, since this would obviously not be satisfactory in his work. The manager of a department store, on the other hand, finds it much more desirable to have the amounts of merchandise which he orders on the average as close as possible to the actual quantities needed than to have the precise amount of some items and far too much or too little of others.

The methods of prediction which we shall discuss in the next few chapters are more or less based on the criterion that predictions are good if they come on the average as close as possible to the values which we are trying to predict. *This is an arbitrary choice*, but, as we shall see, it is justified by practical considerations.

If we want to predict (estimate) a set of unknown numbers θ_1, θ_2, θ_3, . . . , θ_n (theta-one, etc.) which are numerical descriptions of any arbitrary set of n events, and if our corresponding predictions are written as θ_1', θ_2', θ_3', . . . , θ_n', our *average error* is given by the expression

$$\frac{\sum_{i=1}^{n} |\theta_i - \theta_i'|}{n} \tag{12.1.1}$$

As in the case of the *mean deviation* (5.3.2) this quantity depends on the *absolute values* of the errors (deviations) of our predictions, in order to compensate for the fact that some errors may be positive while others may be negative. A set of predictions θ_i' will now be considered good predictions of the numbers θ_i if the quantity (12.1.1) is *small*, and bad if it is *large*.

Returning now to the contest which we discussed earlier in this section, the seven numbers which the contestants were asked to predict were, in the order in which they were drawn,

$$\theta_1 = 7, \ \theta_2 = 20, \ \theta_3 = 20, \ \theta_4 = 9, \ \theta_5 = 3, \ \theta_6 = 20, \ \theta_7 = 5$$

and the predictions of E, for example, were

$$\theta_1' = 9, \ \theta_2' = 9, \ \theta_3' = 9, \ \theta_4' = 9, \ \theta_5' = 9, \ \theta_6' = 9, \ \theta_7 = 9$$

Substituting these values into (12.1.1) we will get as before

$$\frac{2 + 11 + 11 + 0 + 6 + 11 + 4}{7} = 6.4$$

As it is inconvenient to work with *absolute value signs*, we shall now use the identical trick of avoiding negative deviations (negative errors) which we used when we defined the standard deviation in Chapter 5. *Instead of basing the goodness of our predictions on the average error, we shall base it on the average of the squares of the errors.* A set of predictions will therefore be said to be **good** if the quantity

$$\frac{\sum_{i=1}^{n} (\theta_i - \theta_i')^2}{n} \qquad (12.1.2)^*$$

is as small as possible. Formula (12.1.2) defines what is customarily referred to as the *error variance* of the set of predictions. If it is small our predictions are good, and if it is large they are bad. As we shall see in the next few chapters, in which we shall study the problem of correlation, which is essentially a problem of prediction, there are many reasons why formula (12.1.2) is more desirable than (12.1.1).

Had the judges of the contest which we described in the beginning of this chapter stated that the award would be given to the contestant whose predictions would be such that the error variance is the least, the wisest method of prediction would have been to predict for each of the drawings the *mean* of the seven numbers. This is equal to 12, and even though none of the original numbers was actually 12, it can easily be shown that the resulting error variance

$$\frac{(12-7)^2+(12-20)^2+(12-20)^2+(12-9)^2+(12-3)^2+(12-20)^2+(12-5)^2}{7} = 50.9$$

is smaller than that of any of the other sets of predictions. It can easily be shown (Exercise 5, page 245) that the method of prediction which predicts for each drawing the number 12, the mean of the seven numbers, will give us a smaller error variance than any other systematic method of prediction.

It could, of course, have happened that the predictions of contestants A, B, C, or D might have had a smaller error variance, but this would have been due either to the psychic powers of the aunt of A, the extra sensory powers of B, or simply to the luck of any contestant. If we disregard all supernatural powers, in the long run our *safest bet* would be the method of prediction which predicts for each value the *mean* of the seven numbers. In general, if we want to predict a set of numbers θ_i, and if the goodness of our predictions is evaluated by means of the error variance which is defined by formula (12.1.2), the best method consists of predicting for each number the *mean* of the quantities θ_i.

12.2 Functional Relationships

The illustration of the contest has shown how we can evaluate the merits and disadvantages of predictions which are not perfect. As we shall see, in most practical problems we must be satisfied with predictions which come close, or better, with predictions for which the error variance (12.1.2) is relatively small.

The task of the five contestants was intentionally simplified in our illustration by telling them the actual values of the seven numbers. We can hardly expect this to be the case in more general problems of prediction. It usually happens that instead of being given such specific information concerning the quantities which we are asked to predict, we are told merely that they are related in some fashion to other quantities which are known. We may thus be asked, for example, to predict a student's success in college on the basis of his high school grades; the total annual sales of a department store on the basis of statistical information concerning wages, taxes, and the purchasing power of the dollar; or we may be asked to predict a person's weight on the basis of information dealing with his age and height. None of these predictions will probably be too accurate, but even under these difficult circumstances we will be able to devise methods which will yield us the best predictions which we can get.

As we have pointed out before, the main task of science is to discover (and prove) general relationships between observable phenomena. It is important, therefore, to know the precise nature of such relationships, because they are the only basis which we shall have for our predictions. These relationships can be extremely complicated like, for example, the relationship between an electric current and its accompanying magnetic field, the relationship between childhood environment and personality development, or the relationship between radioactivity and the age of a rock. Whenever possible, scientists strive to express the relationship between variables in terms of a mathematical formula. They can say, for example, that the relationship between the volume (v) and the pressure (p) of a gas is given by the formula

$$v = \frac{k}{p}$$

provided that the temperature is constant. Similarly, it has been discovered that the relationship between the size of a culture of bacteria and the time that it has been exposed to certain favorable conditions can be written as

$$S = ab^t$$

where S is the size of the culture, t stands for the time, and a and b are numerical constants. This last equation, which incidentally is called an *exponential equation,* plays an important role in many problems of growth as well as in economic problems dealing with production, sales, etc.

In general, if we limit our discussion to relationships between only *two* variables it will be invaluable to know their relationship so that we can predict one on the basis of our knowledge of the other. For example, if we knew the relationship between high school grades and college achievement, we could predict for each student who enters college the index with which he can be expected to graduate, and we would thus have a very useful tool for the purpose of guidance.

The mathematical relationship between two variables is, wherever possible, given by expressing *one variable as a function of the other.* This means that if we denote the two variables (for example, the height and weight of a group of children) by the letters x and y, then y should be expressed as a function of x, or vice versa, depending on which variable we want to predict in terms of the other. Symbolically this is usually written

$$y = f(x) \quad \text{or} \quad x = f(y)$$

which is read "y is a function of x" or "x is a function of y." If we are given a relationship of the type $y = f(x)$, we can substitute a known value of x and solve for the corresponding value of y.

One of the simplest, and for that reason also one of the most frequently used relationships, is the so-called *linear equation*, which is of the form

$$y = mx + b \qquad\qquad (12.2.1)$$

In this equation m and b are two numerical constants which are usually determined on the basis of experimental data, and once they are known, we can predict the y which corresponds to any given value of x. *Linear equations* are useful not only because there exist quite a few relationships which are actually of this type, but also because *they often provide reasonably close approximations to otherwise complex relationships*. We shall limit our study almost exclusively to relationships which are linear, because the treatment of mathematical relationships, which are more complicated, goes considerably beyond the scope of this text. It must be understood, however, that other relationships are also important and should be studied at a slightly more advanced level.

The names *linear equation, linear function,* or *linear relationship* find their origin in the fact that when plotted on ordinary graph paper all points (x,y) which satisfy an equation of the type $y = mx + b$ will fall on a straight line (see Fig. 12.a). Let us consider, for instance, the equation

$$y = 3.3x + 21.9$$

where x stands for the *July rainfall in inches* and y stands for the *yield of corn in bushels per acre*. If the July rainfall is 5 inches in a given year, we can calculate the expected (predicted) yield of corn by substituting $x = 5$ into this equation, which will give us $3.3(5) + 21.9$ $= 38.4$ bushels of corn per acre. Similarly, if the July rainfall is only 3 inches, we can easily check by substitution that the expected yield of corn is now 31.8 bushels per acre. Taking several such values

YIELD OF CORN

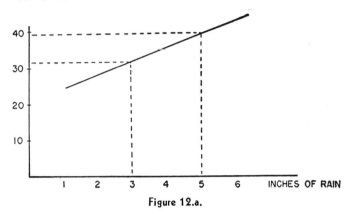

Figure 12.a.

of x and calculating the corresponding values of y, the reader can easily check for himself that all these points will fall on a straight line.

Before we can ever predict y in terms of x on the basis of a linear relationship it will always be necessary to find first the most suitable values of m and b on the basis of some experimental data. By most suitable we mean in this case that the constants m and b should be chosen in a manner which will make the resulting predictions as accurate as possible. How and under what assumptions this can be done is the important problem which will be studied in the next chapter.

REFERENCES

E. B. Mode, *The Elements of Statistics*, Prentice-Hall, New York, 1941, p. 105.
A. E. Waugh, *Elements of Statistical Method*, McGraw-Hill, New York, 1943, p. 114.

EXERCISES

1. Find the error variance of the predictions which contestant C made in the illustration in the text.

2. If, in the illustration in the text, we had wanted to make sure that the *greatest error* which we could possibly have made for any one of the drawings is *as small as possible*, what predictions should we have made?

3. The ages of five finalists in a beauty contest are 17, 29, 17, 24, and 18. How would one predict the ages of the beauties in the order in which they will finally be chosen if (a) one wants to get a correct age as often as possible, (b) the average error should be as small as possible, (c) the error variance

should be the least, and (d) the greatest possible error for any one prediction should be minimum?

4. Show that the quantity $\left(\sum_{i=1}^{n} |\theta_i - k| \right) \Big/ n$ is smallest when the constant k is equal to the *median* of the set of numbers θ_i.

A solution to this problem can be found in the book by Waugh referred to at the end of this chapter.

5. Show that the quantity $\left[\sum_{i=1}^{n} (\theta_i - k)^2 \right] \Big/ n$ is minimum when the constant k is equal to the *mean* of the set of numbers θ_i. This proof can be found in many elementary texts, for example, the book by E. B. Mode referred to above.

13. LINEAR RELATIONSHIPS

13.1 Introduction

Those who have had some previous experience with analyzing numerical data which are plotted as points on a piece of graph paper will probably recall the urge to take a ruler, juggle it around, and fit in this fashion a straight line to the points which represented the data. Of course, there is nothing basically wrong with approximating data by means of such lines, but it is highly questionable whether we should trust our eyesight and our aesthetic preferences in choosing a line which we expect to give us the best possible predictions.

Since there is, logically speaking, no limit to the number of lines which can be drawn on a piece of paper, it is evident that *we will need a criterion on the basis of which we can point to a single line as the one which presents us with the best fit to our data*. The choice of such a criterion is self-evident only in the special case where all points actually do fall on a straight line. However, since we can hardly expect this to happen often if we are dealing with experimental data, we must be satisfied with straight lines which, although they cannot possibly go through all points, will have some less perfect yet still desirable properties. In order to see what such properties might be, let us ask ourselves *why* we are so anxious to fit these lines in the first place.

This question was really answered in the last chapter when we said that it is important to approximate experimental data by means of straight lines and other curves so that we will be able to make predictions. In other words, once we have found the actual equation of a straight line, which is of the form

$$y = mx + b$$

we can find by substitution the predicted value of y for any given value of x.

Let us consider, for instance, the problem of predicting a student's academic success in college on the basis of his average high school grades. Actual studies have shown that, as we should have expected, there exists a fairly strong, though far from perfect, linear relationship between these two variables. In general, it would be unwise to base formulas to be used for predictions on samples which are very small, and we shall do so in the following illustration *only* because this will simplify our calculations, yet will suffice to bring out the general approach to the problem of fitting straight lines to experimental data.

Let us suppose that a study of high school grades and success in college has produced the following results in a sample of six students who were selected at random.

	High school average	College index
Student A	90	1.8
Student B	65	1.1
Student C	95	2.7
Stud nt D	69	1.9
Student E	72	1.6
Student F	80	2.2

It is needless to say that before we start fitting a line to these data (or for that matter, to any kind of data) we should first check whether it is at all reasonable to suppose that a straight line will give us a good fit. This can always be done most conveniently by plotting the points representing our data as we have done in Fig. 13.a. If we have as few as six points it is usually almost impossible to decide whether it is reasonable to treat the two variables as if they were linearly related, but judging from the fact that all points are contained between the dotted lines of Fig. 13.a, we shall go ahead and try to fit a straight line.

If we begin by drawing a more or less freehand line L through our points, as we have done in Fig. 13.b, we can ask ourselves *how good our predictions would have been if we had actually used line L for the prediction of the college indexes of the given six students.* The predicted index of any one student could thus be found by marking his high school average on the horizontal scale (point A of Fig. 13.b), going up vertically until we reach the line L at the point B, and by finally locating the *predicted college index* by going horizontally from B until we hit the vertical scale.

COLLEGE INDEX

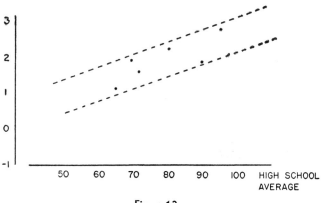

Figure 13.a.

COLLEGE INDEX

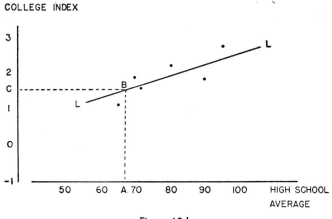

Figure 13.b.

Had we been given such a line L before our six students ever entered college we could have used it to predict their expected success in college. The student who had a high school average of 80, for example, would, according to Fig. 13.c, have had a predicted index of 1.9, and the *error* of this prediction would have been equal to $2.2 - 1.9 = .3$.

Geometrically speaking, the error of this prediction is measured by the *vertical deviation* (distance) from the point representing the actual

COLLEGE INDEX

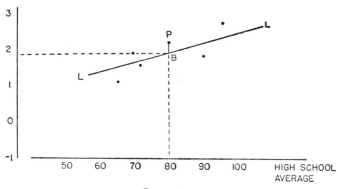

Figure 13.c.

COLLEGE INDEX

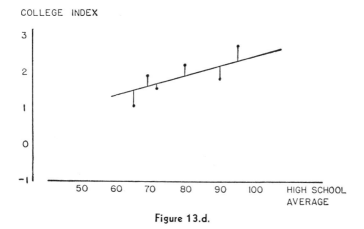

Figure 13.d.

data to the line L which we used for our prediction. In Fig. 13.c this deviation is given by the distance from P to B. Applying this method of prediction to each of the six students used in this example, the six corresponding errors of our predictions are given by the six vertical deviations from the line L (see Fig. 13.d). Denoting the observed index of the ith student by the symbol y_i and the corresponding predicted index by the symbol y'_i, the *error variance* of the six predictions is given by the expression

$$\frac{\sum_{i=1}^{6} (y_i - y'_i)^2}{6} \qquad (13.1.1)$$

which is simply *the average of the squared vertical deviations from the line L.* As it is obviously desirable to make our predictions as accurate as possible. i.e., the error variance (13.1.1) as small as possible, we have now at our disposal a criterion for the goodness of the fit of a straight line. Naturally, we need not use the criterion that the error variance should be minimum, but it seems quite reasonable that straight lines which are fit to our data for predictive purposes should be such that the resulting errors of the predictions will be small.

The line which has the distinction that the sum of the squares of the vertical deviations, the error variance of the y's, is minimum is called the *regression line of y on x.* Had we wanted, instead, to predict x in terms of y we could similarly have asked for a line which minimizes the *horizontal deviations,* or better, the sum of their squares, and we would thus have obtained the *regression line of x on y.* Since it is completely arbitrary which variable is called x and which is called y, we shall simplify our work by limiting our discussion to those lines which minimize the sum of the squares of the vertical deviations, i.e., we shall consider only *regression lines of y on x.*

13.2 The Computation of m and b

In order to treat this problem in a general fashion let us take n pairs of measurements (x_1, y_1), (x_2, y_2), . . . , (x_n, y_n), e.g., the heights and weights of n individuals, and let us suppose that these n points have been plotted on a diagram measuring x and y on the horizontal and vertical scales, respectively. Once we have done this, we can ask for the equation of the line that is such that the sum of the squares of the vertical deviations will be minimum. This means that we must find such numerical values for the two constants m and b which appear in the equation $y = mx + b$ that the line which is thus obtained has the stated properties.

Writing, as before, y'_i for the predicted value corresponding to y_i, this value must be calculated from the equation

$$y'_i = mx_i + b$$

and substituting this predicted value into the formula for the error variance we can rewrite formula (13.1.1) as

$$\frac{\sum_{i=1}^{n} (y_i - mx_i - b)^2}{n} \tag{13.2.1}$$

This expression is called the *error variance about the regression line*, and it will be written as s_e^2 provided, of course, that the two constants m and b are actually such that we do have a regression line. The only two quantities which are *unknown* in (13.2.1) are the two constants m and b (which are also called the *regression coefficients*), since x_i and y_i stand for the n pairs of measurements which we assumed to be known from the start.

The derivation of formulas which will give us such required values of m and b that the resulting line will be a regression line involves partial differentiation and other mathematical techniques which are above the level of mathematics which was assumed as a prerequisite for this study of statistics. Consequently, we shall simply state the results that the necessary values of m and b are given by the two formulas

$$m = \frac{n \sum_{i=1}^{n} x_i y_i - \left(\sum_{i=1}^{n} x_i \right)\left(\sum_{i=1}^{n} y_i \right)}{n \left(\sum_{i=1}^{n} x_i^2 \right) - \left(\sum_{i=1}^{n} x_i \right)^2} \qquad (13.2.2a)^*$$

$$b = \frac{\left(\sum_{i=1}^{n} x_i^2 \right)\left(\sum_{i=1}^{n} y_i \right) - \left(\sum_{i=1}^{n} x_i \right)\left(\sum_{i=1}^{n} x_i y_i \right)}{n \left(\sum_{i=1}^{n} x_i^2 \right) - \left(\sum_{i=1}^{n} x_i \right)^2} \qquad (13.2.2b)^*$$

where n is the number of pairs of measurements, Σx_i and Σy_i are the sums of the x's and the y's, Σx_i^2 is the sum of the squares of the x's, and $\Sigma x_i y_i$ is the sum of their products. All summations go from 1 to n.

Returning now to the illustration of the previous section, we can use formulas (13.2.2a) and (13.2.2b) to find the equation of the actual regression line of y on x. The necessary calculations are usually performed by means of the following kind of table:

x	y	x^2	xy
90	1.8	8100	162.0
65	1.1	4225	71.5
95	2.7	9025	256.5
69	1.9	4761	131.1
72	1.6	5184	115.2
80	2.2	6400	176.0
471	11.3	37695	912.3

and we have

$$n = 6$$
$$\sum x_i = 471$$
$$\sum y_i = 11.3$$
$$\sum x_i^2 = 37695$$
$$\sum x_i y_i = 912.3$$

(If we had used a calculating machine it would have been possible to accumulate these totals directly, and it would thus not have been necessary to write down in detail all the squares x_i^2 and the products $x_i y_i$.)

Substituting these results into formulas (13.2.2a) and (13.2.2b) we get

$$m = \frac{6(912.3) - (471)(11.3)}{6(37695) - (471)^2} = .035$$

$$b = \frac{(37695)(11.3) - (471)(912.3)}{6(37695) - (471)^2} = -.86$$

and we can write the regression line as

$$y = .035x - .86$$

This last formula can be used to calculate the predicted value of y if we are given the corresponding value of x. This can be done either by substituting the known value of x and solving the equation for y, or by first plotting the graph of the equation and using the resulting line to read off the predicted value of y. If we want to plot the line we have only to take two arbitrary values of x, calculate the corresponding values of y, plot the two points, and connect them with a straight line.

Since formulas (13.2.2a) and (13.2.2b) are somewhat tedious to remember it is usually preferable to calculate the values of m and b by solving the two simultaneous linear equations

$$\sum_{i=1}^{n} y_i = m \sum_{i=1}^{n} x_i + nb \qquad (13.2.3a)^*$$

$$\sum_{i=1}^{n} x_i y_i = m \sum_{i=1}^{n} x_i^2 + b \sum_{i=1}^{n} x_i \qquad (13.2.3b)^*$$

This alternative method of finding the two regression coefficients will give us the identical results, and the two equations can easily be remembered by the following rule: formula (13.2.3a) can be obtained by putting a summation sign before every term of the equation $y_i = mx_i + b$, which will give us

$$\Sigma y_i = m\Sigma x_i + \Sigma b$$

and since $\Sigma b = nb$ (Theorem C, page 8), we can also write this as

$$\Sigma y_i = m\Sigma x_i + nb$$

This last formula is identical with (13.2.3a). The second equation is obtained by first multiplying both sides of the equation $y_i = mx_i + b$ by x_i, and then summing on both sides of the equation. This gives us $\Sigma x_i y_i = m\Sigma x_i^2 + b\Sigma x_i$, which is identical with (13.2.3b).

Had we used this second method in our illustration, m and b would have had to be determined by solving the two simultaneous linear equations

$$11.3 = 471m + 6b$$
$$912.3 = 37695m + 471b$$

and we would again have found that $m = .035$ and $b = -.86$.

13.3 The Goodness of the Predictions

Before we can consider adopting the equation

$$\text{Predicted index} = .035(\text{high school average}) - .86$$

even hypothetically as a method of predicting a student's future success in college, we must first check how accurate we can expect the resulting predictions to be. For the sake of argument, let us assume that the above formula was known at the time that the 6 students, who were the subjects of our investigation, entered college. This assumption is really somewhat ridiculous, because the values of m and b were calculated on the basis of the records which the same 6 students established in college, and it would thus have been impossible for us to know this formula. However, let us assume in spite of this obvious objection that as we said, for the sake of argument, we did have this formula when the 6 students entered college. We could then have used it to predict the indexes which our 6 students could have been expected to attain. Substituting their high school averages into the equation $y = .035x - .86$ we could have calculated the predicted values of y which, together with the indexes which the students actually obtained, are shown in the following table.

	Actual index y	Predicted index y'
Student A	1.8	2.29
Student B	1.1	1.41
Student C	2.7	2.47
Student D	1.9	1.55
Student E	1.6	1.66
Student F	2.2	1.96

The goodness of this set of predictions will be evaluated by means of the error variance s_e^2, which is the average of the squared errors $y_i - y_i'$. It can easily be seen that this error variance is equal to approximately .095. Taking the square root of this quantity, we get the so-called *standard error of estimate* (prediction) which in this illustration is $\sqrt{.095} = .31$. This tells us that the average error, defined by the square root of the average of the squared errors, is .31. *If both x and y are normally distributed variables we can say that the error of our predictions can be expected to be less than .31 about 68 per cent of the time.* The standard error of estimate s_e (the square root of the error variance about the regression line) is therefore interpreted as if it were a standard deviation. It follows that if this method of prediction is used a great number of times, we can also say that our errors should not exceed $1.96(.31) = .61$ more than 5 per cent of the time.

The predicted values of y which we obtained in this illustration are so close to the actual values which we had hoped to predict that we might easily be led to believe that we have found a good formula for predicting a student's success in college. However, before we can reach any such conclusion we should remember that the equation was calculated on the basis of the college indexes of the *same* students for whom we made the predictions. It seems only reasonable, therefore, that if we apply a formula to the identical data from which the formula itself was originally obtained, our surprise at the excellent results should really not be much of a surprise at all. Consequently, *if we want to evaluate the goodness of a method of prediction we should apply our formula to data other than those on which the formula itself was based.*

If the true relationship between two variables which we happen to be studying is actually given by an equation of the form

$$y = mx + b$$

the numerical values of m and b which we calculate from a set of experimental or observed data must be considered *estimates* of these true values of m and b. The calculated values of m and b can therefore be expected to vary from sample to sample, and we might speak of their sampling distributions, confidence limits, etc. In other words, we must treat the values of m and b which we calculated like any other *statistic* which has been determined on the basis of a sample.

Inasmuch as most estimates increase in accuracy for increasing values of n, good estimates of the true values of m and b can be obtained only if we have a large number of points, i.e., if we have many pairs of measurements of the two variables x and y. In actual practice we would never have used a sample as small as the one which we have used in our illustration.

The formal study of the accuracy of estimates of the *regression coefficients* m and b is considerably beyond the scope of this book. However, as long as we base the equations which we intend to use for our predictions on reasonably *large samples*, our estimates of m and b will usually be sufficiently close to the true values of the regression coefficients. If we have large sample, therefore, there can be no serious objection to evaluating the goodness of the predictions by applying the equation to the identical data from which it was originally obtained.

The method which we have employed in the determination of m and b consisted of minimizing the sum of the squares of the deviations from the straight line, and it is consequently called the *method of least squares*. This method enabled us to select one line as the line which provides us with the best fit to a given set of points, and it is really in this sense that we *define* what we mean by a good fit. Although we have used the *method of least squares* only for the determination of a best-fitting straight line, it can also be used to give us best-fitting curves in general even though their equations may be of a much more complicated nature.

REFERENCES

M. M. Blair, *Elementary Statistics*, Holt, New York, 1944, Chap. 11.

A. L. Edwards, *Statistical Analysis for Students in Psychology and Education*, Rinehart, New York, 1946, Chap. 13.

E. B. Mode, *The Elements of Statistics*, Prentice-Hall, New York, 1941, Chap. 11.

C. H. Richardson, *An Introduction to Statistical Analysis*, Harcourt, Brace, New York, 1934, Chap. 7.

J. B. Scarborough and R. W. Wagner, *Fundamentals of Statistics*, Ginn and Co., Boston, 1948, Chap. 5.

EXERCISES

1. Use the following data to find the equation of the regression line of y on x.

x	2	1	3	4	5
y	3	1	2	3	5

2. Find the equation of the regression line of y on x using the following data.

x	10	9	11	5	12
y	9	8	13	7	20

3. Use the equation of the regression line which was obtained in Exercise 1 to calculate the predicted value of y for each given value of x. Also find the standard error of estimate.

4. Use the equation of the regression line which was calculated in Exercise 2 to find the predicted values of y for each given value of x. Also find the error variance of this set of predictions.

5. The following table shows the indexes with which 10 students graduated from college and the annual salary which each earned 10 years after graduation.

College index	Salary (in dollars)
2.3	8,000
1.5	4,000
1.6	6,000
2.8	7,000
1.1	6,000
1.2	3,500
1.0	3,000
1.6	3,800
1.8	4,900
2.4	6,400

Find an equation which will make it possible to predict future earnings on the basis of the college index. Use this formula to predict the income of Mr. X ten years after he graduates from college with an index of 2.1.

6. The following table shows the size of the area which is contaminated certain hours after the explosion of an atomic bomb (artificial data).

Hours after explosion	Contaminated area in square miles
5	17
40	19
60	50
100	75
150	132

Calculate the linear equation giving us the size of the contaminated area as a function of the time.

7. The following are the grades which 12 students obtained in two tests in mathematics and physics.

Mathematics	Physics
93	88
85	81
73	76
90	97
87	86
63	72
77	64
85	91
99	94
100	98
86	95
64	72

Plot this information on graph paper and draw freehand a straight line which presents a reasonably good fit to the 12 points. Then find the equation of the regression line which will enable us to predict a student's grade in physics if we know the grade which he obtained in mathematics. Plot the graph of the regression line and compare it with the freehand line.

8. The following table contains the price of oats in cents per bushel and the quantity produced in millions of bushels for the period from 1940 to 1947.

Price	Quantity
36.3	1,246
33.3	1,182
50.2	1,343
52.5	1,140
77.5	1,149
72.1	1,536
71.7	1,498
79.6	1,216

Find the equation of the regression which will enable us to predict the price of oats in terms of the quantity produced.

9. Using the results of Exercise 8, what would have been the predicted price of oats for a year in which the production was 1400 million bushels?

10. Use the results of Exercise 7 to predict the grade which a student who scored 80 in mathematics will receive in physics.

14. THE COEFFICIENT OF CORRELATION

14.1 Introduction

The last chapter was devoted to the problem of finding the equation of the regression line and the error variance which measured the goodness of the resulting predictions, i.e., the closeness of the fit of the regression line to a given set of data. Because the error variance is quite difficult to compute, and further, because it depends on the scale of measurement of the original data, which makes it difficult to interpret, we shall now define another measure of the goodness of the fit of a regression line, which is called the *coefficient of correlation*.

The error variance about the regression line was denoted as s_e^2 and it was defined by the expression

$$s_e^2 = \frac{\sum\limits_{i=1}^{n} (y_i - y_i')^2}{n} \tag{14.1.1}$$

It depends, as we can easily see from this formula, on the scale of measurement of y, and it can therefore happen that the regression line will provide us with a *very poor fit* even though s_e^2 is *small*, simply because the quantities y are small. Similarly, it can also happen if the y's are large, that the error variance will be *large* in spite of the fact that we might have an *excellent fit*. This undesirable feature of the error variance about the regression line as a measure of the goodness of the fit suggests a modification which leads us to the so-called coefficient of correlation. This new measure can be understood most readily if it is defined as a measure which compares the following two methods of prediction:

Method of prediction A. We shall predict each y by means of the regression line $y_i' = mx_i + b$ which was determined from the identical set of data which will also be used to evaluate the goodness of the resulting predictions.

Method of prediction B. We shall predict for each y that it is equal to the *mean* of the y's, i.e., our predictions are now based on the formula $y_i' = \bar{y}$, where $\bar{y}$ is the mean of the same set of data which is used in method A.

The goodness of method A is, as before, given by the error variance about the regression line, namely, by formula (13.2.1), which gave us

$$s_e^2 = \frac{\sum_{i=1}^{n} (y_i - mx_i - b)^2}{n}$$

while *the goodness of method B* is expressed by the error variance

$$s_y^2 = \frac{\sum_{i=1}^{n} (y_i - y')^2}{n} = \frac{\sum_{i=1}^{n} (y_i - \bar{y})^2}{n} \qquad (14.1.2)$$

which is nothing but the square of the *standard deviation of the y's.*

The errors which are made by these two methods of prediction are thus given by the two quantities s_e^2 and s_y^2, and we shall now demonstrate how a comparison of these two quantities can be used to define a new measure of the goodness of the fit of the regression line.

The table given below contains the total savings (personal savings of individuals) in the United States and the number of work stoppages (strikes) for the eight-year period from 1940 to 1947.

Year	Savings in billions of dollars	Number of strikes
1940	2.9	2862
1941	4.9	2508
1942	10.9	4288
1943	16.1	2968
1944	17.5	4956
1945	19.0	4750
1946	11.9	4985
1947	3.0	3693

If we now want to *predict* the number of strikes for any one year on the basis of the total savings recorded for that year, using either method A or method B, we must calculate first the equation of the regression line and the mean of the y's (the number of strikes). The necessary calculations will show that the equation of the regression line is

$$y' = 95x + 2852$$

while the mean of the y's is $\bar{y} = 3876$, so that method B will be based on the formula

$$y' = 3876$$

The relative merits of our two methods of prediction can be judged visually by comparing the vertical deviations (errors) of Figs. 14.a and 14.b. In Fig. 14.a the errors of the predictions of method A are represented by the vertical deviations (solid lines) from the regression line which was obtained by plotting the equation $y = 95x + 2852$. In Fig. 14.b the errors of the predictions of method B are also

NUMBER OF STRIKES

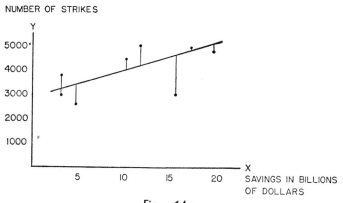

Figure 14.a.

NUMBER OF STRIKES

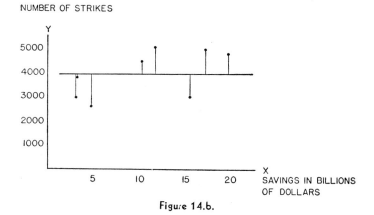

Figure 14.b.

given by the vertical deviations (solid lines) from the horizontal line $y = 3876$, as it is this value of y, namely, $\bar{y} = 3876$, which is predicted by this method for each year regardless of the actual savings.

A casual inspection of these two diagrams gives us the impression that the deviations of Fig. 14.a are slightly smaller than those of Fig. 14.b, implying that method A is slightly more accurate than method B. In order to put the comparison of their respective errors on a more scientific basis let us calculate their two error variances s_e^2 and s_y^2. Using formulas (14.1.1) and (14.1.2) it can easily be seen that

$$s_e^2 = 549{,}012 \quad \text{and} \quad s_y^2 = 887{,}200$$

which verifies our previous rough judgment that the first method of prediction was slightly better than the second. Before we will be able to state *how much better* the first method is, we must look first at another illustration.

The table below contains the average weight of women who are 4 ft. 11 in. tall for ages ranging from 22 to 52.

Age	Weight
22	113
27	116
32	119
37	122
42	126
47	129
52	131

To use the same two methods of prediction we must first find the mean of the y's (the weights) and the equation of the regression line of y on x. These two quantities are

$$\bar{y} = 122.3 \quad \text{and} \quad y' = .62x + 99.34$$

and the errors which are made by methods A and B, applied to this new set of data, are expressed by the vertical deviations from the lines of Figs. 14.c and 14.d, respectively.

In contrast to the first illustration we now find a marked difference between the errors of method A and those of method B. Calculating the two corresponding error variances we find that

$$s_e^2 = .1584 \quad \text{and} \quad s_y^2 = 38.0$$

which demonstrates clearly that the predictions which were based on the regression line were far superior to those which were based on the mean $\bar{y}$.

WEIGHT

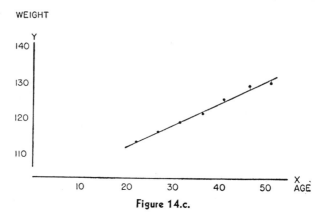

Figure 14.c.

WEIGHT

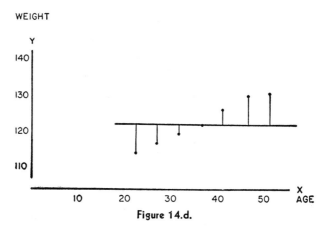

Figure 14.d.

These two examples suggest that a comparison of the given two methods of prediction might provide us with a new measure of the goodness of the fit of the regression line which does not actually depend on the scale of the y's. *If the regression line fits a set of data very closely, the error variance of method A should be much smaller than that of method B.* If, on the other hand, the fit of the regression line is poor, method A provides us with only a slight improvement over method B, as it can be shown mathematically that s_e^2 can never actually exceed s_y^2. This stands to reason, because method A really uses *more information* than method B, and it should therefore be impossible for method B to be more accurate than method A. *It follows, therefore, that s_e^2 is almost as large as s_y^2, i.e., method A has an* *error which is almost as large as that of method B, if the fit of the regression line is very poor.*

As it would obviously be more desirable to put the comparison between s_e^2 and s_y^2 on a less intuitive basis, it has been the custom to define the following measure of the goodness of the fit of the regression line; it is called the *coefficient of correlation*, and is defined by the formula

$$r = \pm \sqrt{1 - \frac{s_e^2}{s_y^2}} \qquad (14.1.3)$$

If the fit is *poor*, s_e^2 will be almost as large as s_y^2, the ratio s_e^2/s_y^2 will be close to 1, and the coefficient of correlation r will be close to 0. On the other hand, if the fit is *good*, s_e^2 will be much smaller than s_y^2, the ratio s_e^2/s_y^2 will be close to 0, and the coefficient of correlation will be close to either plus or minus 1. (The significance of the plus or minus sign of r will be discussed later in Section 14.2.)

The coefficient of correlation which we have just *defined* by means of formula (14.1.3) is by far the most widely used *measure of the strength of the linear relationship between two variables*. It expresses the goodness of the fit of the regression line, which in turn tells us whether or not it is reasonable to say that there exists a linear relationship (correlation) between the two variables x and y. If the numerical value of r which has been computed from a certain set of data is close to 0, we say that *the relationship is weak or nonexistent*; if r is close to either $+1$ or -1, however, we say that *the relationship is strong*, with the tacit understanding that we are referring to a *linear* relationship and nothing else. The statistic r, which we have so far defined merely as a *descriptive measure* of sets of paired observations, is sometimes also called somewhat more elaborately the *Pearson-product-moment coefficient of correlation*.

If we now use formula (14.1.3) to calculate r for our two previous illustrations, we will find that for personal savings and the annual number strikes

$$r = \sqrt{1 - \frac{549,012}{887,200}} = .62$$

whereas for the age and weight of women who are 4 ft 11 in. tall the corresponding value is

$$r = \sqrt{1 - \frac{.158}{38.0}} = .998$$

This shows what we have suspected before, namely, that the relationship between age and weight is very strong (at least for the particular group of women who were studied in the first illustration), while the relationship between savings and strikes is relatively mediocre. Actually, both of our samples were much too small to permit us to make far-reaching generalizations, and confining ourselves to *descriptive statistics* we can safely say only that the second set of data fit a regression line much better than the first. This does not say as much as we might want to say about these variables, but it is as far as we can go without assuming the risk of inductive generalizations.

It is always advisable to be extremely careful in the analysis and interpretation of a value of r which has been calculated from a given sample. Before we can ever say that a value of r which is based on a sample actually implies the existence of a definite linear relationship between two variables we must always ask ourselves whether (1) it is reasonable to say that the relationship is linear, and (2) whether the sample value of r is significant. This second question is very important because *it can easily happen that we obtain a relatively large sample value of r purely by chance even though the two variables are totally unrelated (see Section 14.6).*

In other words, we must always remember that r is merely a descriptive measure of the goodness of the fit of a regression line. If we have no desire to go beyond the mere description of the scattering of the points of our sample, there is nothing more to be said. But if we want to infer from a sample value of r that the variables which we are studying are definitely related (or unrelated), we shall have to worry about all the factors which we discussed in Part Two of this book.

For the moment we shall treat r simply as a descriptive measure of the goodness of the fit of a regression line. After studying the best methods for calculating r both from ungrouped and grouped data, we shall start probing into its precise meaning and significance. This part of our job will therefore be postponed until we reach Sections 14.4, 14.5, and 14.6.

14.2 The Computation of *r* from Ungrouped Data

The coefficient of correlation *can* be calculated directly from formula (14.1.3) in which it was defined. This would make it necessary for us to find first the regression coefficients m and b, which involves a considerable amount of work. Then we must calculate the predicted value of y for each given value of x, using *both* method A and method B, and finally, we must calculate the two error variances and substitute them into (14.1.3).

To avoid a good part of this work we shall now give (without proof) an alternative formula for the calculation of r, which will make most of the above steps unnecessary. This formula which is, mathematically speaking, equivalent to and can be derived from (14.1.3), is in its most suitable form written

$$r = \frac{n \sum_{i=1}^{n} x_i y_i - \left(\sum_{i=1}^{n} x_i\right)\left(\sum_{i=1}^{n} y_i\right)}{\sqrt{n \sum_{i=1}^{n} x_i^2 - \left(\sum_{i=1}^{n} x_i\right)^2}\sqrt{n \sum_{i=1}^{n} y_i^2 - \left(\sum_{i=1}^{n} y_i\right)^2}} \qquad (14.2.1)^*$$

This formula should always be used for the calculation of r from ungrouped data.

To find a coefficient of correlation by use of (14.2.1) it is necessary only to calculate the five summations Σx_i, Σy_i, Σx_i^2, Σy_i^2, $\Sigma x_i y_i$, the sample size n, and substitute all these results into the above formula. Although it is advisable to use a calculating machine whenever possible, we shall show in the following table the detailed work which is necessary to find the various sums which are required for substitution into formula (14.2.1).

Let us suppose that the values of x and y which are given in the following table stand for the scores which 10 students obtained in two successive short quizzes in statistics and that we are asked to compute the coefficient of correlation.

x	y	x^2	y^2	xy
8	6	64	36	48
6	7	36	49	42
10	8	100	64	80
4	5	16	25	20
8	9	64	81	72
9	10	81	100	90
3	5	9	25	15
10	9	100	81	90
6	7	36	49	42
7	4	49	16	28
Totals 71	70	555	526	527

Substituting the totals of these five columns into (14.2.1) we have

$$r = \frac{10(527) - (71)(70)}{\sqrt{10(555) - (71)^2} \sqrt{10(526) - (70)^2}} = .70$$

which describes the strength of the association between the scores which the students obtained in the two successive tests.

Using formula (14.2.1) also for the data pertaining to personal savings and strikes (see page 259) we find that

$$r = \frac{8(362533) - (86.2)(31010)}{\sqrt{8(1228.3) - (86.2)^2} \sqrt{8(127285300) - (31010)^2}} = .62$$

and for the ages and weights of women who are 4 ft 11 in. tall

$$r = \frac{7(32107) - (259)(856)}{\sqrt{7(10283) - (259)^2} \sqrt{7(104948) - (856)^2}} = .998$$

It is interesting to note that these values agree (as they should) with those which we obtained previously, using formula (14.1.3).

As we have said before, formula (14.2.1) should always be used for calculation of r from ungrouped data. Besides the obvious advantage that it eliminates all of the preliminary steps which were necessary when we used formula (14.1.3), *it also tells us automatically whether y increases or decreases when the other variable x increases in size.* The coefficient of correlation is positive, and we shall speak of a *positive correlation* if the linear relationship between x and y is such that *y increases* when x becomes large. Similarly, r is negative, and we shall say that the variables are *negatively correlated* if *y decreases* when x becomes large. (See Figs. 14.e, 14.f, 14.g, and 14.h.) Geometrically speaking, a correlation is positive if the regression line slopes *upward*, and it is negative if the regression line slopes *downward* (going in either case from left to right).

The calculations which are entailed in the determination of a coefficient of correlation can be reduced considerably by use of the following simple trick: since the value of r measures the strength of the relationship between x and y, i.e., it measures the goodness of the fit of the regression line, *its value is independent of the scales of measurement of x and y.* Consequently we can simplify the numbers with which we have to work by *adding or subtracting* any arbitrary number from each x, each y, or both, and by *multiplying or dividing* each x, each y, or both by any arbitrary number.

It is permissible, for instance, to add 20 to every x (if that would help to simplify the numbers), to subtract 15 from every y, and then to divide every adjusted x by 4 and multiply every adjusted y by 3.

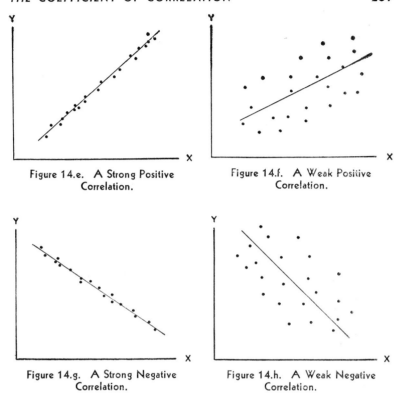

Figure 14.e. A Strong Positive Correlation.

Figure 14.f. A Weak Positive Correlation.

Figure 14.g. A Strong Negative Correlation.

Figure 14.h. A Weak Negative Correlation.

The value of r which is calculated on the basis of these modified x's and y's will be *identical* with the one which we could have calculated directly from the original data. Obviously, these modifications should be made only if they will actually help to reduce the work which is necessary for the calculation of r. When we calculated r for the ages and weights, we could, for instance, have subtracted 37 from every x and 122 from every y.

x (age)	y (weight)
22	113
27	116
32	119
37	122
42	126
47	129
52	131

This would have given us much smaller and much more convenient numbers.

x'	y'
-15	-9
-10	-6
-5	-3
0	0
5	4
10	7
15	9

If we now divide the x' column by 5 and the y' column by 3, we finally get

x''	y''
-3	-3
-2	-2
-1	-1
0	0
1	$1\frac{1}{3}$
2	$2\frac{1}{3}$
3	3

and if we were to calculate r on the basis of this last set of figures we would obtain the *identical* value which we had before.

The numbers which we add or subtract, and by which we multiply or divide, will naturally depend on the actual measurements which we are trying to correlate. As long as we keep in mind that the only purpose of these manipulations is to simplify our calculations, it is generally not difficult to find the most suitable simplifications for any given problem.

EXERCISES

1. Compute r for the data which are given in Exercise 1 on page 256.
2. Compute r for the data which are given in Exercise 2 on page 256.
3. Calculate the coefficient of correlation for the following data representing the heights (x) and weights (y) of 10 college students.

x	72	68	66	70	72	69	64	63	74	71
y	185	163	142	162	171	152	127	123	210	164

4. Find the coefficient of correlation for the number of unemployed in the United States and in Canada on the basis of the following data covering the period from 1940 to 1949.

Number of unemployed (in thousands)

United States	Canada
8,120	454
5,560	193
2,660	134
1,070	75
670	62
1,040	71
2,270	126
2,142	91
2,064	82
3,395	103

5. If you were asked to compute the coefficient of correlation between two variables x and y on the basis of the following data.

x	y
153	6
172	9

would you be surprised if your answer were $r = 1$? Explain.

6. Find the coefficient of correlation between the age and value of second-hand cars on the basis of the following information.

Age	Value (dollars)
10	295
2	1,095
4	795
12	80
4	995
14	75
1	1,395

7. Decide in each case whether you would expect a positive correlation, a negative correlation, or no relationship.

(a) The age of a car and its trade-in value.
(b) The number of crimes committed and the cost of living.
(c) Rainfall and the attendance at football games.
(d) The weights of husbands and wives.
(e) Birth rate and the index of unemployment.
(f) Teachers' salaries and the phases of the moon.
(g) The price of life insurance and the age at which it is bought.
(h) Inches of snow in New York City and the tourist trade of Florida.
(i) Temperature and the number of automobile accidents.
(j) College index and future success in life.
(k) A person's age and the number of teeth he has.
(l) The selectivity and fidelity of a radio.

14.3 The Computation of *r* from Grouped Data

We have demonstrated earlier how the work which is entailed in the calculation of a mean, standard deviation, etc., can be reduced considerably if we first group our raw data into a frequency distribution. Since this is true particularly if we are dealing with large sets of data, and since the calculation of a coefficient of correlation is in that case a somewhat unpleasant task, it seems reasonable to ask whether we cannot achieve a similar reduction in our work if we now group our data into a *two-dimensional frequency distribution*.

To illustrate how paired measurements or observations can be grouped, let us consider the following study of the relationship between the yield of wheat in bushels per acre and the number of pounds of fertilizer which are applied to the soil. Let us suppose that in an agricultural experiment we have made 100 pairs of measurements of these two variables and that the data are shown in the *scattergram* of Fig. 14.i. A study of this diagram makes it apparent that it would

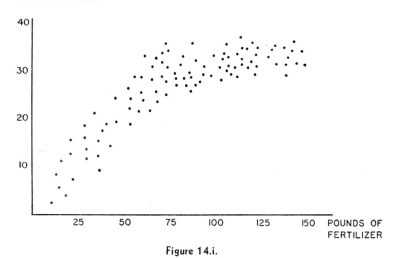

Figure 14.i.

hardly be reasonable to treat the relationship between the amount of fertilizer and the yield of wheat as linear. As a matter of fact this observation is in agreement with the law of *diminishing returns*, according to which the *increase* in the yield of wheat should become smaller and smaller if more and more fertilizer is added to the soil.

Since this chapter is devoted exclusively to the problems of *linear* correlation, we shall use this illustration merely to demonstrate how pairs of measurements are grouped, and we shall therefore not worry about the actual relationship between the two variables. (The problem of nonlinear correlation will be discussed briefly in Chapter 17.)

A frequency table in two variables is usually obtained by dividing the scattergram (see Fig. 14.i) into a network of cells like that shown in the following table. Once the dividing lines of the network have been drawn, we count the number of points which fall into each cell, and denoting these numbers as the *cell frequencies*, we have obtained the two-dimensional frequency distribution. (Instead of drawing the scattergram first, i.e., instead of plotting the points representing our data, we could, of course, choose class intervals for both variables and tally the data directly into this network of cells.)

Yield of wheat
(bushels per acre)

	0–25	25–50	50–75	75–100	100–125	125–150
30–40			8	6	20	12
20–30		2	15	12	4	1
10–20	3	10	1			
0–10	5	1				

Pounds of fertilizer

This distribution tells us, for example, that among the 100 pairs of measurements 15 were such that the amount of fertilizer was between 50 and 75 pounds while the yield was between 20 and 30 bushels, 4 were such that the amount of fertilizer was between 100 and 125 pounds while the yield of wheat was between 20 and 30 bushels per acre, etc.

Whenever we want to group data consisting of paired measurements we construct a similar table. It is only natural that if we do this we must watch out for the same difficulties relating to ambiguities, overlap, open intervals, etc., which we met when we discussed ordinary frequency distributions in Chapter 2. We violated the rule of avoiding overlapping intervals when we chose the classifications of the previous illustration, but since our measurements were given on a continuous scale there was little danger that we would run into trouble.

To illustrate the calculation of r from grouped data, let us consider an important problem belonging to the domain of educational statistics, namely, the problem of checking the *reliability* of an objective test. A test is said to be *reliable* if good students to whom it is administered score high while poor students consistently score low. One method of examining the reliability of a test is to give the same test repeatedly to a number of students and to correlate their repeated scores. A more convenient method is to divide the test into two parts, usually the even problems and the odd problems, and to correlate the scores which a number of students received in both halves of the test. If a test is reliable, good students should score high in both halves, poor students should score low, and the correlation between the two sets of scores should be very high.

Let us suppose that the following data represent the scores which 25 students obtained in a given test, the total of the even-numbered problems being given as x and the total of the odd-numbered problems as y.

x	31	38	22	42	32	39	26	48	33	40	33	29	45
y	35	43	24	38	37	33	28	44	27	38	39	34	33

x	34	37	27	43	31	34	40	33	36	29	41	32
y	31	39	26	39	33	34	38	35	37	27	37	30

Since we want to show how to compute r from grouped data, let us now choose class intervals for both x and y and group these pairs of scores into a frequency table. Although it is not necessary to select equal class intervals for each variable, it is most certainly desirable, and we shall therefore group both x and y into classes going from 21–25, 26–30, 31–35, 36–40, etc. (It should be noted that it is definitely *not* necessary to choose the same classifications for both variables, and we have done so in this illustration only because of the nature of the measurements with which we are dealing.) Following the customary procedure of writing the x scale on the top of the table (increasing from left to right) and the y scale on the left-hand side (increasing downward) we shall obtain the following table into which we have tallied the given data.

	21–25	26–30	31–35	36–40	41–45	x scale
21–25	/					
26–30		///	/			
31–35		//	̶/̶/̶/̶/̶	//		
36–40			/	////	/	
41–45			/	///		
46–50					/	

y scale

Once we have obtained such a tally and the corresponding two-dimensional frequency table we can also present it as a *three-dimensional histogram* (see Fig. 14.j). The *heights* of the various blocks

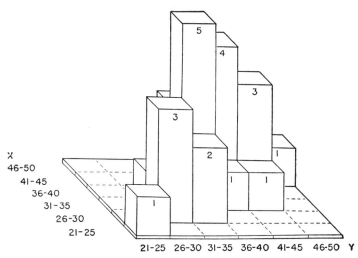

Figure 14.j. The Three-Dimensional Histogram of the Distribution of the Scores.

which stand on top of the cells are proportional to the cell frequencies just as the heights of the rectangles were previously proportional to the class frequencies in the ordinary case. In principle, there is therefore no difference between the histograms which we studied in Chapter 2 and the ones which we can now draw of our two-dimensional frequency tables.

When we calculated the mean and standard deviation of grouped data in Chapters 4 and 5, we succeeded in reducing our work considerably by introduction of a new scale of measurement. This can also be done now, where we are working with two variables, if we replace the x scale by a suitable u scale and the y scale by a suitable v scale. As before, this is done by first selecting a class mark for the zero point of each of the two new scales, and then numbering the successive class marks -3, -2, -1, 0, 1, 2, . . . , depending on how many classifications there are in each scale of the table. If we do this in our illustration we will get the following table in which the class marks are shown in the new scales.

	-2	-1	0	1	2	u scale
-2	1					
-1		3	1			
0		2	5	2		
1			1	4	1	
2			1	3		
3					1	

v scale

As we have pointed out earlier in this chapter, a coefficient of correlation will *not* be affected if we add or subtract arbitrary numbers from both variables or if we multiply or divide them by any constants. *This means that if we calculate r in terms of the u's and v's we should get precisely the same result as if we had used the corresponding class marks of the original scales.* Consequently, making the necessary changes in formula (14.2.1), allowing for the fact that we are now dealing with *grouped* data, *the short formula for the calculation of a coefficient of correlation from grouped data* becomes

$$r = \frac{n(\Sigma uvf) - (\Sigma uf_u)(\Sigma vf_v)}{\sqrt{n(\Sigma u^2 f_u) - (\Sigma uf_u)^2} \sqrt{n(\Sigma v^2 f_v) - (\Sigma vf_v)^2}} \qquad (14.3.1)^*$$

The six summations which are needed if we want to calculate r by means of this formula are usually determined in the following kind of scheme.

					(1) v	(2) f	(3) vf_v	(4) v^2f_v	(5) uvf
1					-2	1	-2	4	4
	3	1			-1	4	-4	4	3
	2	5	2		0	9	0	0	0
		1	4	1	1	6	6	6	6
		1	3		2	4	8	16	6
				1	3	1	3	9	6
(6) u -2	-1	0	1	2		25	11	39	25
(7) f_u 1	5	8	9	2	25				
(8) uf_u -2	-5	0	9	4	6				
(9) u^2f_u 4	5	0	9	8	26				
(10) uvf 4	3	0	10	8	25				

To simplify the general picture which is presented by this arrangement we have put the u and v scales at the bottom and right-hand side of this *correlation table*, where they are labeled as row (6) and column (1), respectively. Column (2) contains the frequencies which correspond to the various values of v, and it is obtained by adding the cell frequencies of each of the rows of this table. The products vf_v are then calculated by multiplying the corresponding values of columns (1) and (2) and recording their products in column (3). Similarly, the values of column (4) are obtained by squaring each v of column (1) and multiplying it by the corresponding frequency of column (2), giving us thus the products v^2f_v.

The figures which are given in rows (7), (8), and (9) can then be obtained by performing the identical operations on the u's and f_u's. The values of row (7) stand therefore for the sum of the cell frequencies of the columns of the correlation table, the numbers in row (8) stand for the products of the entries of rows (6) and (7), and those in row (9) for the products of the squares of the v's and the frequencies of row (7). The total number of cases, which is again written as n, can be found either from the total of column (2) or the total of row (7).

The rows and columns which we have discussed in the last paragraph provide us with n, Σvf_v, Σv^2f_v, Σuf_u, Σu^2f_u, but we still lack

Σuvf. This last summation is obtained in a somewhat more complicated fashion. We multiply the cell frequencies of a given row of the correlation table by the corresponding values of u, marking these products in the lower right-hand corner of each cell. Then we must add these products for each row, multiply the sums by the corresponding value of v, and enter these products in column (5). Interchanging u and v we could, similarly, have calculated Σuvf from the entries of row (10) which were found in a manner analogous to column (5).

To illustrate the calculation of Σuvf, let us consider, for example, the fourth row of our correlation table. Taking its cell frequencies and multiplying them by the corresponding values of u, we get $0(-2) + 0(-1) + 1(0) + 4(1) + 1(2) = 6$, and multiplying this total by $v = 1$, which corresponds to this row, we get $6 \cdot 1 = 6$, which is entered in column (5). It is, of course, unnecessary to find both column (5) and row (10), but since their totals must be the same, they afford a good check on our calculations. Returning now to the totals of the rows and columns of the correlation table, we have

$$
\begin{array}{rl}
\text{From column (2)} & n = 25 \\
\text{column (3)} & \Sigma vf_v = 11 \\
\text{column (4)} & \Sigma v^2 f_v = 39 \\
\text{column (5)} & \Sigma uvf = 25 \\
\text{row \ (8)} & \Sigma uf_u = \ \ 6 \\
\text{row \ (9)} & \Sigma u^2 f_u = 26 \\
\text{row (10)} & \Sigma uvf = 25
\end{array}
$$

Substituting these summations into formula (14.3.1) we finally have

$$
r = \frac{25(25) - (6)(11)}{\sqrt{25(26) - (6)^2} \ \sqrt{25(39) - (11)^2}} = .77
$$

which measures the strength of the correlation between the two parts of the test. It seems reasonable to conclude that since r is as large as .77, the test which we set out to investigate is fairly reliable.

Whenever r is computed on the basis of grouped data it can happen that a slight error is introduced because of our choice of the groupings. However, when n is large the grouping error is usually small and we can save time by grouping our data before we calculate a coefficient of correlation. The reader may feel that calculation of r from grouped data is quite involved, but after trying a few problems he will soon discover that it is actually much less work than the calculation of r for ungrouped data by use of formula (14.2.1).

EXERCISES

1. Calculate the coefficient of correlation for the following data, x representing scores in an English examination and y representing the scores which the same students obtained in a history test.

	1–20	21–40	41–60	61–80	81–100 x scale
1–20	1	1			
21–40		3	2	1	
41–60		2	3	6	
61–80			5	8	2
81–100				1	4

y scale

2. Calculate r from the following correlation table.

	1–3	4–6	7–9	10–12	13–15 x scale
15–19			1	3	5
20–24		2	5	9	14
25–29	1	3	8	7	6
30–34	3	5	4	5	1
35–39	9	10	6	1	
40–44	7	5	2		
45–49	4	1			

y scale

3. Group the following data into a correlation table and calculate r. The variables x and y stand for the height and chest measurements (in inches) of a group of 40 college freshmen.

x	y	x	y	x	y	x	y
64	30.7	68	32.5	72	36.5	67	32.6
70	36.3	67	31.4	73	37.4	70	35.8
73	35.5	70	36.2	70	34.8	72	37.2
69	31.1	70	34.8	67	33.8	75	38.0
67	30.2	68	34.2	69	33.2	71	36.5
68	31.0	66	31.6	75	38.3	72	37.1
64	30.7	72	33.9	72	36.8	69	31.4
73	38.2	69	32.5	70	34.6	68	32.0
69	33.3	73	36.4	69	32.9	68	30.9
69	34.1	70	37.0	68	34.5	70	33.7

14.4 The Interpretation of r

There is no difficulty in explaining the meaning of a coefficient of correlation which is either 0 or ±1.   If r is 0, we know that the fit of the regression line is so poor that we would be just as well off not using it at all if we want to predict values of y.   A correlation of +1 or −1, on the other hand, tells us that all points fall precisely on a straight line, and that we can thus make extremely accurate predictions of y by use of the equation of the regression line.   Values of r which fall *between* 0 and 1, however, are somewhat more difficult to explain.   Somebody who has no knowledge of statistics may easily be led to believe that a correlation of .50 is half as good as a correlation of 1.00, or that a correlation of .90 is three times as good as a correlation of .30.   This is a serious misconception which can lead to unwarranted and ridiculous conclusions.

To clarify the meaning of values of r which lie between 0 and 1 let us return to the original definition of r which was given on page 263 by formula (14.1.3).   In that formula r was based on the comparison of the two methods of prediction which used the equation of the regression line and the mean $\bar{y}$, respectively.   Figures 14.k and 14.l

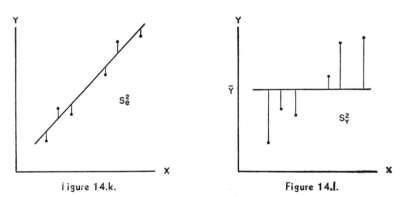

Figure 14.k.   Figure 14.l.

again illustrate the fact that if there exists a strong correlation, s_e^2 is considerably smaller than s_y^2.   The two error variances are, as in previous illustrations, measured by the vertical deviations from the solid lines.

To compare the methods of prediction which we studied in Section 14.1, we asked ourselves how large s_e^2 was as compared with s_y^2, and we used the ratio s_e^2/s_y^2 to express their relative sizes.   In the illustration which we used in that section and which dealt with personal savings and the annual number of strikes, the values of s_e^2 and s_y^2 were

$$s_e^2 = 549,012 \quad \text{and} \quad s_y^2 = 887,200$$

This told us that $s_e^2/s_y^2 = .619$, or better, that the error variance of method A was 61.9 per cent of that of method B. It follows that if we use the regression line (method A) we can reduce the error variance of our predictions by $100 - 61.9 = 38.1$ per cent. This can also be interpreted as implying that *38.1 per cent of the total variation of the y's is accounted for (caused) by their relationship with the variable x.*

If a coefficient of correlation is 1, *all* variations of the y's can be ascribed to corresponding variations of the x's, i.e., it can be said that the variations of the y's are *caused* by the x's. Figures 14.k and 14.l demonstrate what is meant by the fact that the variation of the y's, or a certain part of it, is accounted for by the relationship with x. The vertical deviations of the y's of Fig. 14.l vary considerably about the mean $\bar{y}$, giving us thus the impression that the variable y has a considerable spread. However, if we look at Fig. 14.k we will note that most of the variation of the y's is due to the fact that the y's correspond to different values of x. The variation of the y's which remains *after* we have eliminated the effect of the x's is therefore only the error variance s_e^2, which can also be called the chance variation of the y's. This chance variation of the y's is given by their total variation *minus* that part which is accounted for by the relationship with x.

The differences between these various types of variations will be easier to grasp if we consider a concrete illustration. Let us suppose, therefore, that the identical achievement test has been given to all students of a certain school regardless of their differences in age. The resulting variation between their scores can then be attributed partly to their *differences in age*, partly to their *differences in ability*, and partly to *chance*. We should thus be able to assign parts of the total variation of the y's (the scores) to the known factors of age and ability, and the remainder to chance. If one known factor, say age, accounts for a large portion of the total variation of the y's, we are justified in saying that there exists a strong relationship (correlation) between the score obtained in the achievement test and the student's age.

Limiting ourselves to *one known factor*, we can break the total variation of the y's into two parts, namely, s_e^2, which is the chance variation, and $s_y^2 - s_e^2$, which stands for that part of the total variation of the y's which is accounted for by the linear relationship with the variable x. The *fraction of the total variation* which can thus be attributed to the factor x is equal to

$$\frac{s_y^2 - s_e^2}{s_y^2} \qquad (14.4.1)$$

which can also be written

$$1 - \frac{s_e^2}{s_y^2}$$

Comparing this last formula with formula (14.1.3), we note that it is actually equal to *the square of the coefficient of correlation. This implies that if a coefficient of correlation between two variables x and y is equal to r, then $100r^2$ per cent of the total variation of the y's can be attributed to their relationship with the variable x.*

If a sample value of r is .70, for example, *49 per cent* of the variation of the y's is accounted for (caused) by differences in the variable x; if $r = .30$, only *9 per cent* of the total variation of the y's is due to the relationship with the variable x.

In the sense of *proportion of variation accounted for* we can say that if one value of r is *twice as large* as another, the first relationship is *4 times as strong* as the second. Whereas a correlation of .20 tells us that the variable x accounts for but 4 per cent of the variation of the y's, a correlation of .40 implies that x accounts for 16 per cent. We can therefore say that in the second case the variable x accounts for 4 times as much of the variation of the y's, and *in this sense* the second correlation is 4 times as strong as the first.

This discussion should also have made it clear that if r is small there is little to be gained if we choose method A (the regression line) in preference to method B (using only $\bar{y}$). If $r = .10$, for instance, we can reduce the error variance of our predictions *only by 1 per cent*, i.e., only 1 per cent of the variation of the y's can be attributed to the relationship with x, and it would hardly be worth while to go to the trouble of calculating and using the regression line.

We paid no attention to the sign of r when we discussed its interpretation in the last few pages, because a correlation of $+.80$, for example, is as strong as a correlation of $-.80$. The difference between $r = +.80$ and $r = -.80$ lies merely in the fact that in the first case *the regression line slopes upward*, while in the second case *it slopes downward.* This has nothing to do with the goodness of the fit of the regression line or the strength of the relationship between the two variables x and y.

14.5 Confidence Limits for a Coefficient of Correlation

If a small sample gives us a large value for r, say $r = .90$, this does not necessarily mean that the two variables must be related at all. Whenever a coefficient of correlation is computed on the basis of a sample we must check whether we can generalize from this information so that we will be able to infer something about *the actual relationship* between the two variables with which we are concerned. This means that we are faced with the familiar problem of having to generalize from the sample value of r to the actual relationship between x and y in the population from which our sample was obtained. This will make it necessary for us to distinguish between a *sample value of r* and a *true value of r (population value of r)*, and in order to avoid confusion we shall follow the customary procedure of denoting the population value by the letter ρ (rho). It follows that we shall now have to see how we can *estimate ρ* on the basis of a sample value of r just as we estimated m on the basis of a sample mean $\bar{x}$, and p on the basis of a sample value of f_n.

Logically speaking, there is no reason why we cannot duplicate the general procedures which we studied in Chapters 9 and 10 and look for the sampling distribution of r, confidence intervals of ρ, and a significance test for r under the assumption of a suitable null hypothesis. When we refer to the sampling distribution of r, it must be understood that, as always, we are referring to the distribution of the r's which we would expect to obtain if we were to take repeated samples from the same population. The reader will find it very helpful actually to construct such a sampling distribution of r by performing the experiment which is suggested in Exercise 5 on page 285.

Most sampling distributions which we have discussed in previous chapters had the desirable feature that they were either closely approximated by a normal curve, or they were at least given by some other well-known distribution. The sampling distribution of r is unfortunately so complicated that we shall leave its theoretical study to others and content ourselves with using tables of confidence limits of ρ which are based on the actual sampling distribution of r and which are similar in nature to the confidence limits of p which are given in Table III.

Table VI on page 395 provides us with 95 per cent confidence limits of ρ for samples of size 5, 10, 25, 100, and 400.   Use of this table is identical with that of Table III, which gave us the 95 per cent confidence limits of p.   Once we have calculated r on the basis of a sample, we mark its value on the horizontal scale of Table VI, go up vertically until we hit the two lines which correspond to the size of our sample, and then read the desired confidence limits from the points of the vertical scale which we have thus obtained.

If a sample of size 25 gives us a coefficient of correlation of .40, it can easily be seen from Table VI that the 95 per cent confidence limits of ρ are .01 and .67.   This means that we are 95 per cent sure that this interval will cover the true value of ρ.   Similarly, if $r = .30$ and $n = 10$, the 95 per cent confidence interval of ρ goes from $-.39$ to .76. This demonstrates clearly that sample values of r which are based on small samples are *extremely unreliable*.   On the other hand, if $r = .85$ and $n = 400$, the confidence limits for the true value of ρ are .84 and .87, and we have therefore an accurate estimate of ρ.

If the sample size which is used in a given problem is different from the values given in Table VI, it will be necessary simply to interpolate between the lines of the table.   Also, if it is more desirable to use a degree of confidence of .98 or .99, the appropriate tables can be found in the third reference on page 290.

There exist several other methods which can be used for the construction of confidence limits of ρ.   One method, which we are mentioning only because it is still widely used, employs the so-called *z-transformation* (not to be confused with the z values of the normal curve).   The statistic z is a function of r and it is defined as

$$z = \tfrac{1}{2} \log_e \left(\frac{1 + r}{1 - r} \right) \qquad (14.5.1)$$

(Natural logarithms are used here; the base is $e = 2.718...$)   If we are dealing with very large samples (n should be greater than 100) it is quite reasonable to say that the quantity z is normally distributed with the standard deviation

$$\sigma_z = \frac{1}{\sqrt{n - 3}} \qquad (14.5.2)$$

We can therefore use normal curve tables to construct confidence limits for the true value of z, which in turn can be converted into confidence limits for ρ by means of formula (14.5.1).   This process is quite tedious unless we use special tables which convert z into r and r into z. Such tables can be found in many elementary statistics texts, e.g., in the reference to Guilford at the end of this chapter.

14.6 A Significance Test for r

The definite need for a test of significance which tells us whether a sample value of r means anything is brought out very clearly in the following illustration. Let us suppose that we take two dice, one red and one green, and that we roll them five times and get the results which are given below.

Red die	Green die
1	2
4	6
5	4
6	4
2	2

If we calculate r for these five pairs of numbers we will obtain the astonishingly high value of $r = .67$. This leads to the obvious question whether this large sample value of r contradicts the natural assumption that there should be no relationship whatsoever between the rolls of the two dice, i.e., the assumption that the red die is in no way affected by the behavior of the green one. To answer this question we must investigate our chances of obtaining such a large value of r *purely by chance*, even though there is actually no relationship between the two variables. In other words, we shall have to construct a criterion on the basis of which we can decide whether a deviation from an expected value of r, in this case 0, is sufficiently large to enable us to say that it could not have happened purely by chance.

To *test the significance of a sample value of* r, we shall begin by formulating *the null hypothesis that ρ is equal to 0*. This means that we are following the customary procedure of assuming what we are trying to disprove, and that the relationship which we observed on the basis of a sample may be considered as indicative of the existence of an actual relationship *only if this null hypothesis can be rejected.* If we cannot reject it at a given level of significance we can say only that the sample value of r is not sufficiently large to permit us to say that it is significant, i.e., it might be that it means nothing.

Under the null hypothesis that $\rho = 0$, it is quite reasonable to say that *the sampling distribution of r is closely approximated by a normal curve whose mean and standard deviation are equal to*

$$m = 0 \quad \text{and} \quad \sigma_r = \frac{1}{\sqrt{n - 1}} \qquad (14.6.1)^*$$

Using a level of significance of .05, we can thus say that a coefficient of correlation is *significant* if the sample value of r exceeds $1.96\sigma_r$ or is less than $-1.96\sigma_r$. Substituting (14.6.1) for the *standard error of r* (σ_r), we can also write the criterion for testing the null hypothesis that $\rho = 0$ as:

> *Reject the null hypothesis that $\rho = 0$* if r is less than $-1.96/\sqrt{n - 1}$ or if it is greater than $+1.96/\sqrt{n - 1}$.
>
> *Reserve judgment* if r falls between these two critical values.

Had we wanted to use a different level of significance, e.g., .02 or .01, we would have had only to replace 1.96 by 2.33 or 2.58, respectively.

To illustrate this test of the significance of a coefficient of correlation, let us consider a sample of size 50 which has produced a correlation of $r = .40$. The dividing lines of our criterion are $\pm 1.96/\sqrt{50 - 1} = \pm.28$, and since .28 is exceeded by our sample value of .40, we are justified in saying that there exists a significant relationship between the two variables which were studied in the given sample. Had we used this criterion, on the other hand, to test the significance of an r which was based on a sample of size 5, we would have found that it would have required a correlation of $\pm 1.96/\sqrt{5 - 1} = \pm.98$ to prove the existence of a significant relationship. This shows, as we should really have suspected, that the value of r which we obtained when we studied the 5 rolls of the two dice was *not significant*.

The assumptions on which the above criterion is based are closely approximated when n is equal to 25 or more. Even if n is less than 25, however, it is safe to use this criterion, because our error would be such that the level of significance would be actually *smaller* if we were to evaluate the stated criterion by means of the actual sampling distribution of r instead of the normal curve. We can thus say that *our criterion for testing the significance of a sample value of r permits us to reject the null hypothesis that $\rho = 0$ at a level of significance of at most .05 regardless of the size of our sample.*

EXERCISES

1. Find 95 per cent confidence limits of ρ for each of the following samples.

   (a) $n = 25,\quad r = .70$
   (b) $n = 100,\quad r = -.10$
   (c) $n = 10,\quad r = .80$
   (d) $n = 400,\quad r = .65$
   (e) $n = 50,\quad r = -.38$
   (f) $n = 20,\quad r = .75$
   (g) $n = 200,\quad r = -.23$
   (h) $n = 150,\quad r = .17$

2. Find a 95 per cent confidence interval for the actual strength of the correlation between the heights and weights of the college students of Exercise 3, p. 268.

3. Find 95 per cent confidence limits for the actual strength of the relationship between unemployment in the United States and in Canada on the basis of the results of Exercise 4, p. 268.

4. Calculate r for the data which are given in Exercise 5 on page 256, and construct 95 per cent confidence limits for the true strength of the relationship between college grades and future success in life.

5. (Group exercise) Roll two dice, one red and one green (or otherwise distinguishable), and take a large number of samples consisting of 5 rolls of each die. Calculate r separately for each sample, group these data into a frequency distribution, and compare the standard deviation of this sampling distribution with the value which should have been expected according to formula (14.6.1). Check on probability graph paper whether this sampling distribution is close to a normal curve.

6. Test at a level of significance of .05 whether the sample value of r in each of the following samples is significant.

   (a) $n = 25,\quad r = .23$
   (b) $n = 50,\quad r = -.64$
   (c) $n = 100,\quad r = .24$
   (d) $n = 65,\quad r = -.14$
   (e) $n = 37,\quad r = .32$
   (f) $n = 485,\quad r = -.05$

7. Repeat Exercise 6, using a level of significance of .01.

8. Test, at a level of significance of .05, the significance of the value of r which was determined in Exercise 1 on page 277.

9. Use a level of significance of .02 to test the significance of the correlation between unemployment in the United States and Canada, using the results of Exercise 4, page 268.

10. Use a level of significance of .01 to test the significance of the relationship between the heights and chest measurements of Exercise 3, p. 277.

14.7 Correlation by Ranks

At times it is convenient to describe the correlation (relationship) between paired observations by calculating r on the basis of their *ranks* instead of their actual numerical values. The advantage of this modification lies in the fact that, as we shall see, it is much less laborious than the calculation of the ordinary coefficient of correlation by any standard formula.

If we take, for example, the illustration of page 259, where we discussed the relationship between savings and the number of strikes, we can replace each value of x and y by its corresponding rank within the sample. It does not matter whether we rank the x's and y's in ascending or descending order, *as long as we are consistent*. If we were to rank, by mistake, one of the variables in an ascending order and the other variable in a descending order, the resulting coefficient of correlation would have the wrong sign.

The data which were originally given on page 259 are reproduced in the first two columns of the following table, while their corresponding ranks are given in columns (3) and (4).

	Savings x	Number of strikes y	Rank of x	Rank of y
1940	2.9	2862	1	2
1941	4.9	2508	3	1
1942	10.9	4288	4	5
1943	16.1	2968	6	3
1944	17.5	4956	7	7
1945	19.0	4750	8	6
1946	11.9	4985	5	8
1947	3.0	3693	2	4

Since x was least in 1940, its rank is 1; the 1947 savings, 3.0, comes next and is given rank 2; then comes 4.9, which is given rank 3, etc. The y's are ranked in a similar fashion by assigning rank 1 to the smallest value, which is 2508; rank 2 to the next value, which is 2862, etc., until we reach 4985 which is the largest value and which is therefore given rank 8.

Instead of calculating r from the values of the first two columns representing the actual measurements, we can now apply formula (14.2.1) to columns (3) and (4) and study the strength of the relationship on the basis of these ranks.

This could be done by applying formula (14.2.1) directly, but it can be shown that *for the correlation of ranks* this formula reduces to

$$r_r = 1 - \frac{6\Sigma d_i^2}{n(n^2 - 1)} \qquad (14.7.1)^*$$

and this formula will give us the identical result much faster and with much less work. In this formula d_i stands for the *differences* between the ranks of the corresponding x's and y's, n, as always, for the size of the sample, while r_r itself is called the *coefficient of rank correlation*. The summation Σd_i^2 which is needed for substitution into (14.7.1) can easily be found by using the following scheme.

Rank of x	Rank of y	d	d^2
1	2	-1	1
3	1	2	4
4	5	-1	1
6	3	3	9
7	7	0	0
8	6	2	4
5	8	-3	9
2	4	-2	4
			32

Substituting the total of the last column and $n = 8$ into (14.7.1) we obtain

$$r_r = 1 - \frac{6(32)}{8(64 - 1)} = .62$$

which, oddly enough, is exactly the same as the value of r which we found for the x's and y's on page 263. It would be quite unreasonable to suppose that r and r_r will always be identical. As a matter of fact, if both x and y are normally distributed it can be shown that the relationship between r and r_r is given approximately by the formula

$$r = 2 \sin\left(\frac{\pi}{6} r_r\right) \qquad (14.7.2)$$

The only trouble which we might encounter in the ranking of numerical data is that one (or more) values of x or y occur more than once within the sample. Had we wanted to rank, for example, the following numbers

27,   48,   63,   63,   63,   70,   84,   84,   93,   98, we would have had no difficulty in ranking 27 first and 48 second. However, since 63 occurs three times we might easily be tempted to assign to each of these three numbers rank 3.   There is no reason why this kind of ranking cannot be used in other types of problems, but it is *not* the proper procedure if we want to use the ranking for the computation of r_r.   *In that case the proper procedure is to assign, in the case of ties, to each value the average of the ranks which they jointly occupy.*   Since the three 63's occupy positions three, four, and five, each must be given the rank 4.   Similarly, since 84 occurs twice, in seventh and eighth position, we must assign to each 84 the rank 7.5 (which is the average of 7 and 8).   The 10 numbers are thus ranked as follows:

Numbers	Ranks
27	1
48	2
63	4
63	4
63	4
70	6
84	7.5
84	7.5
93	9
98	10

It is interesting to note that the numbers which occurred only once were all given their proper ranking within the set of numbers.

A further advantage of the coefficient of rank correlation is that it can be used also in certain types of problems in which we are dealing with qualitative rather than with quantitative data.   It can be used in problems in which the variables can be *ranked* even though they cannot be measured on a numerical scale.

We could use r_r, for instance, to evaluate the consistency of two judges of a pie-baking contest at a county fair, or we could use it to correlate two people's preference for certain colors.   In either case formula (14.7.1) provides a convenient method of calculating the strength of the relationship, although we are not dealing with numerical data.

EXERCISES

1. Find the coefficient of rank correlation between the number of automobiles registered and the mileage of rural roads of the following 10 states.

	No. of cars (in thousands)	Road mileage (in 1000 miles)
Alabama	492	60
Colorado	429	76
Florida	705	39
Indiana	1160	82
Maine	284	21
New York	2923	81
Ohio	2264	86
Rhode Island	209	2
Virginia	711	48
Wisconsin	990	85

2. Calculate r_r for the following data representing the grades in history (x) and psychology (y) of 20 college freshmen.

x	85	73	69	73	48	52	70	69	93	100
y	73	84	70	70	62	70	83	66	84	97

x	18	57	93	73	52	61	77	96	88	73
y	22	66	89	70	54	63	79	89	85	68

3. Find the coefficient of rank correlation for the data of Exercise 5, p. 256.
4. Calculate r_r for the data of Exercise 7, p. 257.
5. Calculate r_r for the data of Exercise 8, p. 257.

14.8 Correlation and Causation

Whenever one observes a strong correlation between two variables, it is a considerable temptation to call one variable the *cause* and the other the *effect*, interpreting thus the correlation as a cause-effect relationship. At times this may be quite reasonable, but it can also lead to utterly ridiculous conclusions. One of the best-known illustrations of a strong correlation which cannot possibly be interpreted as a cause-effect relationship deals with teachers' salaries and the annual consumption of liquor in the United States. It can be shown that there exists a very strong linear correlation between teachers' salaries and the consumption of liquor, but it would be silly to infer from this that an increase in the consumption of liquor is a *cause* of changes in the salaries of teachers, or vice versa. Actually the high correlation between these two variables is due to the fact that *both are effects of a common cause*, in this case, the general standard of living. If two variables show a strong correlation because of their relationships with a *third* variable, we are faced with a situation which is a good deal more complicated than the problems which we have so far discussed. Problems of this type require the use of the much more advanced *multiple and partial correlation* techniques, which will be studied briefly in Chapter 17.

The above example has taught us that we are safe only if we interpret a coefficient of correlation as a measure of *association* rather than as a measure of *causation*. Furthermore, we should never forget that r measures the strength of *linear relationships only*. A set of data for which r is small (or even 0) may yet display a very strong non-linear relationship whose determination requires different measures of correlation like, for example, the *correlation ratio*, which will be discussed also in Chapter 17.

REFERENCES

M. M. Blair, *Elementary Statistics*, Holt, New York, 1944, Chap. 12.

F. E. Croxton and D. J. Cowden, *Applied General Statistics*, Prentice-Hall, New York, 1946, Chap. 22.

F. N. David, *Tables of the Ordinates and Probability Integral of the Distribution of the Correlation Coefficient in Small Samples*, Biometrika Office, London, 1938.

A. L. Edwards, *Statistical Analysis for Students in Psychology and Education*, Rinehart, New York, 1946, Chap. 5.

J. P. Guilford, *Fundamental Statistics in Psychology and Education*, McGraw-Hill, New York, 1950, p. 616.

C. H. Richardson, *An Introduction to Statistical Analysis*, Harcourt Brace, New York, 1934, Chap. 8.

A. E. Waugh, *Elements of Statistical Method*, McGraw-Hill, New York, 1943, Chap. 8.

15. THE CORRELATION
OF QUALITATIVE DATA

15.1 Introduction

The material covered in the previous chapter dealt with the relationships of quantitative variables. We defined the coefficient of correlation as a measure of the strength of such (linear) relationships, and its very definition, formula (14.1.3), makes it clear that its applicability is limited to variables which are expressed in terms of numbers. This restriction does not detract from the importance of the coefficient of correlation, but there do exist a considerable number of problems which will require a separate and somewhat different treatment.

The following are just a few illustrations in which either one or both variables which we want to correlate are not of a quantitative nature. A sociologist may be interested, for example, in studying the relationship between intelligence and racial background or the relationship between criminal tendencies of parents and the social adjustment of their children; many problems in biology deal with an analysis of the hereditary traits of successive generations; an economist may be interested in investigating the correlation between the social structure of a community and the marketability of a product, and a psychologist may want to study the relationship between neurotic tendencies and deficiencies in the brain structure. These are just a few examples of problems in which we *cannot* evaluate the strength of whatever relationship may exist in terms of the coefficient of correlation.

In the special case in which *both* variables are such that they permit only one of two possible alternatives, we could study their relationship by a technique which we have already discussed in Chapter 10. If we take, for instance, the following observations dealing with the educational background and social adjustment of 150 individuals who were chosen at random, we could test for the significance of the

<table>
<tr><td></td><td colspan="2">Rating in a
social adjustment test</td></tr>
<tr><td></td><td>low</td><td>high</td></tr>
<tr><td>College graduate</td><td>26</td><td>74</td></tr>
<tr><td>High school only</td><td>24</td><td>26</td></tr>
</table>

difference between the percentages of well-adjusted people belonging to these two groups and decide, on this basis, whether there exists a relationship between education and social adjustment. The proportion of college graduates who scored high in social adjustment was $74/(74 + 26) = .74$, while the corresponding proportion for those who finished only high school was $26/(26 + 24) = .52$. Using the technique of Section 10.5, we can now test the null hypothesis that there exists no difference between the actual percentages, i.e., the hypothesis that there is no relationship between educational background and social adjustment. If the difference, in this case $.74 - .52 = .22$, is significant we can conclude that there is some relationship between education and social adjustment although we cannot say (on the basis of this method) *how strong such a relationship might be.*

The table which contained the data of the investigation of the previous paragraph is called a *two-by-two table*. There exist numerous ways of measuring the strength of the relationship between two variables which are given in a two-by-two table, but since there also exist fairly easy techniques which can be used regardless of the number of rows and columns, i.e., regardless of the number of categories into which we divide our variables, we shall devote no more time to this special problem.

If a table into which our data have been classified contains more than two rows or columns, it is obviously no longer possible to apply the simple technique of testing for the significance of the difference between percentages. The method which we shall use instead can be outlined, in principle, as follows. First, we ask ourselves for the frequencies which we could *expect* to find in the various cells of our table under the assumption that there is *no relationship* between the two variables. Second, we compare these expected cell frequencies with the corresponding frequencies which were actually observed, and finally, we decide by comparing these two sets of frequencies whether their discrepancies are large enough to permit us to reject the null hypothesis that the variables were *independent* (unrelated). *If the null hypothesis can be rejected, we have shown that there exists a significant relationship between our two variables.* The criterion on which this decision is based is, as we shall see in Section 15.4, constructed with the use of the *chi-square distribution* which we have already met in Chapters 9 and 10.

15.2 The Calculation of the Expected Cell Frequencies

Before going into a detailed study of the correlation of qualitative variables, it will probably be helpful to illustrate the general procedure first by means of a concrete example. For this purpose we have chosen the following (fictitious) study of the relationship between hair color and self-control:

	Very self-controlled	Average	Very impulsive	Row total
Blonde	15	64	28	107
Redhead	18	52	23	93
Column total	33	116	51	200

The sample which furnished this information consisted of the observation of 200 individuals among whom 15 were very self-controlled blondes, 64 were blondes with average self-control, and 28 were very impulsive blondes. Among the 93 redheads of this sample 18 were very self-controlled, 52 showed average self-control, and 23 were very impulsive. Adding the number of individuals who belong to the respective rows and columns, we find that our sample contained 107 blondes, 93 redheads, 33 very self-controlled individuals, 116 with average self-control, and 51 who are very impulsive.

In order to determine the cell frequencies which we might have *expected* if there had been no relationship between hair color and self-control, let us now copy this *two-by-three table*, but let us record *only the totals of the rows and columns*, omitting thereby the cell frequencies which were actually observed. This will leave us with the following table:

	Very self-controlled	Average	Very impulsive	Row total
Blonde				107
Redhead				93
Column total	33	116	51	200

and we can now ask ourselves *what frequencies we could expect to find in the various empty cells of this table, knowing only the totals of the rows and columns and making the assumption that there exists no relationship between hair color and self-control.*

To answer this question let us first try to find the number of self-controlled blondes which we could expect under the various assumptions. We know from the totals of our table that $107/200 = 53.5$ per cent of our sample consisted of blondes, and that, similarly, the percentage of very self-controlled individuals is $33/200 = 16.5$ per cent. Under the assumption that self-control is *independent* of hair color—which is equivalent to the assumption that the two variables are not related—we can multiply these two ratios, and we can say that $(.535)(.165) = .0883$ or 8.83 per cent of our total sample could have been expected to consist of very self-controlled blondes. Multiplying this percentage by 200 (the size of the sample) we can now state that we could have expected approximately 18 very self-controlled blondes under the assumption that hair color and self-control are not related. This last assumption was necessary because we could otherwise not have multiplied the two ratios (see the dis cussion of page 133).

The number of very self-controlled redheads which we could have expected can now be found very easily by simply subtracting 18, the expected number of very self-controlled blondes, from 33, the total number of very self-controlled people in our sample. It follows that the expected number of very self-controlled redheads is $33 - 18 = 15$.

If we want to find the expected number of blondes with average self-control, we shall have to go once again through the identical steps. Since $116/200 = 58$ per cent of our sample consisted of people with average self-control, we can say that $(.58)(.535) = .310$ or 31 per cent of our total sample could have been expected to consist of blondes with average self-control. Multiplying this figure by 200, the expected number of blondes with average self-control turns out to be $200(.31) = 62$. Subtracting this number as well as the number of very self-controlled blondes from the total number of blondes in our table, we find that the remainder, or $107 - 62 - 18 = 27$, gives us the expected number of very impulsive blondes.

The cell frequencies which are still unknown can now be found by subtracting the frequencies which have been calculated from the totals of the respective rows and columns. This gives us $33 - 18 = 15$ for the expected number of very self-controlled redheads, $116 - 62 = 54$

for the expected number of redheads with average self-control, and $51 - 27 = 24$ for the expected number of very impulsive redheads.

Having found all expected cell frequencies, we can now compare the observed and the expected frequencies and decide on the basis of this comparison whether our assumptions were reasonable. If the observed frequencies agree very closely with the expected ones which we have computed, we have a good indication that our assumption was correct, and that the two variables are *not related*. If there are great differences, on the other hand, we have an indication that our assumptions were wrong, i.e., that the variables were actually related. This comparison can be made most conveniently by reproducing the original *two-by-three table*, giving the expected cell frequencies in parentheses below the frequencies which were actually observed. If we do this we will get the following table:

	Very self-controlled	Average	Very impulsive
Blondes	15 (18)	64 (62)	28 (27)
Redheads	18 (15)	52 (54)	23 (24)

A casual inspection of these two sets of frequencies shows that the differences are extremely small, and that it seems quite reasonable to conclude that our assumptions were correct. Hence we can say that there is *apparently* no relationship. Before attempting to put the comparison of the two sets of frequencies on a more precise and less intuitive basis, let us first investigate how the expected cell frequencies can be computed in general, regardless of the number of rows and columns, under the assumption that the two variables are independent, i.e., under the hypothesis that there exists no relationship.

15.3 Contingency Tables

To study the most general case, let us consider two variables A and B, each of which permits a certain number of alternative descriptions. The variable A, for instance, may be subdivided into the categories $A_1, A_2, A_3, \ldots$, while the variable B is subdivided into the classifications $B_1, B_2, B_3, \ldots$. In our previous illustration the variable A stood for self-control, B stood for hair color, while

A_1 = very self-controlled.
A_2 = average self-control.
A_3 = very impulsive.
B_1 = blonde.
B_2 = redhead.

Repeating the work which we have just done in this special case, we can now consider a set of data which has been grouped into the following *contingency table* consisting of a rows and b columns:

	A_1	A_2	A_3	.	A_b	Row totals
B_1	n_{11}	n_{12}	n_{13}	.	n_{1b}	$n_{1.}$
B_2	n_{21}	n_{22}	n_{23}	.	n_{2b}	$n_{2.}$
B_3	n_{31}	n_{32}	n_{33}	.	n_{3b}	$n_{3.}$
.	.	.	.	.	.	.
B_a	n_{a1}	n_{a2}	n_{a3}	.	n_{ab}	$n_{a.}$
Column totals	$n_{.1}$	$n_{.2}$	$n_{.3}$	.	$n_{.b}$	n

The observed cell frequencies are represented by the letters n_{11}, n_{23}, n_{45}, . . . , and in general by the symbol n_{ij}, where the *subscript i* refers to the *row* while the *subscript j* refers to the *column* to which the respective cell belongs. For example, the number of items which belonged to the cell which is contained in the second row and third column is written as n_{23}. The total of the first row is denoted as $n_{1.}$, and in general, the total of the ith row will be given as $n_{i.}$. Similarly, the total of the jth column will be written as $n_{.j}$ while the grand total of all cases is, as always, given by the letter n.

Using the identical arguments on the basis of which we calculated the expected cell frequencies in our previous illustration, namely, the assumptions that (1) the two variables A and B are independent, and (2) that the totals of the rows and columns are fixed, we can now calculate the expected cell frequencies which, to avoid confusion, will be written as e_{ij}.

Since the totals of the rows and columns are by assumption fixed, we can say that the proportion (fraction) of items which fit description A_j is given by the ratio $n_{.j}/n$, while the proportion which should fit description B_i is given by the ratio $n_{i.}/n$. Consequently, the proportion (fraction) of the total cases which, under our assumptions, should fit *both* of these descriptions is given by the product $(n_{.j}/n)(n_{i.}/n)$. This last step was possible only because we assumed that the two variables were independent and so we were able to employ formula (7.3.4).

Finally, multiplying this proportion of the cases which fit both description A_j and description B_i by the number n, we obtain the *expected frequency* of the cell which belongs to the ith row and the jth column. This means that the *expected frequency* e_{ij} which corresponds to the *observed frequency* n_{ij} is given by the formula

$$e_{ij} = \frac{(n_{.j})(n_{i.})}{n} \qquad (15.3.1)^*$$

and we can now use it to calculate the expected frequencies which correspond to the various cells of our contingency table. This formula is easy to remember because it tells us that *in order to find the expected frequency of a given cell we have simply to multiply the totals of the respective row and column and divide this product by the total size of the sample.*

To illustrate the use of formula (15.3.1) for the calculation of the expected frequencies of a contingency table, let us consider the following study of the relationship between the intelligence and standard of clothing of a certain group of school children:

	Intelligence low	average	high	Row totals
Very well dressed	51	202	198	451
Well dressed	56	67	29	152
Poorly dressed	12	11	10	33
Column totals	119	280	237	636

Under the assumption that there is no relationship between intelligence and the standard of clothing, formula (15.3.1) tells us that the expected number of school children with low intelligence who are very well dressed is

$$\frac{(119)(451)}{636} = 84$$

and that the expected number who have average intelligence and who are very well dressed is

$$\frac{(280)(451)}{636} = 199$$

Having found these two expected frequencies, it follows immediately that the expected number who are highly intelligent and who are very well dressed is $451 - 84 - 199 = 168$.

Using formula (15.3.1) twice more we find that the expected number who are well dressed but below average in intelligence is

$$\frac{(119)(152)}{636} = 28$$

and that the expected number who are well dressed and have average intelligence is

$$\frac{(280)(152)}{636} = 67$$

We have now used formula (15.3.1) altogether *four times*, and since the totals of the rows and columns of the expected frequencies must equal those of the original table we can find the expected frequencies which are still lacking by subtracting those which we have calculated from the totals of the appropriate rows and columns.

Writing, as before, the expected cell frequencies in parentheses below the frequencies which were actually observed, we can now compare the observed and the expected frequencies by means of the following table:

	Intelligence low	average	high
Very well dressed	51 (84)	202 (199)	198 (168)
Well dressed	56 (28)	67 (67)	29 (57)
Poorly dressed	12 (7)	11 (14)	10 (12)

Since we assumed that our two variables, namely, intelligence and the standard of clothing, were *not related* we can try to decide on the basis of the agreement or lack of agreement of these two sets of frequencies whether or not our assumption was right. If the observed frequencies agree closely with the ones which we might have expected, it seems only reasonable to say that at least we have *no evidence* that there was anything wrong with our original hypothesis. On the other hand, if the discrepancies between the n_{ij} and the e_{ij} are sufficiently large, we will be able to reject the assumption (null hypothesis), and we can conclude that there actually is some relationship between the standard of clothing and the intelligence of the school children.

15.4 The Chi-Square Criterion

The comparison of the observed and the expected cell frequencies of a contingency table can be put on a precise, scientific basis with the use of the statistic

$$\chi^2 = \sum \frac{(n_{ij} - e_{ij})^2}{e_{ij}} \qquad (15.4.1)^*$$

which is called *chi-square* and which, as we might have suspected from its name, has the sampling distribution which was introduced in Chapter 9 as the chi-square distribution. The summation of formula (15.4.1) extends over all cells of the contingency table, which means that we must compute the quantity

$$\frac{(n_{ij} - e_{ij})^2}{e_{ij}}$$

separately *for each cell* and then add all these results.

If the agreement between the observed and the expected frequencies is close, the differences $n_{ij} - e_{ij}$ and consequently also χ^2 will be small. If, on the other hand, some of the differences $n_{ij} - e_{ij}$ are large, the value of χ^2 which is computed from (15.4.1) will also be large.

If χ^2 is computed on the basis of a sample—which is the case in our problem—we must consider the fact that, like any other statistic, it is subject to the chance variations which are displayed by its sampling distribution. This distribution is, as always, the distribution which we could expect to obtain if we were to group values of χ^2 which have been calculated on the basis of repeated experiments of the same type. If we assume that the two variables which are represented in the contingency table are *independent* it can be shown that the sampling distribution of the statistic which we have defined in (15.4.1) is very closely approximated by the identical chi-square distribution which we used in Chapter 9 for the construction of confidence intervals of a standard deviation. To give the reader an idea of the shape of this distribution, a more or less typical illustration is given in Fig. 15.a.

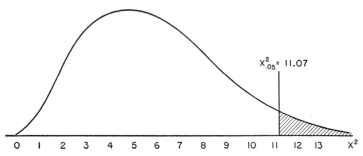

Figure 15.a.   The Chi-Square Distribution for Five Degrees of Freedom.

To test the null hypothesis that the two variables of the contingency table are not related we shall now use the statistic χ^2 and its sampling distribution.   As large values of χ^2 are indicative of serious discrepancies between the observed and the expected cell frequencies, *we shall reject the null hypothesis that the variables are not related if our sample value of χ^2 exceeds a certain critical value $\chi^2_{.05}$*, provided, of course, that we are satisfied with a level of significance of .05.

A small value of χ^2 is usually understood to imply that the differences between the two sets of frequencies may be attributed to chance, and that we are therefore not able to prove the existence of a significant relationship.   It might be argued that an extremely small value of χ^2 could imply that our results were *too good*, inferring that we should suspect that the experiment was not conducted in an unbiased fashion.   This is of course possible, but we shall not worry about it at this time.

When we first introduced the chi-square distribution in Chapter 9 we pointed out that the exact shape of the distribution, and consequently its areas, depend on the size of the sample on which our statistic is based.   Rather than associating a definite chi-square distribution with the size of the sample, however, it is more common to say that the chi-square distribution depends on something called the *number of degrees of freedom*.   When we computed the expected cell frequencies of the three-by-three table of our last illustration, we pointed out that after we had calculated four of the expected cell frequencies by means of formula (15.3.1), the remaining five could be found directly by substracting the known cell frequencies from the totals of the respective rows and columns. We could, in this sense, say that we had *four degrees of freedom*, which simply means that if four of the cell frequencies are known (calculated or assumed) then we have *no more freedom* in filling in the remaining cells.

In general, if a contingency table consists of a rows and b columns, the number of degrees of freedom is given by the formula

$$d.f. = (a - 1)(b - 1) \qquad (15.4.2)^*$$

If we take a *four-by-five table*, for instance, the number of degrees of freedom is according to (15.4.2) equal to $(4 - 1)(5 - 1) = 12$.

Once we have determined the number of degrees of freedom for a given problem, we can determine the desired value of $\chi^2_{.05}$, i.e., the critical value of our criterion, directly from Table IV (page 392), locating the proper row of the table by checking the number of the degrees of freedom in the right-hand column which is marked $d.f.$

Returning now to the illustration which dealt with the intelligence and the standard of clothing of the 636 school children, we shall first have to compute χ^2, which is most conveniently done by means of the following scheme:

(1) n_{ij}	(2) e_{ij}	(3) $n_{ij} - e_{ij}$	(4) $(n_{ij} - e_{ij})^2$	(5) $\dfrac{(n_{ij} - e_{ij})^2}{e_{ij}}$
51	84	−33	1089	12.96
202	199	3	9	.04
198	168	30	900	5.35
56	28	28	784	28.00
67	67	0	0	.00
29	57	−28	784	13.75
12	7	5	25	3.57
11	14	−3	9	.64
10	12	−2	4	.33
				64.64

The first two columns contain the observed and expected frequencies which we have calculated earlier; column (3) contains their differences $n_{ij} - e_{ij}$; column (4) the squares $(n_{ij} - e_{ij})^2$; and column (5) finally the values of column (4) divided by the corresponding values of column (2), i.e., the quotients $(n_{ij} - e_{ij})^2/e_{ij}$.

The total of column (5) gives us the desired value of χ^2, which in this example is equal to 64.64. Whether or not this value is sufficiently large to enable us to conclude that we have *a significant correlation* will depend on the value of $\chi^2_{.05}$, which is found from Table IV. Since we have, according to formula (15.4.2), $(3 - 1)(3 - 1) = 4$ degrees of freedom, Table IV provides us with the information that $\chi^2_{.05} = 9.488$, and it follows that we can *reject* the null hypothesis; therefore the relationship between the intelligence and the standard of clothing of the school children is *significant*.

Had we applied the chi-square criterion to our study of the correlation between hair color and self-control, we would have found that our sample value of χ^2 is 1.30. This is considerably less than the critical value, which for *two degrees of freedom* is equal to 5.991. Consequently, we would not have been able to reject the null hypothesis, and our experiment did not prove that the two variables were related. The fact that the sample value of χ^2 was as small as 1.30 as compared with the critical value of 5.991 is a good indication that the two variables were independent, although we can make no definite statement to this effect without assuming the risk of a *type II error*.

One point which should be added about the use of the chi-square criterion is that *it can be used only if every expected cell frequency is at least equal to five*. If it happens that one cell frequency is less than five, it will be necessary to combine adjacent cells in order to raise the expected cell frequency above the necessary minimum. Whenever this must be done, it is important to note that having thus reduced the number of cells, we have also lost a degree of freedom.

To conclude our discussion of contingency tables let us briefly outline the steps which were necessary to test the null hypothesis that the two variables were independent:

1. Calculation of the expected cell frequencies e_{ij} by use of formula (15.3.1).
2. Calculation of χ^2 on the basis of the observed and the expected cell frequencies, using formula (15.4.1).
3. Calculation of the number of degrees of freedom from formula (15.4.2).
4. Determination of the critical value of χ^2 from Table IV and comparison with the sample value of χ^2 which was obtained in step 2. If the level of significance is .05, .02, or .01, the corresponding critical values of χ^2 are $\chi^2_{.05}$, $\chi^2_{.02}$, or $\chi^2_{.01}$, respectively.

15.5 The Contingency Coefficient

The chi-square criterion enables us to decide whether or not the relationship between two qualitative variables is significant. *It does not tell us, however, to what extent one variable depends on the other, i.e., it does not yet provide us with a measure of the strength of the correlation.*

Because the expected cell frequencies were determined on the basis of the assumption that the two variables were independent, it follows that the greater the difference between the two sets of frequencies, the stronger is the relationship between the two variables, and, consequently, *the greater the value of* χ^2, *the stronger will be the correlation.* Using this argument, we can now define a measure of the strength of the relationship which is displayed by the variables of a contingency table. This new measure of correlation is called the *contingency coefficient* and it is given by the formula

$$C = \sqrt{\frac{\chi^2}{\chi^2 + n}} \qquad (15.5.1)^*$$

In this expression n is as always the size of the sample (and *not* the number of cells), while χ^2 is the sample value which is obtained from the contingency table by means of formula (15.4.1).

A contingency coefficient is in many respects similar to an ordinary coefficient of correlation, and it is usually interpreted more or less like a value of r. It is advisable to be careful, however, in the interpretation of a sample value of C, because the *maximum* value of C can be considerably less than 1 if the contingency table has a small number of rows and columns. If we are dealing with a two-by-two table, for example, it can be shown that the contingency coefficient can never exceed .707, which must thus be interpreted as a perfect correlation (equivalent to $r = 1$). Similarly, the maximum value of C for a four-by-four table can never be greater than .866.

Had we computed the contingency coefficient C to measure the strength of the correlation between the intelligence and the standard of clothing of the school children, we would have had

$$C = \sqrt{\frac{64.64}{64.64 + 636}} = .30$$

which indicates a significant though not strong correlation between the two variables. The fact that it is significant was shown earlier by means of the chi-square criterion.

REFERENCES

F. E. Croxton and D. J. Cowden, *Applied General Statistics*, Prentice-Hall, New York, 1946, Chap. 22.

A. L. Edwards, *Statistical Analysis for Students in Psychology and Education*, Rinehart, New York, 1946, Chap. 6.

R. A. Fisher, *Statistical Methods for Research Workers*, Hafner, New York, 1948, Chap. 3.

M. J. Hagood, *Statistics for Sociologists*, Holt, New York, 1947, Chap. 19.

P. G. Hoel, *Introduction to Mathematical Statistics*, Wiley, New York, 1947, Chap. 5.

J. F. Kenney and E. S. Keeping, *Mathematics of Statistics (Part II)*, Van Nostrand, New York, 1951, Chap. 8.

EXERCISES

1. Decide on the basis of the information which is given in the following two-by-three table whether there is a relationship between political views and levels of income (use a level of significance of .05):

	Low income	Average income	High income
For candidate A	32	84	25
For candidate B	18	72	57

2. Use the data given in the following table to decide whether there exists a relationship between intelligence and a person's choice of his occupation (use a level of significance of .05):

	Occupations					
	A	B	C	D	E	F
Low intelligence	33	28	49	19	23	51
Average intelligence	118	94	53	72	44	68
High intelligence	52	13	37	64	17	6

3. Test whether the following three materials react equally well under thermal shock treatment (use a level of significance of .05):

	Broke completely	Showed slight defects	Remained perfect
Material I	25	40	35
Material II	45	35	20
Material III	40	35	25

4. Decide on the basis of the information given in the following table whether there exists a correlation between a student's ability and interest in the subject of statistics (use a level of significance of .05):

		Ability		
		low	average	high
Interest	low	28	17	15
	average	20	40	20
	high	12	28	40

5. Calculate the contingency coefficient for each of the above four exercises.

16. FURTHER APPLICATIONS OF THE CHI-SQUARE CRITERION

16.1 The Goodness of the Fit of a Normal Curve

The chi-square criterion which we discussed in the previous chapter served the purpose of putting the comparison of the observed and the expected cell frequencies of a contingency table on a scientific basis. When the value of χ^2 which was calculated from a sample was large, larger than some critical value $\chi^2_{.05}$, we were able to conclude that the discrepancies between the two sets of frequencies was *significant*. On the other hand, when χ^2 was small, smaller than $\chi^2_{.05}$, we could say only that the differences might be attributed to chance.

Since χ^2 was defined in formula (15.4.1) as *a measure of the compatibility of two sets of frequencies* it suggests itself that it might also be used to compare frequencies other than those of the contingency table. Indeed, one of the most common and most valuable applications of the chi-square criterion is its use in testing *whether we are justified in treating a set of experimental data as if it had come from a normally distributed population*. In the second part of this book we have approximated many different sampling distributions with normal curves and we have often assumed that our samples were taken from normal populations. This practice gives rise to the question as to when, how, and under what conditions we are actually justified in making such assumptions. To be precise, we should really have checked in each case whether our observed distributions were sufficiently close to be treated as if they were normal curves.

When we first studied theoretical distributions and the normal curve in particular in Chapter 6, we learned in Section 6.5 how to fit a normal curve to a set of grouped data. At that time we were satisfied with basing the goodness of the fit on visual comparison of the observed and the corresponding normal curve frequencies. Now we shall see how this comparison can be put on a more precise basis by use of the chi-square criterion, which will serve to decide whether the two sets of frequencies are sufficiently close for us to say that there is *no significant difference.*

Before going into any theoretical detail, let us illustrate this new application of the chi-square criterion, using the set of data which we discussed earlier in this connection on page 115. There we used the normal curve areas of Table I to compute the frequencies which we could have *expected* to find in the various class intervals of the distribution of the weights of the recruits *if* the original **data** had been normally distributed. The normal curve which we thus fitted to our data had the same mean, standard deviation, and total frequency as the observed distribution, because these are the three quantities which must always be known for the determination of a normal curve. The final results which we obtained on page 118 were

Weights	Observed frequencies	Normal curve frequencies
150–158	9	9
159–167	24	26
168–176	51	52
177–185	66	71
186–194	72	68
195–203	48	45
204–212	21	20
213–221	6	7
222–230	3	1

It was evident from Fig. 6.n, in which we showed the histograms of the two distributions, and it is evident now from this table, that the agreement between the observed frequencies and the expected normal curve frequencies is close. If we want to be more specific, we must first calculate χ^2 with the formula

$$\chi^2 = \sum \frac{(n_i - e_i)^2}{e_i} \qquad (16.1.1)^*$$

which differs slightly from the formula for χ^2 which we gave in Chapter 15. This modification of our symbolism and the resulting modification of the formula for χ^2 is necessary because we are now dealing with *a single column* of observed (or expected) frequencies instead of the *two-dimensional array* of cell frequencies which we found in the contingency table.   This makes it possible to write the observed class frequencies as n_i and the corresponding expected class frequencies as e_i.

If we now square the differences between the observed and the expected frequencies, divide each square by the expected frequency, and finally add all these quantities, we obtain

$$\chi^2 = \frac{(9-9)^2}{9} + \frac{(24-26)^2}{26} + \frac{(51-52)^2}{52} + \frac{(66-71)^2}{71}$$
$$+ \frac{(72-68)^2}{68} + \frac{(48-45)^2}{45} + \frac{(21-20)^2}{20} + \frac{(9-8)^2}{8}$$
$$= 1.23$$

Before we could actually make these calculations we had to combine the last two classes of the frequency table because, as we have said before, the chi-square criterion cannot be used if any expected cell frequency is less than five.   Combining the last two classes of the distribution we obtained an observed frequency of $6 + 3 = 9$ and an expected normal curve frequency of $7 + 1 = 8$, which is above the necessary minimum of five.

If we now want to use the calculated value of χ^2, e.g., the 1.23 which we obtained in our illustration, to decide upon *the goodness of the fit of the normal curve*, we discover that in order to determine the critical value $\chi^2_{.05}$ from Table IV we must know the number of *degrees of freedom*.   In our discussion of the expected cell frequencies of a contingency table we observed that we could *not* fill in all cell frequencies in an arbitrary manner, because the totals of the rows and columns had to agree with the corresponding totals of the observed data.   This imposed a certain restriction on our choice of the expected cell frequencies and a corresponding loss in the number of the degrees of freedom.   In other words, *this means that the number of degrees of freedom was given by the total number of cells minus the number of the restrictions which were imposed by the observed data.*   It is apparent that this definition of the number of the degrees of freedom is slightly different from that which was given in Chapter 15, but it can easily be seen that the two definitions are actually equivalent.

Using this last definition of the number of the degrees of freedom we can say that since our distribution had eight classifications—there were originally nine but we had to combine the last two—we now have $8 - 3 = 5$ degrees of freedom.   *The reason why we must subtract three from the total number of cells is that we used in our calculation of the expected frequencies three quantities which were obtained from the observed data;* these were the mean, the standard deviation, and the total frequency.

It follows, therefore, that *whenever we fit a normal curve to a set of experimental data the resulting χ^2 will have $k - 3$ degrees of freedom,* where k is the number of classes into which we have grouped our data.

Since the distribution which we discussed in our illustration had eight classes we have accordingly *five degrees of freedom.* Choosing a level of significance of .05, the critical value $\chi^2_{.05}$ can easily be found in Table IV, and in our example it is 11.070. Comparing this critical value of χ^2 with our sample value of 1.23, it is evident that the difference between the observed and the normal curve frequencies is not significant, and it seems quite reasonable to say that the original distribution was closely approximated by a normal curve.

If the calculated value of χ^2 is less than the critical value which, for a given level of significance, is obtained from Table IV, we shall agree to say that we have a *good fit,* and that we are consequently permitted to treat our distribution as if it were a normal curve. Whenever we make such a decision we should perhaps keep our fingers crossed, that the type II error which we are thus risking is not too large.

16.2 The Goodness of the Fit of Other Theoretical Distributions

The technique which we have just outlined can be used, in general, to test the goodness of the fit of any theoretical distribution provided, of course, that we know how to compute the theoretical frequencies which we should have expected, corresponding to our observed distribution. In any problem of this type we must always determine first the expected frequencies, then calculate χ^2 by substituting the observed and the expected frequencies into formula (16.1.1), and finally decide on the basis of the critical value which is found from Table IV whether we have a good fit.

The only difference in the general method of testing the goodness of fit of different theoretical distributions lies in the number of degrees of freedom. This will always depend on the number of quantities which are first obtained from the observed data and then used in the calculation of the expected frequencies. For the normal curve we had $k - 3$ degrees of freedom, and in general, we will have $k - s$, where k stands for the number of classifications and s for the number of restrictions which the observed data impose on the expected frequencies.

The theoretical distribution which throughout our work has ranked second only to the normal curve is the *binomial distribution*. This distribution was defined by formula (3.3.1) in Chapter 3 as the formula which tells us the probabilities of obtaining x successes in n trials. For example, if we toss four coins a great number of times we can *expect* the resulting number of heads to be distributed according to the binomial distribution for which $p = .50$ and $n = 4$. Let us suppose that an experiment consisted of tossing 4 coins 112 times and that it produced the following results:

Number of heads	Frequency
0	11
1	26
2	39
3	31
4	5
	112

Under the assumption that the four coins are honest, i.e., under the assumption that each coin has a fifty-fifty chance of coming up heads, we can evaluate by use of formula (3.3.1) the probabilities of getting 0, 1, 2, 3, or 4 heads. Substituting $p = .50$ and $n = 4$ into the formula of the binomial distribution, we find that these five probabilities are $\frac{1}{16}$, $\frac{4}{16}$, $\frac{6}{16}$, $\frac{4}{16}$, and $\frac{1}{16}$, respectively. Since we tossed the four coins 112 times, we can now find the *expected* frequencies by multiplying each of these probabilities by 112 and we will get

Number of heads	Observed frequencies	Expected frequencies
0	11	7
1	26	28
2	39	42
3	31	28
4	5	7

These two sets of frequencies can be compared roughly on the basis of their superimposed histograms, which are shown in Fig. 16.a. Judging from this figure it seems that there is a close agreement between the observed and the expected binomial frequencies. If we want to make a precise comparison, however, we again must compute the statistic χ^2 according to formula (16.1.1), and we will find that

$$\chi^2 = \frac{(11-7)^2}{7} + \frac{(26-28)^2}{28} + \frac{(39-42)^2}{42} + \frac{(31-28)^2}{28} + \frac{(5-7)^2}{7}$$
$$= 3.53$$

The number of degrees of freedom which correspond to this value of χ^2 and which are needed for the determination of the critical value of

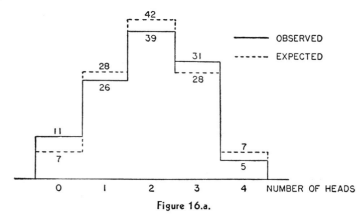

Figure 16.a.

$\chi^2_{.05}$ can be found immediately by use of the rule which we gave on page 309. The only quantity needed for the calculation of the expected frequencies, which was based on the observed data, was the total number of tosses, namely, 112. Since our distribution consists of 5 cells the number of degrees of freedom is $5 - 1 = 4$, and according to Table IV the critical value of χ^2 for a level of significance of .05 is 9.488. It follows that we are justified in saying that our experiment exhibited almost precisely what we should have expected. This result can also be interpreted as evidence for the hypothesis that our four coins were honest.

If it had been necessary to find from the observed data an additional quantity that is needed in the computation of the expected frequencies, we would have lost an additional degree of freedom. This would be the case, for example, in problems in which we do not assume a value for the probability p but in which p is determined on the basis of the observed distribution.

The same general technique could also be used to test, for instance, the goodness of the fit of a Poisson distribution. If we were given a formula which would enable us to calculate the expected Poisson frequencies, we could compare these expected frequencies with those which were observed (e.g., those representing the number of deaths resulting from the kick of a horse) on the basis of the chi-square criterion. The only difference would be that we might have a different number for the degrees of freedom, which must always be given by the number of classes (cells) minus the number of restrictions (conditions) which are imposed on the expected frequencies by the observed data.

EXERCISES

1. Test the goodness of the fit of the normal curve which was fitted to the data used in Exercise 10 on page 120. Use a level of significance of .05.

2. Test the goodness of the fit of the normal curve which was fitted to the distribution of the aptitude scores in Exercise 11, p. 120. Use a level of significance of .02.

3. Test the goodness of the fit of the normal curve which was fitted to the distribution of heads in 100 tosses of 10 coins in Exercise 12, p. 120. Use a level of significance of .05.

4. Use the following two sets of frequencies to test the goodness of the fit of the normal curve. Use a level of significance of .05.

Observed frequencies	Expected normal curve frequencies
19	17
107	104
211	208
135	143
28	27
2	1

5. Use the χ^2 criterion to test the closeness of the agreement between the observed and the expected frequencies of Exercise 5, p. 45. Use a level of significance of .05.

6. The following table contains the observed and the expected distribution of the number of heads obtained in 320 tosses of six coins. Test the goodness of the fit of these expected binomial frequencies at a level of significance of .01.

Number of heads	Observed frequencies	Expected frequencies
0	12	5
1	28	30
2	69	75
3	103	100
4	85	75
5	16	30
6	7	5

16.3 The Multinomial Case

The binomial distribution applies only to those problems in which the outcome of each trial must be one of two possible alternatives. It can be used, for instance, in problems in which we have heads or tails, rain or no rain, death or recovery, passing or failing, success or bankruptcy, etc.   It cannot be used, however, if the outcome of each trial permits a greater number of alternatives like, for example, the six faces of a die, the A, B, C, D, or F which a student can receive in a college course, and the many different types of weather which a meteorologist might predict.   All these illustrations belong to the so-called *multinomial case*.   Since the mathematical development of the multinomial problem is quite involved we shall limit our discussion to some of the most simple comparisons of observed and expected multinomial frequencies.

Let us suppose, for instance, that the president of a college sends a directive to his faculty instructing them to make their grades fit the following distribution:

Grade	Percentage
A	10
B	20
C	40
D	25
F	5

He understands, of course, that this exact distribution can be obtained only in the long run, but he is still curious to find out whether the grades which were given by his faculty in the subsequent semester compare even remotely with his suggested distribution.   The grades which the students actually received were:

Grade	Number of students
A	42
B	127
C	530
D	283
F	18
	1000

while those which the president of the college would have expected were 100 A's, 200 B's, 400 C's, 250 D's, and 50 F's.

In order to be able to judge the closeness of these two sets of frequencies let us again compute χ^2 by formula (16.1.1).   This gives us

$$\chi^2 = \frac{(42-100)^2}{100} + \frac{(127-200)^2}{200} + \frac{(530-400)^2}{400}$$
$$+ \frac{(283-250)^2}{250} + \frac{(18-50)^2}{50}$$
$$= 135.18$$

while the critical value of $\chi^2_{.05}$ for $5 - 1 = 4$ degrees of freedom is 9.488. Since the sample value of χ^2 is so much larger than this critical value, the president of the college would definitely be justified in appointing a committee to investigate the tremendous discrepancy between the two sets of grades.

Many important applications of the chi-square criterion which, in principle, are much like the previous illustration, can be found in biology, particularly in the field of genetics. The following data were taken from a classical experiment which was originally conducted by Mendel in his investigation of the crossbreeding of plants. Crossbreeding two kinds of plants, one of which had round yellow seeds while the other had wrinkled green seeds, Mendel obtained the following second generation of seeds:

Type of seed	Number
Round and yellow	315
Wrinkled and yellow	101
Round and green	108
Wrinkled and green	32
	556

According to his theory of the inheritance of characteristics, he expected that $\frac{9}{16}$ of the seeds would be round and yellow, $\frac{3}{16}$ would be wrinkled and yellow, $\frac{3}{16}$ would be round and green, and $\frac{1}{16}$ would be wrinkled and green. Multiplying these expected fractions by the total size of the sample, namely, by 556, we have the following *expected* frequencies:

Type of seed	Number
Round and yellow	313
Wrinkled and yellow	104
Round and green	104
Wrinkled and green	35
	556

If we calculate χ^2 on the basis of these observed and expected frequencies we will get the small value of .52. Since the only quantity required from the *observed data* for the calculation of the expected frequencies was the size of the sample, we have $4 - 1 = 3$ degrees of freedom. For a level of significance of .05 the critical value of χ^2 is 7.815, and we are therefore most certainly justified in saying that there exists a very close agreement between the observed and the expected frequencies. Thus the result of this experiment provides strong confirmative evidence for the Mendelian theory of the inheritance of characteristics.

Although it is impossible to devote more time and space to the many interesting and important applications of the chi-square criterion, the material we have discussed in this and the previous chapters should be sufficient to emphasize the fact that the chi-square criterion plays a vital role in many of the problems in which we want to compare experimental results with theoretical expectations. It provides us therefore with a method of confirming or disproving scientific theories on the basis of experimental or observed data.

REFERENCES

F. E. Croxton and D. J. Cowden, *Applied General Statistics*, Prentice-Hall, New York, 1946, Chap. 11.

W. J. Dixon and F. J. Massey, *Introduction to Statistical Analysis*, McGraw-Hill, New York, 1951, Chap. 13.

R. A. Fisher, *Statistical Methods for Research Workers*, Hafner, New York, 1948, Chap. 4.

M. J. Hagood, *Statistics for Sociologists*, Holt, New York, 1941, Chap. 19.

P. G. Hoel, *Introduction to Mathematical Statistics*, Wiley, New York, 1947, Chap. 10.

A. E. Waugh, *Elements of Statistical Method*, McGraw-Hill, New York, 1943, Chap. 8.

EXERCISES

1. If 300 rolls of a die have produced 34 ones, 58 twos, 61 threes, 42 fours, 77 fives, and 28 sixes, test the hypothesis that this die is balanced, at the level of significance of .05.

2. If we plant an equal number of pure red and pure white plants we can expect the next generation to be 75 per cent red and 25 per cent white, since red is a dominating characteristic. Use the χ^2 criterion to decide whether the results differ significantly from these theoretical considerations if under the stated conditions we obtained 359 red plants and 137 white ones.

3. If 100 random drawings from a deck of cards produced 28 hearts, 19 clubs, 31 diamonds, and 22 spades, would you consider these results unusual?

4. If a public opinion poll claims that 60 per cent of the voters favor candidate A, 30 per cent favor candidate B, and 10 per cent favor candidate C, test the hypothesis that this claim is reasonable if an independent survey produced the following results:

For candidate A	427
B	114
C	59

Use a level of significance of .05.

5. A manufacturer of automobile tires claims that 98 per cent of his products are perfect. If a sample of his tires contains 481 good ones and 19 bad ones, use the χ^2 criterion and a level of significance of .02 to test whether his claim is valid.

6. In a biological experiment dealing with flowers a certain investigator obtained the following results:

Characteristic	Observed frequency	Expected frequency
AB	164	180
Ab	78	60
aB	65	60
ab	13	20

Compare these two sets of frequencies.

17. MULTIPLE, PARTIAL, AND NONLINEAR CORRELATION

17.1 Multiple Correlation

The study of multiple and partial correlation is generally omitted in an introductory course of statistics because there is really enough material to be covered without these more advanced topics. Nevertheless, the fundamental ideas of multiple and partial correlation are not difficult to understand once the reader has grasped the meaning of an ordinary coefficient of correlation. Consequently, the first half of this chapter is devoted to a brief and nontechnical introduction to this subject because (1) the reader should at least know what these terms mean, and (2) because it should broaden his understanding of the subject of correlation in general.

The coefficient of correlation was defined in Chapter 14 as a measure of the goodness of predictions which were based on an equation of the form

$$y' = mx + b$$

in which m and b were numbers which were evaluated on the basis of a set of observed data by use of the *method of least squares*. We observed at that time that y could be predicted accurately on the basis of information concerning the variable x *if and only if* the points of the scattergram fitted closely to a straight line, i.e., if there existed a strong linear relationship between x and y.

It is true that it is often possible to predict a variable y, whatever it might be, on the basis of *one* other variable alone, but in the vast majority of the problems which a scientist can expect to meet it will be necessary to consider *more than one* variable in order to make sufficiently accurate predictions.   If we want to predict, for example, how long it will be before a bridge collapses, we must know the material it is made of, the length of its beams, their cross sections, the number of supports, etc.   Similarly, if we want to predict the grade which a certain student can be expected to score in a given test it would help to know his age, his I.Q., his high school record, and possibly also the state of his health and other relevant factors.   Most predictions can be improved considerably by inclusion of additional factors, although we can usually expect to reach a saturation point after which the addition of further information will no longer increase the accuracy of our predictions appreciably.

The mathematical relationships which we may come across if we consider more than two variables can be extremely complex, and in order to make predictions which consider several variables at all possible it is customary to use a formula like

$$x_1 = ax_2 + bx_3 + cx_4 + \ldots \tag{17.1.1}$$

which provides often a fair approximation to the actual relationship. It is indeed fortunate that many sets of variables actually do satisfy *linear relationships*, i.e., equations like the one given in (17.1.1).

Formula (17.1.1) is a *linear equation* which expresses the variable which we want to predict, namely, x_1, in terms of all the other variables.   It is advisable to use subscripts to differentiate between the variables rather than call them x, y, z, . . . , because we may not only have to consider a great number of variables, but because this symbolism will also lend itself to a much more uniform treatment in the development of the necessary formulas for multiple and partial correlation.

The ordinary coefficient of correlation was introduced in Chapter 14 by means of a comparison of the errors of the two methods of prediction which were based on the regression line and the mean of the y's, respectively.   Proceeding now in identical fashion, we can define the *coefficient of multiple correlation* by comparing the predictions of x_1 which are based on a formula like (17.1.1) with the predictions of x_1 which are based on the mean $\bar{x}_1$ alone.

To illustrate the meaning of such a coefficient of multiple correlation, let us consider the most elementary case, namely, prediction of a variable x_1 on the basis of two other variables x_2 and x_3.   Among the many problems which are exactly of this type we may find, for example, the problem of predicting (estimating) a person's weight on the basis of his age and height; the problem of predicting a college index on the basis of a student's high school record and I.Q.; or the problem of predicting the expected yield of corn on the basis of the total rainfall and the amount of fertilizer which was applied to the soil. Taking the first of these illustrations, let us suppose that the following measurements represent the weight, age, and height, of 10 individuals who were chosen at random among the inhabitants of a certain town:

Weight x_1 (pounds)	Age x_2 (years)	Height x_3 (inches)
129	27	62
172	35	70
151	18	68
138	36	64
212	49	72
173	52	69
154	43	66
191	22	74
147	19	70
196	51	71

To get a rough idea of the relationship between these three variables we might, as before, try to plot a scattergram. However, it will immediately become apparent that this is not as easy as it may sound because we are now dealing with more than two variables, three to be exact, and the resulting scattergram must be a three-dimensional figure. An illustration of the corresponding three-dimensional scattergram, one dimension representing each of the three variables, is shown in the projective diagram of Fig. 17.a.

In the two-dimensional case we proceeded to fit a straight line using the method of least squares, but now we find that the graph (geometrical configuration) which corresponds to equation (17.1.1) is a *plane* and not a straight line. In spite of this complication we can still carry through the analogy and fit a plane (see Fig. 17.a) which will provide us with the best fit to the given data, the word *best* meaning in this case that the plane and its corresponding equation will give us the most accurate predictions in the sense of *least squares*.

The goodness of the fit of such a plane, which is appropriately called a *regression plane*, is measured by the magnitude of the deviations from this plane in the x_1 direction, just as we previously measured the goodness of the fit of a regression line by the size of the vertical deviations. If all points are such that they lie fairly close to a plane

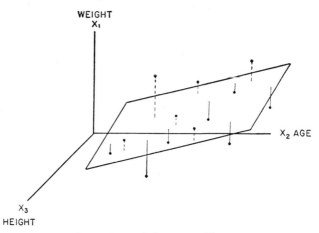

Figure 17.a. A Regression Plane.

we will have a good fit, and we will subsequently be able to say that there exists a strong multiple correlation among the three variables. If, on the other hand, the points which represent our data are widely scattered, the plane will not give us a good fit, and the correlation among the three variables is said to be weak.

To measure the actual strength of such a multiple relationship *we must compare, as before, the error variance of the predictions which are based on the regression plane with the error variance of the predictions which are based on the mean $\bar{x}_1$ alone.* The error variance of this first method of prediction can be written as $s_e'^2$, and it is equal to the average of the squared deviations of Fig. 17.a. The error variance of the second method of prediction is again only the standard deviation of the x_1 values which will be written as s_1^2. Analogous to the definition of r which was given on page 263 by means of formula (14.1.3) we can now define the *coefficient of multiple correlation* as

$$r_{1.23} = \sqrt{1 - \frac{s_e'^2}{s_1^2}} \qquad (17.1.2)$$

in which we have used the symbol $r_{1.23}$ to make it clear that we are predicting the variable x_1 in terms of the two variables x_2 and x_3. Since this definition is in principle identical with that of formula (14.1.3), the coefficient of multiple correlation can be understood and interpreted in a manner analogous to the ordinary coefficient of correlation.

We have given formula (17.1.2) only to *define* the multiple correlation coefficient, and even if we were to calculate this coefficient for the data which were given on page 319, we would not use this formula because, as in the case of r, there exist alternative (equivalent) formulas which lead to a much more rapid evaluation of the multiple correlation coefficient. We shall not calculate $r_{1.23}$ at this time, however, since it has been our purpose only to introduce the reader to the fundamental ideas of multiple correlation and not to make this subject a formal part of our introductory study of statistics.

It is customary to use the symbol $r_{1.23}$ to denote the multiple correlation coefficient which was defined in (17.1.2) because there really exist several coefficients of multiple correlation in the case of three or more variables *depending on which of the variables we want to predict in terms of the others*. Had we wanted to predict the variable x_2 in terms of x_1 and x_3, for example, we could have defined a similar coefficient of multiple correlation $r_{2.13}$, which would have told us how well we can predict the variable x_2 by means of an equation of the type

$$x_2 = ax_1 + bx_3 + c$$

The numerical constants a, b, and c must be determined, like the m and b in the ordinary case, by means of equations which are based on the method of least squares.

It must be understood, of course, that $r_{1.23}$ as well as all other multiple correlation coefficients which are based on methods of prediction using a formula like (17.1.1) are measures of *linear relationships* only, and that there could therefore exist a strong nonlinear correlation in spite of the fact that $r_{1.23}$ might be equal to 0. (The problem of nonlinear multiple correlation is so complicated that it is seldom discussed even in more advanced texts.)

We found no particular obstacles in trying to demonstrate the analogy between multiple and ordinary linear correlation. Our task would have been more difficult if we had considered the general case in which we base our predictions on the values of k other variables. In that case we would have had to plot our data (points) in a $k + 1$ dimensional scattergram, fitting a k-dimensional (hyper) plane using the method of least squares. Unfortunately, these geometrical concepts are beyond the human scope of visualization, and we must be satisfied with pointing out that even in the more general case *the basic ideas and methods are still the same*.

17.2 Partial Correlation

We showed in our brief comments on *correlation and causation* in Section 14.8 that a high correlation between two variables x and y does not necessarily imply that one can be considered the *cause* of the other. As we pointed out, it can happen quite often that a high correlation between two variables can be ascribed almost completely to their relationships with a third variable which is, so to speak, their *common cause*.

A simple illustration which demonstrates how a third variable can play havoc with the value which we might obtain for an ordinary r is given by the following example in which

> $x_1 =$ the total amount of hot chocolate which is sold
>   at a summer resort per season;
>
> $x_2 =$ the number of tourists who visit the resort;
>
> $x_3 =$ the average temperature for the tourist season.

In order to avoid ambiguities concerning the variables, we must write the ordinary coefficient of correlation between the variables x_1 and x_2 as r_{12} and define r_{13} and r_{23} in similar fashion. Let us now suppose that a given set of data pertaining to the values of these three variables for several years has produced the results: $r_{12} = -.30$; $r_{13} = -.70$; $r_{23} = .80$. The second of these three coefficients of correlation, namely, r_{13}, seems to agree with what we should have expected, since most people do not drink much hot chocolate in hot weather. Consequently, since small values of x_1 go with high values of x_3, and large values of x_1 go with low values of x_3, there should be a fairly strong negative correlation. The third coefficient of correlation, i.e., r_{23}, also agrees with what we might have expected, since more tourists are likely to visit this resort in warm weather, and a high positive value of r would thus fit the situation.

However, the first of these three coefficients of correlation seems to be quite unreasonable, since a negative value of r, in this case $-.30$, implies that if there are many tourists they actually drink a correspondingly smaller amount of hot chocolate.

A careful analysis of this situation reveals that (1) if the temperature is high there will be a great number of tourists, and (2) if the temperature is high much less hot chocolate will be consumed. The negative correlation between x_1 and x_2 must therefore be due entirely to the dependence of both of these variables on the temperature x_3.

In order to study the actual effect that the number of the tourists might have on the sales of hot chocolate, *we must investigate their relationship under the condition that all other factors, primarily the temperature, are being held constant.* The strength of the relationship between two variables, when one or more other variables are assumed to be held fixed, is precisely what we are asked to express or measure in problems of *partial correlation.*

Since it is seldom possible (we have seldom sufficient data) to make a separate study of the relationship of two variables when all other (relevant) factors are fixed, it has been found that the statistic which is called the *coefficient of partial correlation* does a fair job of eliminating the disturbing effects of other variables. This coefficient of partial correlation which, in our example, should measure the strength of the correlation between x_1 and x_2 while x_3 is being held fixed is written as $r_{12.3}$, and it is defined by the formula

$$r_{12.3} = \frac{r_{12} - (r_{13})(r_{23})}{\sqrt{(1 - r_{13}^2)(1 - r_{23}^2)}} \qquad (17.2.1)*$$

This formula can easily be generalized to take care also of the case where more than one variable is being held fixed. (The derivation of this formula and similar formulas for the more general case will not be discussed in this chapter. They can be found in all texts which treat the subject of correlation on a more advanced level.)

We can now study the actual relationship between the number of tourists and the sales of hot chocolate, regardless of the weather, i.e., the temperature, by substituting the ordinary coefficients of correlation which were given on page 322 into formula (17.2.1). This gives us

$$r_{12.3} = \frac{(-.30) - (-.70)(.80)}{\sqrt{[1 - (-.70)^2][1 - (.80)^2]}} = .62$$

and it demonstrates what we should have expected, namely, that there exists a *positive* correlation between the number of tourists and the sales of hot chocolate. The negative value of r_{12} was therefore due entirely to the third variable, which in this case was the temperature.

Formula (17.2.1) provides a measure of the strength of the correlation between the variables x_1 and x_2 while the variable x_3 is being held fixed. Had we wanted to study the relationship between x_1 and x_3, for instance, holding x_2 fixed, we could have obtained a formula for $r_{13.2}$, the corresponding coefficient of partial correlation, simply by interchanging the subscripts 2 and 3 wherever they occur in formula (17.2.1).

The above illustration has been given primarily as a brief introduction to the problem of partial correlation. At the same time it has also served the purpose of emphasizing again the fact that an ordinary coefficient of correlation can lead to extremely misleading conclusions unless it is interpreted carefully. A large value of r *can* imply that one variable is the cause of the other, but it *can also* imply that both variables are the effects of a common cause.

17.3 Nonlinear Correlation

We cannot repeat often enough that all different measures of correlation which we have so far discussed (save those of Chapter 15) are measures of *linear relationships* and nothing more. The fundamental ideas which underlay the techniques of evaluating or describing the strength of *nonlinear* or *curvilinear* relationships are actually not much different from those which we used in our definition of r, although the resulting formulas and calculations are of a slightly different and much more complicated form. As a matter of fact, the mathematical manipulations which are involved in problems of nonlinear correlation are so cumbersome that this subject is hardly ever covered in an introductory course.

The ordinary coefficient of correlation was originally defined in Chapter 14 in terms of the error variances of the two methods of prediction which were

$$\text{Method A} \quad y' = mx + b$$
$$\text{Method B} \quad y' = \bar{y}$$

and its formula was given as

$$r = \pm \sqrt{1 - \frac{s_e^2}{s_y^2}}$$

where s_e^2 is, as always, the average of the squared deviations from the regression line, which are again illustrated in Fig. 17.b, while s_y^2 is the average of the squared deviations from the mean $\bar{y}$ (shown in Fig. 17.c) or simply the standard deviation of the y's.

If the relationship between x and y is *not linear*, we could repeat the identical argument which we used above with the only exception that the regression line would now be replaced by some other mathematical curve (see Fig. 17.d). Comparing the predictions which

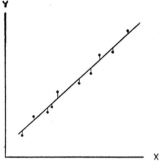

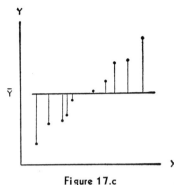

Figure 17.b.   Figure 17.c

could have been based on this curve with the corresponding predictions which are based on $\bar{y}$ alone (see Fig. 17.e), *we can now define a measure of the goodness of the fit of this curve, i.e., a measure of the strength of this curvilinear correlation by means of the formula*

$$\text{Index of correlation} = \sqrt{1 - \frac{s_e^2}{s_y^2}} \qquad (17.3.1)$$

which gives us the so-called *index of correlation*. It should be noted that in this formula s_e^2 must be interpreted as *the error variance about the regression curve*, provided that the equation of the curve was again determined by use of the method of least squares. This error variance s_e^2 measures the magnitude of the deviations of Fig. 17.d, while s_y^2 is given by the corresponding deviations of Fig. 17.e.

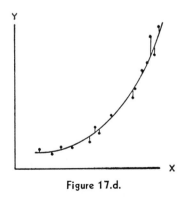

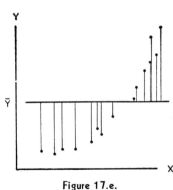

Figure 17.d.   Figure 17.e.

Theoretically speaking, it was not difficult to generalize the ideas of linear correlation to handle also problems of nonlinear correlation, but as we have said before, the mathematical detail is likely to become involved. We would not only have to decide first what type of curve to fit to our data, but we would also have to calculate the equation of this curve, using the method of least squares, compute the predicted values of y for the various values of x, determine s_e^2 on the basis of the errors of these predictions, and finally substitute our results into formula (17.3.1). Although there do exist methods which will reduce this work to some extent we shall not discuss them, since we had hoped to show only that the basic principles of nonlinear correlation are practically identical with those which we used in Chapter 14 for the definition of r. This is brought out clearly by the fact that formula (17.3.1) is identical in form with formula (14.1.3).

17.4 The Correlation Ratio

One of the most difficult questions with which we are faced in problems of nonlinear correlation is the selection of the type of the mathematical curve which is supposed to express the relationship between our two variables. Sometimes this choice is dictated by theoretical reasons, but most frequently it is simply left to our personal judgment. One way to avoid this difficulty altogether is to use a so-called *curve of means* and the correspondingly defined *correlation ratio* which we shall discuss in this section. Let us suppose that the points of the scattergram of Fig. 17.f represent measurements of the

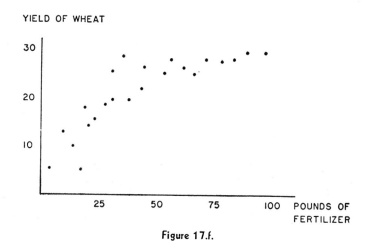

Figure 17.f.

yield of wheat and the amount of fertilizer which is applied per acre. Instead of approximating these points by means of some complicated curve we shall divide the figure more or less arbitrarily into a number of columns, compute the mean of the y's (the yield of wheat), *separately for the points of each of the columns*, and construct in this fashion the *step function*, called a *curve of means*, which is shown by the solid lines of Fig. 17.g. In this figure $\bar{y}_1$ is the mean of the y's of the first column,

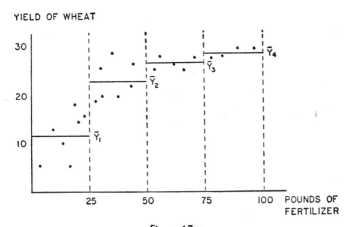

Figure 17.g.

i.e., the average yield of wheat for those samples in which the amount of fertilizer was from 0 to 25 pounds per acre; $\bar{y}_2$ is the mean of the y's corresponding to the points of the second column, etc.

The method of prediction on the basis of which we shall now predict the expected yield of wheat consists of predicting for a known amount of fertilizer the $\bar{y}$ of the corresponding column. If we know, for example, that 90 pounds of fertilizer are applied per acre, the predicted yield of wheat is given by the $\bar{y}$ of the fourth column, which, judging from Fig. 17.g, is about 28 bushels per acre.

The mathematical curve which we are here using for our predictions is the *curve of means*, which consists of the horizontal lines of Fig. 17.g. The advantage of this curve of means rests in the fact that we need not specify a definite mathematical equation for the curve which we fit to our data and that, as we shall see, we will now be able to define a useful measure of the strength of the curvilinear correlation, which is much easier to handle than the one which was defined in (17.3.1). It should be noted that the choice of the dividing lines between the columns of Fig. 17.g is essentially arbitrary, but the columns are usually chosen in such a manner that they will bring out the relationship between the two variables x and y.

In place of the error variance about the regression line or regression curve, we can now speak of the *error variance about the curve of means*, which, as always, measures the accuracy of the predictions which are based on this curve. This error variance is given by the average of the squared deviations of Fig. 17.h. Writing the error variance

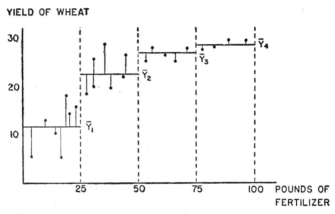

Figure 17.h.

about the curve of means as S_e^2, we can define (analogous to the ordinary coefficient of correlation) the *correlation ratio* η (*eta*) as

$$\eta = \sqrt{1 - \frac{S_e^2}{s_y^2}} \qquad (17.4.1)^*$$

where s_y^2 is, as always, the standard deviation of all of the y's.

The correlation ratio, which is not difficult to compute, provides us with a valuable measure of the strength of a nonlinear correlation. It also plays an important role in the test of the hypothesis that the relationship between two variables is really linear. In that case we first calculate both r and η and then decide on the basis of their respective values whether it is reasonable to treat our variables as if they were linearly related. If the difference between r and η is small, this is understood to imply that it is quite reasonable to treat the relationship as if it were linear. If their difference is large, however, we must reject the null hypothesis that the relationship is linear, and we will consequently not be justified in using linear correlation techniques in the discussion of the two variables.

It is easy to see how important this criterion is, because the ordinary coefficient of (linear) correlation is all too often used in examples in which the correlation is definitely *not* linear and in which a calculated value of r can be extremely misleading.

REFERENCES

M. M. Blair, *Elementary Statistics*, Holt, New York, 1944, Chaps. 23, 24.

J. P. Guilford, *Fundamental Statistics in Psychology and Education*, McGraw-Hill, New York, 1950, Chap. 16.

P. G. Hoel, *Introduction to Mathematical Statistics*, Wiley, New York, 1947, Chap. 7.

C. H. Richardson, *An Introduction to Statistical Analysis*, Harcourt Brace, New York, 1934, Chap. 9.

G. W. Snedecor, *Statistical Methods*, The Iowa State College Press, Ames, 1937, Chap. 13.

PART FOUR:

SPECIAL TOPICS

18. FURTHER DESCRIPTIONS
AND INDEX NUMBERS

18.1 Further Descriptive Measures

The major part of this book has been devoted to problems of inductive statistics including those of estimation, prediction, and the testing of simple hypotheses. The reason for this emphasis on inductive methods is *not* that we consider it unimportant for the beginning student to learn how to describe numerical data, but because we think that he will benefit more in a first course by learning the meaning of statistical methods and by achieving an understanding of the role which these methods play in everyday life as well as in modern science.

Since the calculation of a mean, the drawing of a histogram, and even the computation of a coefficient of correlation could reasonably be performed by a high school student who has attained a fair skill in arithmetic, we have spent most of our time studying, instead, the concepts and ideas which are essential for a meaningful analysis and intelligent interpretation of the results of statistical investigations. This has made it necessary to omit certain subjects which are ordinarily covered in an introductory course, and to compensate for this shortcoming we shall now devote the next two chapters to material which actually belongs to the domain of descriptive statistics and which is of interest particularly to students of business and economics.

The descriptive measures which we have discussed in Part One of this book were limited mainly to descriptions of the most characteristic features of frequency distributions or sets of ungrouped data. It is easy to point to examples in which we are forced to describe features of sets of measurements or observations which are quite different from the ones which we have so far discussed in our work. Indeed, it happens quite often that particular problems require statistical methods which must be developed especially to fit the features of the data which we want to describe.

One of the most fundamental tasks of a scientist is to describe what he observes and to describe it in such a manner that he will be able to bring out whatever relevant information can possibly be obtained from his observations or measurements. If a scientist wants to distinguish, for example, between a parrot and a stork, it would certainly not be appropriate for him to describe them both simply as birds; similarly, if he wants to distinguish between iron and gold, he might refer to their molecular weights, but he would not get anywhere by describing them both as metals. Whatever distinction he will be able to discover depends mainly on the particular features which he chooses to describe, and it is therefore of great importance to him to be able to describe whatever features are the most relevant for any given problem. As we have said before, this may frequently require the development of new formulas, new descriptive statistics. Actually there is no limit to the many different ways in which sets of numerical data can be described.

To illustrate such a situation, let us consider a relatively important problem in which our so-called standard statistical procedures do not supply an appropriate description. Let us suppose that in a psychological experiment a number of rats are put into a maze and that they have the choice of three different paths which may or may not lead them to the food which they are seeking. The three paths are labeled A, B, and C, and the piece of cheese or whatever reward is awaiting the correct choice of the path can be reached only through path B. Let us now put 100 rats through this maze, record the paths which they select, and let us assume that this first run of the experiment has produced the following results:

35 rats chose path A
32 rats chose path B
33 rats chose path C

After the rats have been given some time to acquaint themselves with the pattern of the maze, they are again put through the same experiment and the results of the second run are:

10 rats chose path A
79 rats chose path B
11 rats chose path C

This can be interpreted as positive proof of the fact that the rats have *learned* how to reach their goal in the maze.

Since some kinds of animals can obviously be expected to learn faster than others, it seems desirable from the point of view of the psychologist to devise a statistical measure which might express the degree to which the behavior of the animals has changed after they have been put through the maze a certain number of times.

What can he do? He cannot compute a mean, median, standard deviation, etc., since he is dealing with a categorical rather than with a numerical grouping. It would not help him much to compute a coefficient of correlation, a chi-square, or any of the other descriptive measures which we have discussed, and he would, consequently, be forced to *invent* some new descriptive measure which will display the information that he is trying to express.

The solution that we shall suggest to this psychologist is merely one of many possible statistical measures which he might conceivably use. Whether it is a particularly good way to describe the results of the previous experiment is something which we shall not discuss at this time, being satisfied that we have at least given one possible answer to his problem.

Our method of describing the process of learning which is being studied in this experiment consists, first of all, of arranging the three alternative paths according to the frequencies with which they were chosen by the rats. This gives us for the first run of our experiment the distribution of Fig. 18.a, and for the second run the distribution of Fig. 18.b. If we now *arbitrarily* denote the path which was chosen

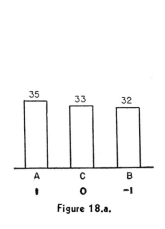

Figure 18.a.

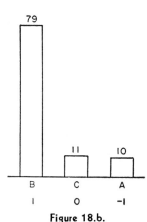

Figure 18.b.

with the highest frequency with the number 1, the path which has the next highest frequency with the number 0, and the one which has the lowest frequency with the number -1, we can treat the distributions of Figs. 18.a and 18.b as if they were ordinary frequency distributions. Once we have gone this far there is no reason why we cannot compute, for instance, the mean of each distribution and denote it with the letter W (one of the few letters of the alphabet which we have not used so far).

Calculating the means W for the two distributions which represent the two runs of our experiment, we obtain in the first case

$$W = \frac{35(1) + 33(0) + 32(-1)}{100} = .03$$

and in the second case

$$W = \frac{79(1) + 11(0) + 10(-1)}{100} = .69$$

These results must be interpreted as follows. If the behavior of the rats is more or less random, i.e., if they have not learned the path which will lead them to the piece of cheese, *the value of W should be close to or equal to 0.* On the other hand, the better the rats have learned which path will actually lead them to the cheese, *the closer will the resulting value of W be to the number 1.* We have therefore constructed a descriptive measure which enables us to evaluate the degree to which the learning process has advanced during the course of the experiment.

Let us repeat that we have not given this illustration to add one more method to the long list to which the beginner has already been introduced. No, we have given it *only* to show that there exist problems in which our standard procedures do not help and in which we therefore must use our ingenuity to invent suitable descriptions of the phenomena which we want to investigate. There are many different ways in which we could have described the change in the behavior of the rats. As a matter of fact, it is quite likely that there exist methods which are much more desirable than the one which we have invented in this section. *All this does not matter, however, since it has been our purpose only to show how statistical methods can be developed more or less arbitrarily to suit any given problem and to fit any feature of a set of numerical data which we may want to describe.*

18.2 Graphical Presentations

There are some features of numerical data which can be described by means of simple and elementary formulas, but there are others which require elaborate and complicated techniques. For many of the latter it is safest, perhaps, to let the data speak for themselves, leaving them in a tabular form or improving their appeal with the aid of graphical or pictorial presentations.

There exist many ways in which we can emphasize information which would otherwise be hidden in a mass of numerical data by using *pictographs, pie charts, bar charts,* and other pictorial devices which should be familiar to everyone through the daily newspapers, advertising in popular magazines, textbooks, and financial and other reports.

All these graphical presentations are aimed to serve the purpose of attracting the layman's attention to otherwise relatively dull facts and unattractive statistical information. Although it is true that pictographs are often shunned in scholarly expositions like theses, they play an ever-increasing role in advertising and other media which have the primary function of presenting statistical facts in a dramatic fashion to the general public.

18.3 Index Numbers

Some of the most widely used and the most easily understood statistical descriptions are those which tell us how large one quantity is as compared to another. If Joe Smith earned $3,000 in 1948 and is making $4,500 in 1951, then his income is now (in 1951) 150 per cent of what it was in 1948; if the population of Egypt has increased from 16 million in 1937 to 19.5 million in 1948, it has increased during this period of time by 22 per cent; and if the total production of corn has changed from 108 million metric tons in 1930 to 139 million metric tons in 1949, this marks an increase of 29 per cent, or better, the 1949 total is 129 per cent of the production of corn in 1930.

In each of these three illustrations we have limited our comparison to two numbers, and we have simply expressed the relative changes by giving one of the two numbers as a percentage of the other. Such percentages or percentage changes are the most elementary members of a large group of statistics, called *index numbers*, which serve the express purpose of comparing two numbers, or in general, two sets of numerical data. They are the most elementary kinds of index numbers because a statistical measure which is used to express *relative changes* can be anything from a simple ratio to one of the elaborate formulas which we shall meet later on in this chapter.

It is true that index numbers are generally associated with the study of economic data, business conditions, etc., but there is no reason why they cannot be used also to make comparisons in other branches of the social and the natural sciences. However, since most index numbers that are used in fields other than business and economics are only ordinary ratios about which there is relatively little to be said, we shall concern ourselves primarily with index numbers referring to changes in prices, production, unemployment, import-export, etc.

Index numbers that are used to describe relative changes of economic phenomena are usually more complex inasmuch as they must refer to the relative changes which have taken place *at the same time* in a number of different commodities. If we hear someone mention the increasing (or decreasing) index of the cost of living, for example, we know that he is referring to the relative changes which have taken place in a combination of the various items which make up the average budget. Similarly, if someone complains about the declining purchasing power of the dollar, we know that he is talking about a mythical drop of the value of the dollar, which is really nothing but a reflection of the increases of the prices of certain commodities which were selected as the most representative for this particular purpose.

All index numbers are, by definition, measures of relative changes, and they must therefore be given relative to some arbitrarily chosen standard. If somebody were to tell us, for example, that Norway's cost of living index for 1949 was 164 per cent, this would mean absolutely nothing unless we were also told that this index compares the 1949 figures with those of 1937. Had we, instead, wanted to compare them with those of 1945, a brief check in the *Statistical Yearbook* of the United Nations would have revealed that the 1949 index would have been 102.5, indicating thus an increase of only 2.5 per cent as compared with the 64 per cent which we had before. This shows very clearly that an index number is meaningful only if we specify a standard of comparison, i.e., a year (or period) which is to be used as the basis of the comparison and which is consequently called the *base year* (or *base period*). We shall not go into the difficult problem of selecting suitable base years or base periods at this time because this is really a problem of economics rather than a problem of mathematics or

statistics. It is important to note, however, that the basis selected
for most business indexes is usually a period of economic stability, and
often an *average* taken over a considerable period of time. It is
evident that the choice of the base year or period must, of course,
depend on whatever we are trying to show and whatever we might
intend to do with an index once it has been constructed. Had we
wanted to compare, for instance, the 1951 production figures of the
United States with those of World War II, the choice of our base
period would be one of the years from 1941 to 1945 or better, perhaps,
an average covering these five war years.

An index number need not necessarily compare quantities referring
to two different periods of time. Had we wanted to study, for
example, the 1948 hourly wages paid in the manufacturing industries
of Australia and Great Britain, we would have found that the two
respective figures were 44.5 and 34.9 pence per hour. Dividing these
two numbers we can show that the index comparing the wages paid
in that year in Australia with those paid in Great Britain is 44.5/34.9
= 127.5. This provides us with a *geographical comparison* instead
of the usual comparison pertaining to two different periods of time.
Since there is, fundamentally speaking, not much difference between
these various kinds of indexes, we shall save time by limiting our
discussion to those index numbers which express changes which have
taken place (or will take place) with respect to time.

Once we have chosen the base year (or period) on which an index
is to be based, our next task is to decide which commodities or which
quantities are to be included in the comparison. It is evident that
if we want to construct, for example, an index of the cost of living, it
would be virtually impossible to include every item from toothpicks
to shoelaces which might conceivably appear in some person's budget.
This means that we must select a limited number of items which will
cover the over-all picture and which will include a sufficiently wide
and representative selection of the most important items that make
up the average person's cost of living.

If the choice of the base year and the selection of the items which
are to be considered in an index were the only problems which we
might have to face, our task would be easy, and a satisfactory index
could easily be defined by means of any one of the formulas which are
given in Section 18.4. Unfortunately, the real difficulties start once
we realize that we cannot simply add or average the various prices or
other quantities and that we shall have to *weight* them in some fashion

to account for the different roles which they play in the total phenomenon that the index is supposed to describe. This is essentially the same problem which we first met when we discussed the *weighted mean* in Chapter 4.

The weights which are assigned to the various items (commodities) are measures of their *relative importance* and they must therefore be chosen with great care to avoid misleading and biased results. Whenever we compare prices, i.e., whenever we try to construct a *price index*, the most suitable weights are the *quantities or amounts* which are either produced, manufactured, or sold of the items which are included in the index.

Since most of the important index numbers refer to prices, we shall limit our work to this kind of index and we shall consider as weights only the corresponding *quantities*. We shall therefore denote the weights with the letter q in order to distinguish them from the corresponding prices, which will be given by the letter p. Since we will have to refer to prices and quantities which belong to different years or, in general, to different periods of time, we shall write the prices and quantities of the base year as p_0 and q_0 and the prices and quantities of the given year (the year which we want to compare) as p_n and q_n. This symbolism could be improved further with the use of subscripts or primes which distinguish between the various items to which the p's and q's refer.

18.4 Unweighted Index Numbers

In order to illustrate one of the most straightforward examples of an index number which combines several commodities, let us suppose that we want to compare the 1947 prices of certain kinds of meat with their corresponding prices in 1940 and that we are given the following information:

	1940	1947
Round steak	36.4	75.6
Pork chops	27.9	72.1
Sliced bacon	27.3	77.7

all prices being given in cents per pound.

One possible way of comparing these meat prices is to construct a so-called *simple aggregate index*, which is defined by the formula

$$I = \frac{\Sigma p_n}{\Sigma p_0} \qquad (18.4.1)^*$$

and which is obtained by simply dividing the sum of all 1947 prices by the sum of their corresponding values in 1940. Substituting the given information into formula (18.4.1) we have

$$I = \frac{75.6 + 72.1 + 77.7}{36.4 + 27.9 + 27.3} = \frac{225.4}{91.6} = 2.46$$

which is usually written without the decimal point as 246, and which tells us that the combined 1947 prices are 246 per cent of what they were in 1940.

An alternative method of comparing these two sets of prices would be to calculate first a separate index (ratio) for *each* of the three kinds of meat and then to average the ratios p_n/p_0, which are also called the *price relatives*, by means of any one of the measures of central tendencies which we have studied in Chapter 4. If we calculate the separate ratios (price relatives) for our data, we obtain

Price relatives

	Price relatives
Round steak	$\dfrac{75.6}{36.4} = 208$
Pork chops	$\dfrac{72.1}{27.9} = 258$
Sliced bacon	$\dfrac{77.7}{27.3} = 285$

and in order to construct an over-all index we must now combine these three numbers by finding their mean, median, or some other average. If we decide to use the mean of these price relatives, we will have defined the index number which is called, appropriately, the *simple mean of the price relatives*, and which can be written symbolically

$$I = \frac{\sum \dfrac{p_n}{p_0}}{k} \qquad (18.4.2)^*$$

where k is the number of the commodities which are included in our calculations.

In our illustration, dealing with the three kinds of meat, this formula would give us

$$I = \frac{208 + 258 + 285}{3} = 250$$

which is close but not equal to the result that we previously obtained with the first index. Instead of the ordinary mean (the arithmetic mean) we could also have found the *median of the price relatives* which in this case would have been 258, or the *geometric mean of the price relatives*, which would have been

$$\sqrt[3]{(208)(258)(285)} = 248$$

This last index is defined as kth root of the product of the k price relatives p_n/p_0, and in this example it is given by the cube root of the product of 208, 258, and 285.

A discussion of the relative merits of the various index numbers which we have so far studied in this section would be practically identical with our earlier study of the advantages and disadvantages of the different measures of central tendencies in Chapter 4. We might add, perhaps, that the geometric mean is usually considered the most desirable statistic for averaging ratios, but that it is also very laborious to compute and difficult to explain to the average layman.

Plainly, the index numbers which we have mentioned in this section are really of little value in most practical situations because it is seldom that we can average prices or price relatives without paying any attention to the relative importance which is played by each individual item. This shortcoming will be corrected in the more complicated types of index numbers which we shall treat in the following section.

EXERCISES

1. The following are the average prices received by farmers in the United States in dollars per 100 pounds:

	1930	1935	1940	1945
Hogs	8.84	7.05	5.17	13.80
Cattle (beef)	9.07	5.17	7.19	11.00
Sheep	6.75	3.35	3.95	6.18
Lambs	11.10	6.77	7.79	12.90

Use this information to calculate (a) the simple aggregate index of the 1945 prices relative to those of 1935; (b) the simple aggregate index of the 1945 prices relative to those of 1930; (c) the mean of the relatives comparing the 1945 prices with those of 1935; (d) the mean of the relatives comparing the 1945 prices with those of 1930; (e) use formulas (18.4.1) and (18.4.2) to construct the corresponding index numbers, comparing the 1940 prices with those of 1930.

2. Use formulas analogous to (18.4.1) and (18.4.2) to construct index numbers which compare the 1945 coal and coke production in the United States with that of 1935. (Values are given in millions of net tons.)

	1935	1940	1945
Bituminous	372	461	576
Pennsylvania anthracite	52	51	54
Coke	35	57	67

3. Use the information given in the previous exercise to construct a simple aggregate index comparing 1945 with 1940.

4. The following national incomes are given in millions of pesos:

	1944	1946	1948
Argentina	14.3	20.0	31.0
Mexico	13.4	19.2	12.7
Chile	37.0	48.9	76.0

Construct a simple aggregate index comparing the 1948 national incomes of these countries with those of 1944.

5. Use the data of the previous exercise to find the mean of the relatives comparing the 1946 national incomes with those of 1944.

18.5 Weighted Index Numbers

We shall illustrate the definition and the construction of index numbers which account for the difference in the importance of various commodities with the following study of the 1930 and 1947 prices of certain farm products:

	1930 Prices	1947 Prices
Oats	43.1	79.6
Barley	53.9	136.0
Rye	85.7	218.0
Buckwheat	97.3	141.0
Potatoes	137.8	128.0
Sweet potatoes	103.1	220.0

all prices being given in cents per bushel. A generalization of the *simple aggregate index* which was defined by formula (18.4.1) can easily be found by defining, analogous to (4.10.3), the *weighted aggregate index* as

$$I = \frac{\Sigma p_n w}{\Sigma p_0 w} \tag{18.5.1}$$

In this formula the weights w must be such that they express the relative importance of the roles which are played by the different farm products. As we have said before, the weights which are most commonly used in the construction of a price index are the corresponding *quantities* which are produced of each of the given commodities.

This leaves us the freedom of using either the quantities which correspond to the base year, which we shall write as q_0 ,or the quantities which correspond to the given year (the year which we want to compare), which will be written as q_n. Omitting for the time being other possibilities for the choice of the weights we can thus use either set of weights and define a *weighted aggregate index of the prices* as

$$I = \frac{\Sigma p_n q_0}{\Sigma p_0 q_0} \qquad (18.5.2)^*$$

or as

$$I = \frac{\Sigma p_n q_n}{\Sigma p_0 q_n} \qquad (18.5.3)^*$$

Since the selection of the weights is, fundamentally speaking, arbitrary, we must expect to get somewhat different results if we use different weights or different formula. The fact that index numbers which compare economic phenomena are *not unique* should not surprise us, however, because we have (as in the case of the mean, median, and mode) different descriptions of the same general situation, and there is no reason why such descriptions should necessarily all be the same.

If we want to use formula (18.5.2) or formula (18.5.3) to construct a weighted index of the farm commodities which we have studied before, we must know the *quantities* which are produced of each of the commodities in either 1930 or 1947. If the q_0's and q_n's are

	Quantity produced	
	1930	1947
Oats	1274	1215
Barley	302	279
Rye	45	26
Buckwheat	7	7
Potatoes	344	384
Sweet potatoes	54	57

all quantities being given to the nearest million bushels, we can substitute these values, together with our earlier data, into formula (18.5.2) or (18.5.3) and we will get

$$I = \frac{(79.6)1274 + (136)302 + (218)45 + (141)7 + (128)344 + (220)54}{(43.1)1274 + (53.9)302 + (85.7)45 + (97.3)7 + (137.8)344 + (103.1)54}$$
$$= 162 \text{ per cent}$$

by use of formula (18.5.2) and

$$I = \frac{(79.6)1215 + (136)279 + (218)26 + (141)7 + (128)384 + (220)57}{(43.1)1215 + (53.9)279 + (85.7)26 + (97.3)7 + (137.8)384 + (103.1)57}$$
$$= 158 \text{ per cent}$$

by use of formula (18.5.3). This tells us that the over-all increase in the price of the combined farm commodities which we have studied is either 62 or 58 per cent, depending on which formula we choose.

A weighted index, which is in many ways better than either (18.5.2) or (18.5.3) inasmuch as it does not express any preference for either of the two sets of weights, and which also satisfies certain highly important criteria which will be discussed in Section 18.6, is the so-called *ideal index*. Since this index was originally developed by Irving Fisher it is often referred to as *Fisher's index* and it is defined as the square root of the product of the two index numbers which are given by formulas (18.5.2) and (18.5.3). The ideal index can, therefore, be written

$$I = \sqrt{\frac{\Sigma p_n q_0}{\Sigma p_0 q_0} \cdot \frac{\Sigma p_n q_n}{\Sigma p_0 q_n}} \qquad (18.5.4)*$$

Had we used this formula in our example we would have obtained

$$I = \sqrt{(162)(158)} = 160$$

which expresses an over-all increase of 60 per cent in the price of the chosen farm commodities.

There are actually numerous ways in which we can define weighted or unweighted index numbers. We could, for example, have weighted the price relatives and have constructed, in this fashion, a weighted index which is a generalization of (18.4.2). Had we done this it would have been more desirable, however, to use *values* rather than *quantities* as the weights which we would have had to assign to the various ratios p_n/p_0. Since the value, i.e., the total amount of money which is spent on a commodity, is given by the product pq (price times quantity) it can easily be shown that the resulting index (based on the values of the base year) would have reduced to the index which was defined by formula (18.5.2).

Additional index number can be defined by taking weighted geometric or other means or by selecting entirely different sets of weights. It should also be noted that all index numbers which we have defined in the last few sections were *price indexes*, i.e., statistics which measure the relative changes of prices. Interchanging p and q in most of these formulas we could, similarly, have defined *quantity index numbers*, which accordingly express the relative changes which have taken place in the corresponding quantities. Finally, substituting the products pq for the p's of either formula (18.4.1) or (18.4.2), we could also have defined a *value index number*, which compares the total amounts of money which are spent on the various commodities.

EXERCISES

1. Compute the weighted aggregate index of the following dairy products, comparing the 1947 prices with those of 1945. Use the 1945 quantities as weights. (The quantities given are the per person consumption of eggs in dozens, milk in quarts, and butter in pounds. The prices are given in cents per respective units.)

	Quantities		Prices	
	1945	1947	1945	1947
Eggs	33.0	32.0	60.2	69.6
Milk	397.0	396.0	16.5	19.6
Butter	10.8	11.2	49.8	80.5

2. Find the weighted aggregate index of the dairy prices which are given in the previous exercise. Compare the 1947 prices with those of 1945 and use the 1947 quantities as weights.

3. Find Fisher's index for the data given in Exercise 1 (base year 1945).

4. Calculate a weighted aggregate index of the prices of the fuels which are given in the following table. Compare the 1945 prices with those of 1939, using the 1939 quantities as weights. (The prices are given per ton of coal, gallon of fuel oil, and 1000 cu ft of natural gas. The quantities are given per 1 million of the respective units).

	Prices (cents)		Quantities	
	1939	1945	1939	1945
Coal	914.3	1188.7	46.2	74.7
Fuel oil	4.2	6.4	730.8	848.4
Natural gas	48.7	46.3	191.1	326.3

5. Find Fisher's index for the data given in Exercise 4, comparing (a) the 1945 prices with those of 1939, (b) the 1939 prices with those of 1945. If these two index numbers are multiplied, is the answer equal to 1?

18.6 Properties of Index Numbers

Since index numbers are supposed to be designed for the comparison of two sets of figures, it seems only reasonable that if an index for 1950 with the base year 1935 is equal to 200, the same index for 1935 with the base year 1950 should be equal to 50. In other words, if Peter is twice as tall as Paul it stands to reason that Paul is half as tall as Peter. This intuitively necessary and desirable property of an index number is, surprisingly enough, *not* satisfied by most index numbers which we have studied in the previous sections.

If we want to determine whether an index has this property, that the interchange of the functions of the base year and the given year produces the *reciprocal* of the original index, we have only to interchange the subscripts 0 and n wherever they may appear in the formula of the index. If the resulting new index is equal to 1 divided by the original index, we say that our index satisfies the *time reversal test* and that it is, in this sense, satisfactory. The reader can easily check for himself that among the index numbers which we have given only those which were defined by (18.4.1) and (18.5.4) satisfy the time reversal criterion.

A second desirable property of an index number is that it satisfies the so-called *circularity test*. If, for example, the 1950 price of a certain commodity is twice what it was in 1945, and its 1945 price is again twice what it was in 1935, then its 1950 price must be *four times* what it was in 1935. This means that we should be able to get an index for 1950 relative to the base year 1935 by multiplying the index for 1950 relative to 1945 by the corresponding index for 1945 relative to 1935.

It is advantageous to use index numbers which satisfy the circularity test because we can then adjust them from year to year without referring each time to the original basis. Among the index numbers which we have so far discussed only that given by formula (18.4.1) satisfies this second criterion.

A third property which a good index number should have is that it passes the *factor reversal test*. We have mentioned very briefly at the end of the last section that a *price index* can easily be converted into a *quantity index* if we replace the p's by q's and q's by p's wherever these symbols appear in the formula of an index number. Using this correspondence between a price index and a quantity index, the factor reversal test demands that the product of a price index and its corresponding quantity index should present us with a *value index*, i.e., it should be equal to the ratio V_n/V_0 where

$$V_n = \Sigma p_n q_n \quad \text{and} \quad V_0 = \Sigma p_0 q_0$$

If we take, for example, Fisher's index and interchange the p's and q's, we obtain a quantity index which is defined by the following formula:

$$I_q = \sqrt{\frac{\Sigma q_n p_0}{\Sigma q_0 p_0} \cdot \frac{\Sigma q_n p_n}{\Sigma q_0 p_n}} \qquad (18.6.1)$$

Multiplying this new index number by Fisher's original (price) index number which was defined by (18.5.4), we will find that their product is equal to the quantity

$$\frac{\Sigma q_n p_n}{\Sigma q_0 p_0}$$

which equals the desired ratio of the two values V_n and V_0. Fisher's index does therefore satisfy the factor reversal test, and it is, incidentally, the only one among the index numbers which we have defined which satisfies this third criterion.

Our reasons for insisting that an index number should satisfy the factor reversal test are fairly easy to see. After all, if the price of a certain commodity has doubled, and if one sells three times as much, the value (amount of money) which one can expect to receive should be $2 \cdot 3 = 6$ times as much.

The over-all problem of construction of reliable and unbiased index numbers is not an easy one. It is of great importance to the banker who compares the values of stocks and bonds, to the economist who compares economic phenomena from depressions to inflations, and even to the average person who tries to understand the world in which he lives. The main difficulties in the construction of suitable index numbers lie in the selection of the basis of the comparison, in the choice of the commodities (or other quantities) which are to be included, and in the selection of the most appropriate weights. Actually, these questions are not really of a mathematical nature, and as far as the statistical aspects of the problem are concerned, the various formulas which we have studied should suffice as an introduction to the general problem of index numbers. For most practical purposes Fisher's index will provide an index number which is perfectly adequate for the comparison of economic data.

REFERENCES

W. C. Brinton, *Graphic Presentation*, Brinton Assoc., New York, 1939.

R. R. Lutz, *Graphic Presentation Simplified*, Funk & Wagnalls, New York, 1949.

B. D. Mudget, *Index Numbers*, Wiley, New York, 1951.

W. A. Neiswanger, *Elementary Statistical Methods*, Macmillan, New York, 1948, Chap. 11.

J. R. Riggleman and I. N. Frisbee, *Business Statistics*, McGraw-Hill, New York, 1938, Chap. 9.

19. TIME SERIES

19.1 Introduction

The business world would be Utopia if it were possible to predict economic phenomena as accurately as an astronomer can predict, for example, the position of the planet Mars. Most businessmen and ∩conomists must make decisions on the basis of the regularities and patterns which they have discovered in the behavior of statistical information concerning supply, demand, employment, taxes, stocks, etc., with the tacit understanding that the same patterns and regularities will continue also into the future. The mere fact that economists and businessmen use information about the past to predict the behavior of economic phenomena does not distinguish them from other scientists; but the inherent difficulty of discovering sufficient generalities in the statistical information which they have at their disposal makes their task unwieldy and makes it necessary for them to comb through a wealth of economic data hoping to find hints that will enable them to make better predictions.

Statistical data which are collected, observed, or recorded at successive intervals of time form what is generally called a *time series*. This definition does not limit the applicability of the term time series solely to economic data although it is practically always used in this sense. If a patient's temperature is taken at regular intervals and recorded on a chart at the foot of his bed, if a county clerk records the number of marriage licenses which are issued each day, and if a police bureau records the number of robberies which are committed per month, we have in each case a time series which refers to information which is not of an economic nature. Although we shall limit our discussion mainly to economic data, it should be understood, therefore, that all techniques which we shall develop apply also to data belonging to any of the other natural or social sciences.

It is almost impossible nowadays to open a newspaper, enter into an office, or even go to school without having to face the graphs of time series showing the behavior of stocks and bonds, reports on weekly or monthly sales, and charts of the daily attendance. Some of these graphs look like straight lines, others look like smooth curves, but most, and above all those which represent economic data, give the impression of the haphazard scrawlings of a three-year-old child. It is for this reason that special statistical techniques have been devised which will help us to bring some order into the irregular patterns and the seemingly erratic appearances of the time series of business data.

Since we shall devote only one relatively short chapter to this sizable task it must be evident that we can at best analyze a few of the basic problems and indicate a few of the most general methods. If the reader's main interests lie in fields other than business and economics, a casual reading of this chapter should help him to understand and, perhaps, interpret more critically the time series which he cannot help but meet in his everyday life. On the other hand, if business and economics are his main fields of interest, the material which is covered in this chapter should suffice to clarify the basic problems of time series, while the methods which we shall present on a more or less sample basis should provide a sufficient background for more advanced courses on this subject.

19.2 The Behavior of Time Series

It is customary to divide the fluctuations of a time series into four general types of variation which, superimposed and all acting at the same time, give the time series its irregular and almost haphazard appearance. These four types of patterns or movements of a time series can be classified as:

1. Random and erratic variations.
2. Secular or long-term trends.
3. Seasonal patterns.
4. Business cycles.

1. *Random and erratic fluctuations* of time series are those types of variation which are either completely unpredictable or which are caused by isolated special events such as elections, floods, and wars. If we consider, for example, the monthly sales of refrigerators, there

are certain chance factors which, like those determining the flips of a coin, are unpredictable taken one at a time yet which in the long run more or less compensate for one another. Whether Mr. Jones buys his new refrigerator today or whether he decides to wait until the next summer might be determined by economic or psychological factors, but it might also be purely a matter of chance. If it is chance, there is little to be said or done about the fluctuations which can thus be caused in the behavior of a time series.

Variations which are due to the occurrence of special (unusual) events can fortunately be handled much more readily. Most of the time they can be recognized and correlated with the political changes, weather conditions, or sociological upheavals by which they are caused, simply by direct inspection of our data.

The main value of the discovery and analysis of fluctuations which are due to rare events is that we can subsequently disregard or eliminate these variations in our search for the trends and seasonal patterns which might otherwise have been obscured by the erratic behavior of the time series.

It is well known that the stock market is greatly affected by such events as elections, international complications, crop fluctuations, and that even the sales of a new style of dress can vary tremendously if it is worn by a movie star or if it is seen at a social event. The study of the erratic fluctuations of a time series requires, therefore, a knowledge of subjects which can deal with almost anything from psychology to politics, and it does *not* require the development of fancy new statistical techniques.

2. The *long-term or secular trend* is not only difficult to define but it also presents us with mathematical difficulties which are considerably above the level of this study of statistics. Intuitively we might say that *the trend of a time series displays the general sweep of its development,* or better, that it characterizes the gradual and consistent pattern of its changes.

In most elementary problems trends are thought of as *straight lines* (see Fig. 19.a) which are fitted to the time series and which are thus indicative of the gradual growth or decline of the quantities described by our data. For example, if insurance sales increase from year to year we are accustomed to say that there is an *upward trend.* There can be a trend in public opinion, a gradual shifting from one point of view to another, and there can be a trend in politics from one ideology to another. In each of these examples the trend is indicative of a

BILLIONS
OF DOLLARS

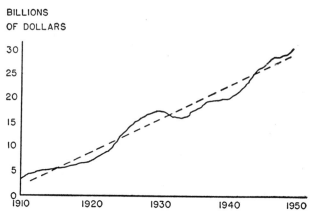

Figure 19.a.   Ownership of Industrial Life Insurance in the United States.

gradual sweeping development of the phenomena which we have tried to describe.

Although it is quite common to picture trends as straight lines, few are actually of such a simple type. Complicated mathematical curves, particularly exponential curves (see page 242), are often much more representative of the gradual development of an economic phenomenon. Time series which, for example, give us the growth of an industry are usually exponential curves, and it would be rather misleading to measure their changes by means of straight-line trends. Yet for reasons of simplicity linear trends are by far the most widely used, and allowing for the mathematical background which we have assumed of our reader we shall limit our study almost exclusively to straight-line trends. It must be understood, of course, that just as in our earlier experiences with the problems of curve fitting, straight lines should be used only if we can be reasonably sure that they will give us a good fit.

3. The type of variation which is, perhaps, the easiest to understand is the *seasonal variation*, which consists of regularly repeating patterns like, for example, those which are shown in Fig. 19.b. Although the name which we have given to this type of variation implies a connection with the seasons of the year, like the variation which we might find, for instance, in the monthly production of eggs or the weekly sales of a department store, it is used to indicate any kind of variation which is of a *periodic* nature (provided that its repeating cycles are relatively short).

THOUSANDS OF CARS

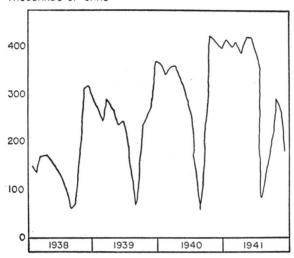

Figure 19.b. Monthly Passenger Car Production in the United States.

Simple illustrations of seasonal patterns can be found, for instance, in the hourly statistics of the number of passengers who travel on the subways of New York City, or in monthly statistics of the price of raspberries. It is easy to see that the rush hours during which people travel to and from work in the morning and in the afternoon present a pattern which repeats every working day. Similarly, the price of raspberries is always low in the months during which they are harvested, and high when the supply is scarce.

Most business time series show seasonal patterns depending on crops, weather conditions, paydays, vacation seasons, etc., and the study of these seasonal patterns is therefore a very important part of the analysis of a time series.

Since it is usually easy to see by inspection whether we are dealing with a monthly pattern, an annual pattern, or one that repeats every week or every day, determination of the *length* or the *period* of the seasonal cycle does not present undue difficulties. Leaving this problem aside for the moment let us now see how a seasonal pattern can best be described. If we take another look at Fig. 19.b, we will note that it represents the time series of the monthly production of automobiles in the United States from 1938 to 1941. Taking, for example, the year 1941, we will find (from the proper source) that the total production of that year consisted of 3,779,682 passenger cars, or a monthly average of 314,973. If the number of cars which were produced in August, 1941, was 78,500, which is only 78,500/314,973 = .249 or 24.9 per cent of the monthly average, we can say that the *seasonal index* for August is 24.9. Similarly, if 417,700 cars were produced during May, 1941, we can correspondingly say that the index for that month is 417,700/314,973 = 132.6 per cent. Repeating these calculations, we could thus compare each month's production with the monthly average and construct an index for each individual month of the year.

The two indexes which we have just computed agree with what we should really have expected, as it stands to reason that many cars are bought during the months preceding the vacation season (132.6 per cent of the monthly average were produced in May) while few cars are bought towards the end of the summer (24.9 per cent of the monthly average were produced during that August). To simplify matters we did not consider the fact that these figures might have been affected by the international situation. Furthermore, it is evident that a seasonal index which is based on a single year can hardly be expected to be very reliable, and in actual practice it is customary to consider much longer periods of time which will thus account for the patterns which repeat year after year.

4. The *business cycle* is sometimes defined as the variation which remains after the trend, the seasonal variation, and erratic fluctuations have been eliminated. Generally speaking, a business cycle consists of a cyclic variation, an up and down movement of the time series, which differs from the seasonal variation which we have just discussed inasmuch as it extends over much longer periods of time and originates from general economic conditions like, e.g., periods of prosperity, inflation, and depression. Actually there exist not one unique business cycle but many different kinds—and we should add, perhaps, that there exist an even greater number of theories which are supposed to explain their occurrence.

To mention just a few of these cycles, there is ample evidence for the existence of a 40-month cycle in the prices of industrial stocks, a nine- to ten-year cycle in industrial activity, a building cycle which fluctuates between 15 and 20 years, and a 50-year cycle which is noticeable primarily in commodity prices. Theoretical explanation of these different cycles vary from such scientific theories as the *price-dislocation theory*, the *overconfidence theory*, *over-* and *undersavings theories*, etc., to the less scientific theory which attributes these cycles to changes in sun spots and similar phenomena.

Putting these theoretical considerations aside for the time being, let us now devote some time to the more statistical aspects of time series, namely, to the problem of describing the trends and seasonal patterns of a time series by means of relatively simple and straightforward statistical techniques.

19.3 Long-Term or Secular Trends

Whether an upward or downward movement of a time series is a trend or whether it is a phase of a long-term cycle is a question which can be answered only by someone who has sufficient data to study the phenomenon which is expressed by the time series. It is for this reason that it is usually advisable to calculate a trend on the basis of data covering ten, twenty, and preferably even a greater number of years.

The most widely used method of fitting straight-line trends to the time series of economic data is the *method of least squares*, which we have already met in earlier chapters and which will therefore require no further elaboration. The only difference, if we can call it a difference, is that the variable x must now refer to the time or date to which the measurements (observations), the y's, refer. As before, we are interested in predicting y in terms of x, i.e., in predicting the value of a certain commodity for a given time, and we must therefore compute the regression line of y on x.

Since most business data are not accurate inasmuch as they are subject to numerous kinds of errors (variations), application of advanced statistical techniques is often analogous to putting high octane gasoline into a Model T Ford. We shall therefore turn to one of the less accurate yet much easier and much faster techniques of fitting a trend line. The most straightforward method consists simply of the freehand drawing of a straight line, which, with a bit of luck and experience, will for most practical purposes provide us with a sufficiently accurate indication of the general development of the time series. Although this method is often perfectly adequate, it will probably not satisfy the scientifically minded businessman who may want to feel that his methods are slightly above the level of common sense and intuitive judgments.

A method which in accuracy lies somewhere between the method of least squares and the freehand drawing of a straight line is the *method of semiaverages*, which requires the following steps.

1. We first divide our data into two parts, which should preferably be of equal size. If a time series covers the period from 1930 to 1949, for example, we could divide it into two periods, one extending from 1930 to 1939 and the other from 1940 to 1949. (If a time series covers an odd number of years, we can either omit the middle year or make the two groups unequal in size.)

2. Once the data have thus been split into two parts, we calculate the means of the quantities which are expressed by the time series *separately* for each of the two parts and plot these means at the midpoints of the respective intervals. This gives us two points which in turn provide us with a straight line, which, when extended through the two points, represents the required trend.

To illustrate this *method of semiaverages* let us consider the following data which represent the total sales of life insurance in the United States from 1940 to 1949 as reported in the *1950 Life Insurance Fact Book:*

Year	Total sales of life insurance in millions of dollars
1940	10,920
1941	12,260
1942	11,420
1943	12,620
1944	13,580
1945	14,780
1946	22,130
1947	23,000
1948	23,155
1949	23,610

Dividing these annual sales of life insurance into two groups, one from 1940 to 1944 and the other from 1945 to 1949, we can readily calculate the mean of the annual sales of the first period as $12,160 million and that of the second as $21,335 million. If we plot these two averages at points corresponding to the years 1942 and 1947, which are the midpoints of the respective periods, the straight line connecting them provides the desired trend, as is shown together with the time series of the original data in Fig. 19.c.

Once we have found the trend, we can proceed to compare the actual data with the corresponding values on the straight line, and for this purpose it is often convenient to calculate the *trend value*

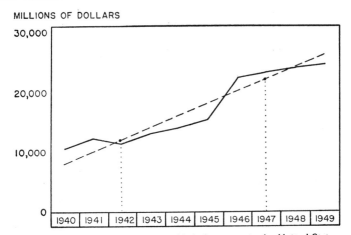

MILLIONS OF DOLLARS

Figure 19.c. Total Annual Sales of Life Insurance in the United States.

for each year which is included among our data. Had we used the method of least squares we could have found these trend values directly from the equation of the straight line (just as we calculated the predicted values of y in Chapter 13). Using the method of semi-averages, however, our task is even simpler, requiring only the following operations. We first take the difference between the means of the two groups, which in our example gives us $21{,}335 - 12{,}160 = \$9{,}175$ million and which marks the increase in the annual sales from 1942 to 1947. Distributing this change over the entire five-year period (1942–1947), we find that the average increase per year is equal to $9{,}175/5 = \$1{,}835$ million. This last quantity is called the *annual trend increment* of the annual sales and it tells us by how much the trend values increase from year to year.

Since we know that the trend value for 1942 is 12,160, we can determine the trend value for any other year by adding or subtracting the annual trend increment an appropriate number of times. This will tell us, for example, that the trend value for 1944 is given by 12,160 plus *twice* 1,835, that the trend value for 1940 is given by 12,160 minus *twice* 1,835, and that the trend value for 1948 can be obtained by either adding 1,835 *six times* to 12,160 or adding it *once* to 21,335, which was the mean of the second group, i.e., the trend value of 1947.

If we proceed in this fashion we will obtain the following table, which contains the actual data together with the corresponding trend values (in millions of dollars):

Year	Actual data	Trend values
1940	10,920	8,490
1941	12,260	10,325
1942	11,420	12,160
1943	12,620	13,995
1944	13,580	15,830
1945	14,780	17,665
1946	22,130	19,500
1947	23,000	21,335
1948	23,155	23,170
1949	23,610	25,005

These trend values tell us what our time series of insurance sales would have looked like if the trend had been the only type of variation present, i.e., if there had been no seasonal variation, no cycles, or other factors involved.

Besides the annual trend increment of the annual data which we have used in our last illustration, it is often necessary to find also the *monthly trend increment of the annual data* or the *monthly trend increment of the monthly data.* The first of these two additional trend increments is found very simply by dividing the annual trend increment of the annual data by 12, since the monthly change must obviously be $\frac{1}{12}$ of the total change per year. Going back to our illustration, the monthly trend increment of the annual data is $1,835/12 = \$153$ million. Similarly, the monthly trend increment of the monthly totals, and this is really the more important one, is found by dividing this last figure again by 12 or the original trend increment by 144. In our example the monthly trend increment of the monthly totals is therefore $1,835/144 = \$12.7$ million. This tells us that the monthly sales have increased on the average by $12.7 million *per month.*

The monthly and the annual trend increments are particularly useful if we want to *eliminate the trend* from our data, i.e., if we want to see what our time series would have looked like if there had been no trend. The picture which we will thus be able to get of our time series is important because it will have no upward or downward trend and it will give us a much clearer picture of the other types of variation which might be present.

If in our illustration we keep the 1940 sales of life insurance fixed, we can *eliminate the trend* by subtracting the annual trend increment of the annual sales *once* from the total sales of 1941, *twice* from the total sales of 1942. *three times* from the total sales of 1943, etc. By

doing this we are counteracting the effects of the trend, and we will
get for our illustration:

Year	Actual sales (millions of dollars)	After elimination of the trend
1940	10,920	$10,920 - 0 \times 1,835 = 10,920$
1941	12,260	$12,260 - 1 \times 1,835 = 10,425$
1942	11,420	$11,420 - 2 \times 1,835 = 7,750$
1943	12,620	$12,620 - 3 \times 1,835 = 7,115$
1944	13,580	$13,580 - 4 \times 1,835 = 6,240$
1945	14,780	$14,780 - 5 \times 1,835 = 5,605$
1946	22,130	$22,130 - 6 \times 1,835 = 11,120$
1947	23,000	$23,000 - 7 \times 1,835 = 10,155$
1948	23,155	$23,155 - 8 \times 1,835 = 8,475$
1949	23,610	$23,610 - 9 \times 1,835 = 7,095$

Plotting the two respective columns of this table on one diagram as
we have done in Fig. 19.d, we can then check whether there is any
indication that there are other types of variation at play in the time
series of the insurance sales.

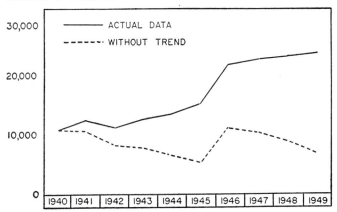

Figure 19.d. Total Annual Sales of Life Insurance in the United States.

One of the main reasons for the elimination of a trend is to enable us
to decide which part of the total fluctuations of a time series can be
attributed to which type of variation. Since Fig. 19.d contains only
annual figures it is of no use for the study of (annual) seasonal patterns. Had we used monthly figures instead of the annual totals,
however, we would then have been able to clear up the following
question. If, for example, the December sales of life insurance are

always higher than those of the September of the same year, it would be interesting to know whether this repeated difference is due to an upward trend or whether it is due to a seasonal variation. This question, and others like it, could probably have been answered if we had eliminated the trend of the monthly data and had then looked at the adjusted time series for traces of a seasonal pattern. It seems, therefore, that if we want to develop precise measures of the effects of the various types of variations, we must eliminate them *one at a time* as we have done so far only with the trend.

EXERCISES

1. Use the method of semiaverages to fit a trend line to the following time series of the index of the purchasing power of the dollar (base period 1923 to 1925):

Year	Index number
1932	130.5
1933	135.9
1934	128.0
1935	123.2
1936	119.9
1937	114.9
1938	117.6
1939	119.3
1940	118.3
1941	114.3

Plot a graph showing both the original data and the trend line.

2. Use the results of the previous exercise to determine the annual trend increment of the index number and find the trend values which correspond to each of the ten years. Also find the monthly trend increment of the index of the purchasing power of the dollar. (It should be noted that since there is a downward trend the trend increments must be taken as negative.)

3. Use the method of semiaverages to fit a linear trend to the time series of the size of the population of the United States which is given in the following table:

Year	Population (in millions)
1931	124.0
1932	124.8
1933	125.6
1934	126.4
1935	127.2
1936	128.0
1937	128.8
1938	129.8
1939	130.9
1940	132.0

1941	133.2
1942	134.7
1943	136.5
1944	138.1
1945	139.6

Plot a graph of this time series together with the line showing its trend.

4. Calculate on the basis of the results of the previous exercise the trend values corresponding to each of the 15 years.

ᐧ 5. Fit a freehand trend to the following time series of the national income of Mexico:

Year	National income (billions of pesos)
1940	6.2
1941	6.9
1942	8.3
1943	10.5
1944	13.4
1945	16.0
1946	19.2
1947	20.9
1948	22.8
1949	25.6

Also use the method of semiaverages to find the annual trend increment of these annual totals and compute the yearly trend values.

19.4 Seasonal Variations

As we might have expected, there is not one but there are many ways in which we can describe the seasonal patterns of a time series. The method which is the most widely used is the method of *link relatives*, which, although it is relatively accurate, has the definite disadvantage that it involves extremely tedious calculations. Since our main purpose in this section is to familiarize the reader with the basic ideas of an *index of seasonal variation*, i.e., with the descriptive measures of the seasonal pattern of a time series, we shall be satisfied with a much more elementary, less involved, and, of course, also relatively less accurate method of defining such an index. The simplicity of the method which we shall employ really does not warrant our giving it a special name, but to distinguish it from the other techniques it is usually referred to as the *simple average method*.

To illustrate the use of this method let us again consider the sales of life insurance, although to bring out the seasonal pattern, we must take the monthly instead of the annual totals. To simplify our work we shall, furthermore, consider only a span of five years, which is generally considered to be sufficient for the calculation of a seasonal index. The first five columns of the following table represent the monthly sales of life insurance in the United States from 1945 to 1949 in millions of dollars (source: *1950 Life Insurance Fact Book*).

	1945	1946	1947	1948	1949	(6)	(7)	(8)	(9)
January	$1,088	$1,375	$1,790	$1,849	$1,821	$1,585	$ 0	$ 1,585	.96
February	1,100	1,547	1,767	1,680	1,711	1,561	13	1,548	.94
March	1,334	1,855	1,900	1,888	2,224	1,840	25	1,815	1.10
April	1,268	2,014	1,847	1,894	1,852	1,775	38	1,737	1.05
May	1,308	2,004	1,886	1,780	1,861	1,768	51	1,717	1.04
June	1,256	1,903	1,887	1,850	1,890	1,757	64	1,693	1.03
July	1,163	1,999	1,918	1,903	1,657	1,728	76	1,652	1.00
August	1,067	1,835	1,668	1,740	1,778	1,618	89	1,529	.93
September	1,034	1,755	1,635	1,625	1,718	1,553	102	1,451	.88
October	1,259	1,836	1,909	1,720	1,861	1,717	114	1,603	.97
November	1,213	1,685	1,849	1,808	1,901	1,691	127	1,564	.95
December	1,499	2,013	2,261	2,303	2,195	2,054	140	1,914	1.16

$19,808

Column (6) contains the averages of the monthly totals calculated separately for each month on the basis of the given five years. The January average of 1,585, for example, which we find at the top of column (6) is simply the mean of 1,088, 1,375, 1,790, 1,849, and 1,821, which are the January totals given in the first five columns of our table.

Column (7) contains the *trend adjustments* which are based on the monthly trend increments of the monthly totals, which we calculated on page 358 as $12.7 million. As we have said before, it is imperative to eliminate the trend *before* we try to evaluate a seasonal index because we could otherwise easily confuse one type of variation with the other. The quantities which must be subtracted from the successive monthly averages in order to eliminate the trend are given in column (7). They are rounded off to the nearest million since it would be unreasonable to ask for more accuracy than we were given in the original data.

Keeping the January average fixed, we must therefore subtract 12.7 *once* from the February average of 1,561, *twice* from the March average of 1,840, *three times* from the April average of 1,775, etc., and we will in this manner obtain the adjusted monthly averages which are given in column (8). The figures which are given in column (8) are therefore those of column (6) minus the corresponding values of column (7).

To construct a seasonal index, which after all, is nothing but a *descriptive measure which compares each month's sales with the over-all monthly average for the entire year,* we now must determine this over-all monthly average from the figures which are given in column (8). Dividing the total of this column, namely, 19,808 by 12, we find that the average monthly sales (after the trend has been eliminated) are $1,651 million. Dividing each number of column (8) by 1,651, we finally obtain the seasonal index which is given in column (9).

This index tells us, for example, that the January sales are 96 per cent, the September sales are only 88 per cent, while the December sales are as much as 116 per cent of those of the average month. Once we have calculated a seasonal index we can use it either *to ask ourselves what the time series would have been like if there had been no seasonal variation,* i.e., we can use it to eliminate the effects of the seasonal variation, or we can use it *to predict future monthly* sales, assuming that we know (or can estimate) the expected monthly average.

To illustrate the first of these two applications, let us take the index which we have just calculated and let us ask *what the life insurance sales might have been in December 1948 if there had been no seasonal variation.* We found that the seasonal index for the month of December is 116, which means that the seasonal pattern makes the December sales 116 per cent of the monthly average. Consequently, in order to eliminate the effect of the seasonal variation we must divide the observed sales of that month by 1.16. Since the sales of December 1948 were $2,303 million, we obtain 2,303/1.16 = $1,985 million as the sales which we could have expected in that month *if there had been no seasonal variation.*

Had we wanted to eliminate the trend as well as the seasonal variation we would have corrected our data first for the trend, adding or subtracting the appropriate trend adjustments (the multiples of the monthly trend increments), and we would then divide the adjusted data by the seasonal indexes corresponding to the respective months. The use of the *simple average method* which we have discussed demands that we know the trend increments from previous calculations. Although this does not present undue complications, since we are most of the time interested in finding the trend anyhow, there do exist methods, among others the method of *link relatives* which we have mentioned before, which automatically eliminate the effects of the trend. These methods can be found in most of the texts which are given as references at the end of this chapter.

To illustrate the use of a seasonal index for prediction of future sales, let us suppose that an insurance executive has estimated the total life insurance sales for 1952 as $24,819 million, and that we are asked to estimate the expected sales for the month of August of that year. Dividing the estimated annual total by 12, we find first that the expected monthly average for 1952 is 24,819/12 = $2,068 million. Since the August index proved to be .93 in our previous calculations, we must now multiply 2,068 by .93 and we will find that the expected insurance sales for August, 1952, are $1,923 million. It should be noted that we are now *multiplying* and not dividing by the seasonal index.

To consider one more example, let us suppose that on the basis of the trend increments and the seasonal index which we have computed in this chapter we are asked to predict the life insurance sales for April, 1953. Using the trend values which we fitted to our time series on page 358, we shall first predict the total expected sales for 1953. Adding *four times* the annual trend increment of 1,835 to the 1949 sales, which were 25,005, we find that the total expected sales for 1953 are 25,005 + 4(1,835) = $32,345 million. Dividing this last figure by 12 it follows that the 1953 expected monthly average is 32,345/12 = 2,695, and finally, multiplying this monthly average by the seasonal index for April which was 1.05, we obtain (1.05)(2,695) = $2,830 million as the expected insurance sales for April, 1953. It must be understood, of course, that this prediction is based on the assumption that the trend as well as the seasonal pattern which we have calculated will continue into the future. As far as the trend of this particular example is concerned this is a somewhat dubious assumption.

EXERCISES

1. The following table contains the number of passengers who have traveled on a certain railroad in three consecutive weeks:

	First week	Second week	Third week
Monday	8421	8451	8645
Tuesday	8364	8391	8417
Wednesday	8489	8397	8492
Thursday	8513	8525	8571
Friday	8715	8728	8809
Saturday	3520	4271	3972
Sunday	1112	958	1034

Assuming that the daily trend increment of the daily number of passengers is 57, calculate a seasonal index representing the number of passengers who travel on this railroad each day of the week.

2. The following table contains the monthly values of the index of the purchasing power of the dollar (base period 1923 to 1925):

	1937	1938	1939	1940
January	117.1	116.3	119.5	119.0
February	116.7	117.2	119.0	118.8
March	115.7	117.2	119.8	118.9
April	115.2	117.2	119.6	119.3
May	114.5	117.5	119.9	118.2
June	114.4	117.2	120.0	117.6
July	114.4	117.5	119.8	117.9
August	114.3	118.3	120.3	118.2
September	113.8	118.3	118.3	117.4
October	113.6	118.5	118.5	118.9
November	114.3	118.8	118.6	118.9
December	114.8	118.5	119.2	118.3

Use the monthly trend increment found in Exercise 2, page 360, and the method indicated in the text to find an index of the seasonal variation of the purchasing power of the dollar. (It should be noted that since there is a downward trend the trend adjustments must be *added* instead of subtracted.)

3. The following table contains the cold storage holdings of frozen eggs in millions of pounds:

	1941	1942	1943	1944
January	73.3	95.5	82.9	102.3
February	53.8	76.3	59.8	81.7
March	45.2	73.8	56.5	98.6
April	63.4	107.4	99.2	148.6
May	99.5	159.6	172.3	218.0
June	142.0	223.8	251.5	292.4
July	178.6	278.5	323.2	354.2
August	195.2	290.5	351.2	388.5
September	194.0	272.0	343.6	371.6
October	178.4	234.9	306.2	332.6
November	153.8	180.3	242.3	279.2
December	129.5	126.3	172.4	219.8

Find a seasonal index, assuming that the monthly trend increment of these monthly figures is 3.0 million pounds.

19.5 Business Cycles and the Calculation of the Normal

There are two reasons why we are interested in the determination of the seasonal index and the trend. First, it is essential to know the trend and the seasonal pattern for predictions which are supposed to account for these two types of variation, and second, we must be able to eliminate these two types of variation so that we will be in the position to discover what other kinds of variation might be at play.

Having studied the first of these applications of the trend and the seasonal index in the previous section, we now turn to a brief discussion of the subject of business cycles and how they can be isolated from the other two types of variation. There are essentially two ways in which we can bring out a business cycle which may (or may not) exist in our data. We can either eliminate the trend and the seasonal variation, using, for example, the method which we have mentioned in the last section, and then compare the adjusted time series with the original data, or *we can ask ourselves what the time series would have looked like if the trend and seasonal variation had been the only two types of variation affecting our data,* and then compare the original time series with the resulting curve which is called the *normal.*

The *normal* of a given time series is therefore the curve which tells us what our time series would have been like if there had been no variations except the trend and the seasonal variation. This is similar to what we did earlier in this chapter when we studied the trend line, which told us what the time series would have been like if the trend had been the only type of variation present.

Considering now the effect of the seasonal variation as well, the *normal* will be obtained by multiplying each monthly trend value by the seasonal index of the corresponding month. Let us illustrate this technique by referring again to the insurance data which we have used before. First, we must calculate the monthly trend values corresponding to the months which we shall include in our study, on the basis of the trend values which are given on page 358. To simplify our work we shall limit ourselves to the three-year period from 1946 to 1948, which is somewhat shorter than the period which we used for the determination of the seasonal index.

The trend value which corresponded to the 1947 insurance sales was \$21,335 million (see page 358), which gives us a monthly average of $21{,}335/12 = \$1{,}778$ million. Since this average must be put in the middle of 1947, halfway between June and July, we add to it one-half the monthly trend increment in order to obtain the trend value which corresponds to July, 1947. This gives us $1{,}778 + 12.7/2 = \$1{,}784$ million (to the nearest million).

Once this value is known we can complete the table of the monthly trend values which is given below by adding (or subtracting) the trend increment of \$12.7 million to each successive month. This will give us the following monthly trend values from January, 1946, to December, 1948.

	1946	1947	1948
January	$1,555	$1,708	$1,860
February	1,568	1,720	1,873
March	1,581	1,733	1,886
April	1,594	1,746	1,898
May	1,606	1,759	1,911
June	1,619	1,771	1,924
July	1,632	1,784	1,936
August	1,644	1,797	1,949
September	1,657	1,809	1,962
October	1,670	1,822	1,974
November	1,682	1,835	1,987
December	1,695	1,848	2,000

where all figures are rounded off to the nearest million. In order to calculate the normal we will now take each of these trend values and multiply it by its month's seasonal index, which was calculated earlier on page 362. Multiplying, therefore, the January figures by .96, the February figures by .94, the March figures by 1.10, etc., we obtain:

	1946	1947	1948
January	$1,493	$1,640	$1,786
February	1,474	1,617	1,761
March	1,739	1,906	2,075
April	1,674	1,833	1,993
May	1,670	1,829	1,987
June	1,668	1,824	1,982
July	1,632	1,784	1,936
August	1,529	1,671	1,812
September	1,458	1,592	1,726
October	1,620	1,767	1,915
November	1,598	1,743	1,888
December	1,966	2,144	2,320

which are the monthly sales (in millions) of life insurance which we could have expected if the trend and the seasonal variation had been the only two types of variation which affected our data.

Once the normal has been found, we can compare it with the original data and decide whether there is any indication that there are further types of variation in the time series. This comparison can be made in a number of ways, most conveniently, perhaps, by simply plotting the original data as well as the normal on one diagram like that of Fig. 19.e. In this figure we have connected the points representing the sales of the successive months by straight lines, solid lines to indicate the normal, and dotted lines to indicate the actual sales.

It must be evident that we can hardly expect to find a business cycle or even a trace of one in a graph which covers as few as three

MILLIONS OF DOLLARS

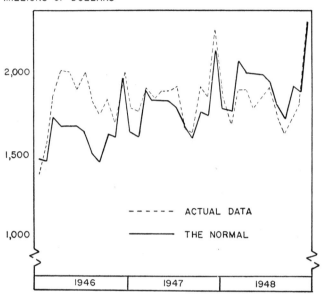

Figure 19.e.   Monthly Sales of Life Insurance in the United States.

years. Mainly for this reason we shall not waste our time trying to apply more refined techniques to our illustration. Instead, we shall merely indicate what can be done to put the comparison between the normal and the observed data on a more precise basis. Such a comparison is generally made by either studying the time series consisting of the *ratios* which are obtained by dividing the actual data by the corresponding values of the normal, or by investigating the *differences* between the same two sets of figures. In either case we will obtain a new time series which is free of trends or seasonal variations and which can thus be investigated for the possible presence of a business cycle.

19.6 The Smoothing of Time Series

In problems in which the trend of a time series is obviously not a straight line and in problems in which we are interested only in the general motion of the time series, be it a trend, a cycle, or possibly both, it is customary to study the behavior of the series by means of a so-called *moving average*.

A moving average is an artificially constructed time series in which each annual figure is replaced by the *average* (mean) of the value of that year and those of a number of the preceding and succeeding years. If we have a *three-year moving average*, for instance, each annual total is replaced by the mean of the total of that year and the totals of the preceding and succeeding years.

The advantage of such a moving average (which can be used, incidentally, also for weekly, monthly, or hourly data) is that it tends to eliminate the ragged appearance of the time series, emphasizing at the same time the general picture of its development. Moving averages are therefore useful in the *smoothing* of time series, i.e., in the elimination of the minor fluctuations which might obscure the over-all picture.

Instead of a three-year moving average we can also compute a *five*-year moving average, a *seven-year moving average*, etc. In a five-year moving average the value of each year is replaced by the mean of the values of the five successive years, of which two precede and two succeed the given year. This provides us, therefore, with the averages of five neighboring years in place of the individual annual totals.

The work which is involved in the calculation of a moving average is shown in the illustration given below, in which we shall calculate a five-year moving average to smooth the time series of the number of automobiles produced in the United States from 1924 to 1947. The first column of our table consists of the actual annual production totals in millions of cars. The second column contains each year's

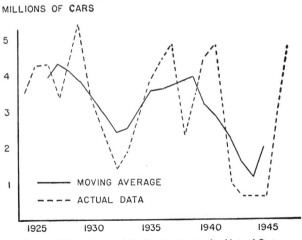

Figure 19.f. Automobile Production in the United States.

production *plus* that of the two preceding and succeeding years, i.e., it contains the five-year production totals, which are entered in this table in line with the year which is in the middle of the respective five-year period. The third column finally contains the five-year moving averages, which are obtained by dividing each of the five-year production totals of the second column by five.

A minor disadvantage of this method of smoothing a time series is that we lose two years at each end of the table. Had we instead computed a three-year moving average, we would have lost only one year at each end of the table; and if it had been a seven-year moving average, we would have lost three. This is not very serious, however, since we can practically always extend our study to include a few extra years, and even if this is impossible the loss of a few years will not affect the general picture to an appreciable extent unless the time series is very short.

The practical effect of the moving average can readily be seen from Fig. 19.f, in which we have plotted the actual annual production totals together with their five-year moving average. It is evident that the moving average has eliminated the lesser fluctuations to some extent, and it has thus smoothed the general appearance of the time series.

Year	Annual production	Five-year totals	Five-year moving averages
1924	3.6		
1925	4.3		
1926	4.3	20.0	4.0
1927	3.4	21.8	4.4
1928	4.4	20.9	4.2
1929	5.4	19.0	3.8
1930	3.4	17.0	3.4
1931	2.4	14.5	2.9
1932	1.4	11.9	2.4
1933	1.9	12.4	2.5
1934	2.8	14.5	2.9
1935	3.9	17.9	3.6
1936	4.5	18.3	3.7
1937	4.8	19.1	3.8
1938	2.3	19.7	3.9
1939	3.6	20.0	4.0
1940	4.5	16.2	3.2
1941	4.8	14.6	2.9
1942	1.0	11.7	2.3
1943	.7	7.9	1.6
1944	.7	6.2	1.2
1945	.7	10.0	2.0
1946	3.1		
1947	4.8		

EXERCISES

1. Use the results of Exercise 1, page 360, and Exercise 2, page 365, to calculate the *normal* of the index of the purchasing power of the dollar from January, 1937, to December, 1940.

2. Fit a three-year moving average to the following data pertaining to the production of butter in the Union of South Africa (in thousands of metric tons):

Year	Production	Year	Production
1930	8.2	1940	20.2
1931	9.4	1941	18.6
1932	9.7	1942	20.2
1933	8.4	1943	20.3
1934	8.5	1944	17.5
1935	12.0	1945	15.5
1936	14.6	1946	16.3
1937	12.9	1947	17.0
1938	15.2	1948	22.0
1939	18.3	1949	21.1

Plot a graph of the given data together with their three-year moving average.

3. Fit a five-year moving average to the time series of the annual import of coffee to the United States:

Year	Import (millions of pounds)	Year	Import (millions of pounds)
1926	1496	1936	1747
1927	1444	1937	1707
1928	1461	1938	1991
1929	1486	1939	2021
1930	1605	1940	2062
1931	1749	1941	2260
1932	1508	1942	1723
1933	1592	1943	2198
1934	1531	1944	2607
1935	1761	1945	2716

Plot a graph showing this five-year moving average together with the original data.

4. Fit a three-year moving average to the time series of the previous exercise.

5. Fit a seven-year moving average to the time series which is given in Exercise 2.

19.7 Conclusions

The inherent inadequacies of most economic data make it unnecessary for us to employ high-powered statistical techniques in elementary problems dealing with the analysis of time series. Therefore the relatively simple techniques which we have studied in this chapter should prove sufficient to handle the problems which the reader can expect to meet in his undergraduate work.

The various methods which we have developed lack many refinements which could possibly have been added. In the calculation of the index of seasonal variation, for instance, we could have considered the fact that different months are not all of equal length, while holidays and other occasions at which business is at a standstill could easily affect our results.

The brevity of this exposition has made it impossible for us to give illustrations dealing with weekly, daily, or even hourly data. However, since there is, fundamentally speaking, no difference between the treatment of these different kinds of data, the study of this chapter should suffice to give the reader a general introduction to the methods used in the analysis of a time series regardless of the kind of data to which it might refer.

REFERENCES

M. M. Blair, *Elementary Statistics*, Holt, New York, 1944, Chaps. 15, 16, 17, and 18.

F. E. Croxton and D. J. Cowden, *Applied General Statistics*, Prentice-Hall, New York, 1946, Chaps. 14, 15, 17, and 18.

F. C. Mills, *Statistical Methods Applied to Economics and Business*, Holt, New York, 1938, Chap. 7.

W. A. Neiswanger, *Elementary Statistical Methods*, Macmillan, New York, 1948, Chaps. 13, 14, and 15.

J. R. Riggleman and I. N. Frisbee, *Business Statistics*, McGraw-Hill, New York, 1938, Chaps. 13, 14, and 15.

20. STATISTICS AND SCIENCE

20.1 Statistics and Science

In the first few pages of Chapter 1 we expressed the hope that besides presenting to the reader an introduction to the basic ideas and methods of modern statistics, this book might also serve to broaden his understanding of the nature, the scope, and the limitations of scientific knowledge. Many readers may have found it difficult to connect our illustrations dealing with such everyday and down-to-earth subjects as the salaries of the employees of the LYX Co., the daffodils of the QRS Bulb Co., and the ham sandwiches of Chapter 7 with their conception of modern science and the role which it plays in our society. This is quite understandable because the word *science* itself means many different things to many different people. If we check its meaning in a dictionary, we will find not one but a whole selection of definitions, and if we look up its origin, we will find that it is derived from the Latin word *scire*, which simply means *to know*.

Our task of relating science and statistics will, perhaps, be easier if we first discuss the so-called scientific method or, better, its modern counterpart, *and then define science simply as the body of knowledge which can be obtained with the use of this method*. Before doing this, let us take a brief look at an argument which has often been raised against those who, like us, have claimed that statistics is a vital and indispensable part of science. Their argument, which sounds quite convincing, is that although statistics has really begun to flourish only in the twentieth century and is, relatively speaking, still in its childhood stage, science has been able to get along without it for many centuries. To this argument we might reply that *the very exactness* of the sciences which were developed first and which apparently had no need for statistics, namely, astronomy and physics, may actually have done a disservice to science in general.   Had our solar system been a little more helter-skelter, had there been several suns near the earth instead of one, then even the earliest scientific problems would have required statistical treatment.   This might have delayed the general progress of science for a few years, but it would probably have led to a much more uniform development of the different branches of science.   This in turn would most likely have prevented the unfortunate line which is so often drawn between the *pure* (natural) and the *impure* (social) sciences.

One of the most important steps which have led to what is commonly called *scientific thinking* was David Hume's critical analysis of the notion of causality.   The British philosopher, who lived from 1711 to 1776, first expressed the view that *causality is only the constant succession or coincidence of events.*   In contrast to his views, the common-sense notion of causality was (maybe still is) that an effect is, in some fashion, *produced* by a cause.   Precisely what is meant by the cause *producing* the effect is difficult to see if we say, for example, that icy roads cause accidents, bacteria cause diseases, and that moist air causes iron to rust.   If we think about this for a moment, it becomes clear that all we can really talk about in any one of these examples is the apparently constant succession of certain events.   If the roads are icy, cars are likely to skid; if a person has certain bacteria in his blood, he is likely to display the symptoms of a disease; and if we leave iron in moist air, it will usually rust.   In other words, we can only observe that certain events are followed by others with a definite regularity.

In the early stages of science Hume's concept of causality was applied only in connection with events which could be expected to occur *100 per cent of the time.*   For instance, if we drop a rock out of a window it will always fall down, if we raise the temperature of water to a sufficient extent it will always boil, and if we heat a metal bar it can always be expected to expand.   In order to arrive at generalizations of this type it was obviously necessary to use *inductive* reasoning.   This type of thinking was illustrated in Chapter 1 with the argument, "all swans which we have seen were white; hence all swans are white."

As early as the beginning of the seventeenth century, Francis Bacon suggested certain methods which should be used if one wanted to discover, as he said, the "causes of things."   This method is known mainly in the form in which it was presented by John Stuart Mill centuries later in his famous work *A System of Logic*, published in 1843, and it is in this form that it is usually referred to as the scientific method. Although this method is undoubtedly of considerable historical interest, judged by twentieth century standards it is totally inadequate for the discovery or proof of scientific relationships. One of the main reasons for this inadequacy of the scientific method as stated by Mill is that in the past century scientists have no longer asked exclusively for relationships which must hold 100 per cent of the time. *Instead, they have extended the concept of a scientific law or fact to relationships which can be observed with regularity a definite percentage of the time.* This trend in the development of science was almost unavoidable because there are few things which we can really expect to happen 100 per cent of the time. To illustrate this change from statements which must be true always to statements which can be asserted only with a certain probability, i.e., statements which must be true only a certain percentage of the time, we have only to look for scientific laws which have been discovered in any one of the social sciences. A sociologist can tell us, for example, that children who have lived in a specific kind of environment are likely to be better adjusted than others. This does *not* mean that every child who has come from a certain kind of home must necessarily be well adjusted; it means only that the percentage of well-adjusted individuals is *consistently higher* among those children who have experienced the preferable environment. Similarly, cars do not always skid even though the roads are icy, people who have bacteria in their blood do not always become actually sick, and iron which is exposed to moist air does not always rust. All these events will occur only *with definite regularity a certain percentage of the time.*

A scientific law (or fact) expresses, therefore, according to the ideas of modern science, a relationship between observable phenomena which must hold a certain percentage of the time, i.e., with a certain probability. If such a percentage happens to be 100, this would be fine and desirable, but it would be nothing but a very *special case.*

20.2 Statistics and the Scientific Method

Any attempt to explain a subject as complex as the scientific method in two or three pages can hardly be expected to be anything but an oversimplification. In spite of this we shall now take a very brief look at Mill's formulation of the scientific method, adapted to permit also relationships which need not necessarily hold 100 per cent of the time.

Mill listed the basic five methods of experimental inquiry as the *Method of Agreement*, the *Method of Difference*, the *Joint Method of Agreement and Difference*, the *Method of Concomitant Variation*, and the *Method of Residues*. Although, when first formulated, these methods marked an important development in human thinking, they are likely to strike us today as only common sense. Of course, this merely goes to show how much we have assimilated these methods into our daily lives.

Let us consider, first, the *Method of Agreement*, which states that if two or more cases of a phenomenon which we are investigating have one and only one factor in common, this factor must be the cause of the phenomenon. For example, since every person having malaria has the same type of bacteria in his blood, we can say that it is the bacteria which are the cause of malaria; if a gas expands each time that we increase the temperature, we can say that the change of the temperature is the cause of the change in the volume, etc. Similarly, the *Method of Difference* states that if there exists a single factor which is such that in its presence a certain event will take place and in its absence it will not, this factor is the cause of the event. To illustrate this *Method of Difference* let us suppose, for example, that we bake two cakes, one with sugar and one without, all other ingredients being the same. Then if the cake which contains the sugar tastes delicious while the other tastes flat, the *Method of Difference* would tell us that the absence of the sugar was the cause of the failure of the second cake.

The *Joint Method of Agreement and Difference* is simply a combination of the previous two and it eliminates to some extent their respective weaknesses. This joint method could, for instance, have saved the *Method of Agreement* from making a serious mistake in the well-known example of the man who drinks Scotch and ginger ale on Monday, gin and ginger ale on Tuesday, rum and ginger ale on Wednesday, and who concludes that, therefore, the common factor which is ginger ale is, according to the *Method of Agreement*, the cause of his getting drunk on each of the three nights.

The *Method of Concomitant Variation* states that if we change the values of one variable and if we then repeatedly observe corresponding changes in another variable, this implies that there exists a causal relationship between the two variables. By use of this method we can show, for instance, that there exists a relationship between the shape and the speed of a bullet, between education and social adjustment, or between production, advertising, and sales.

Finally, the *Method of Residues* claims that if we eliminate from a phenomenon the factors which are already known to be the causes of certain of its aspects, the remaining factors must be the causes of that part of the phenomenon which has remained unexplained. This should remind us of our study of time series, in which we said that the variation which remains after we eliminated the trend and the seasonal variation can be defined as the business cycle. Consequently, using the *Method of Residues*, we can say that the cause of a business cycle must be given by those factors affecting the time series which remain after those causing the trend and the seasonal variation have been eliminated.

This completes our very brief and consequently not very thorough excursion into applied logic, and it would not surprise us if an impatient reader would ask the question: *What has all this to do with statistics?*

Using the word *scientific* in its colloquial sense meaning accurate, systematic, or exact, we shall probably startle the reader by saying that *statistics is needed to make the scientific method really scientific.* The methods which we have outlined so very briefly in the last few pages are supposed to enable us to discover as well as prove the existence of so-called scientific relationships between observable phenomena. This means that we must arrive at general conclusions on the basis of observations or experiments which, at best, give us a *sample* of the phenomena which we want to describe. Consequently, if we find some evidence for the existence of a relationship between the quantities which we are investigating with any one of the five basic methods, we always must ask ourselves whether it is really permissible to generalize from the information which we have thus gathered from a sample. For example, if a sample of 20 people shows that the redheads in the sample are more intelligent than the blondes, we still must ask ourselves whether we can infer the conclusion that redheads *in general* are more intelligent than blondes. In other words, we must ask whether the relationship which is displayed by the sample is really *significant*.

This puts us back into familiar territory. When we said in some of our studies of Parts Two and Three of this book that a relationship was significant, we meant to imply that our chances of getting that particular kind of sample would have been slim indeed if the relationship had not existed. Therefore, in order to decide whether the relationship meant anything at all, we had to compare the sample values which we obtained with the values which we might have *expected* if the relationship had been nonexistent.

When we said a few paragraphs earlier that statistics was needed to make the scientific method precise and accurate, we were simply expressing the fact that statistical criteria are indispensable if we want to be able to decide whether scientific discoveries and proofs are significant (whether they mean anything) or whether they are simply the result of a lucky (or unlucky) coincidence. Therefore, whenever we observe a relationship between variables, we must always ask ourselves whether this is indicative of a scientific law or whether it is something which could have happened purely due to chance.

The role which is thus played by statistics in the general framework of science is the same as that of an appraiser of jewelry who can tell us whether we have a diamond or just a piece of plain glass. Without the expert appraiser we would scarcely be able to tell whether a diamond is pure, and without suitable statistical techniques we would hardly be able to say that the relationships which we have observed mean anything at all. It is difficult to overestimate the importance of statistics, not even mentioning the important function which is performed by descriptive statistics in the handling of numerical data.

20.3 The Analysis of Variance

If the reader understands the meaning of a sampling distribution, the idea of a type I error, the importance of a test of significance, etc., he will discover that the more advanced statistical techniques which he might find in further courses of statistics will not present him with any basic difficulties except, perhaps, those which are of a purely technical nature.

Let us take a brief look, for example, at a somewhat more advanced test of significance which is sometimes discussed even in an elementary course. So far we have learned to test the significance of the difference between two means, the significance of the difference between two percentages, the significance of a coefficient of correlation, and the significance of several other simple types of statistics. In each case we began by formulating the hypothesis that whatever we had wanted to demonstrate was not so, i.e., we began by formulating a null hypothesis with the tacit hope that we might be able to reject it.

Then we calculated some property which we would have expected of our sample had the null hypothesis been true, and finally, comparing what we got with what we could have expected, we were able to decide whether our results were significant. If the discrepancies were so large that they could not reasonably have been ascribed to chance, our results were said to be significant.

Let us now see whether the general procedure which we have just reviewed can also be used in the following problem which, in a sense, is the continuation of a problem which we discussed earlier in Chapter 5. Let us suppose that we are ordering steel for the construction of a bridge and that four different companies have sent us samples of five pieces each, which showed an average (mean) compressive strength of 54,000, 59,000, 62,000, and 64,000 psi, respectively. Since we are obviously interested in buying strong steel, but since there are also other considerations concerning, for instance, the price, we should now ask ourselves whether there is actually a difference in the strength of the steel which is produced by the four companies. In other words, we must ask whether the differences between the four sample means are significant or whether they can reasonably be attributed to chance.

This situation sounds similar to problems which we have solved before, but as we shall see, it cannot be handled with the elementary techniques which we have learned in Part Two of this book. To be able to decide whether the differences between the four means could be ascribed to chance, *we must see what kind of differences, i.e., how much variation, we could expect to find between the four means if there had been no actual difference in the strength of the four kinds of steel.*

Since there is apparently nothing else that we can do, let us investigate whether it might help to take a look at the actual measurements which were taken of the steel as originally submitted by the four companies. Checking the raw data, we find that the results which were reported by the technicians who made the measurements of the compressive strength were:

	Company A	Company B	Company C	Company D
	53,650	60,300	61,400	63,700
	54,210	59,250	63,260	65,250
	54,160	58,700	62,280	64,720
	53,980	58,360	61,470	62,500
	54,000	58,390	61,590	63,830
Mean	54,000	59,000	62,000	64,000

If we study these four samples we cannot help but note the interesting fact that whereas the *ranges* of the samples are 560, 1,940, 1,860, and 2,750 respectively, the range of the four means is as large as 64,000 − 54,000 = 10,000. This is very interesting because, as we know, the range is a measure of variation, and according to what we have said in Chapters 9 and 10, the variation (standard error) of sample means should actually be *much smaller* than the variation of the individual measurements. Had there been no actual differences between the four kinds of steel, it would have been *extremely unlikely* for us to obtain a variation between the sample means which is so much larger than the variation which we found within the individual samples of the four kinds of steel. This is precisely what we have wanted to show. The observed variation (spread) of the four means differs by so much from the variation which we might reasonably have expected (judging from the variations within the four samples) that we can confidently say that the difference between the four kinds of steel is significant.

The significance test which we have just outlined by means of this illustration is actually an *imitation* of a very important statistical technique which is called the *analysis of variance*. Our test was only an imitation because in the analysis of variance we compare the variation of the means with the variation within the samples *not* on the basis of the range, but on the basis of a statistic which is similar to a standard deviation. Of course, the final decision whether the variation is significant is also not made by simply glancing at the two measures of variation as we have done in our example, but by means of a criterion, the F criterion, which, as always, is based on a theoretical distribution.

The fictitious data which we have used in this example were specially chosen to bring out the difference between the *variation of the means* and the *variation within each of the separate samples*. Because we can seldom expect this difference to be so pronounced under ordinary circumstances (even though it may be significant), we must develop techniques which can put this comparison on a more exact scientific basis. This is precisely what is accomplished by the analysis of variance, which incidentally owes its name to the fact that it helps us to analyze and compare, among other things, the two types of variation which we have studied in our illustration. It is also interesting to observe that when we discussed the significance of a coefficient of correlation in Section 14.4 we compared *the variation which was accounted for by the linear relationship* with *the total variation of the y's.* What we did in that section belongs, therefore, to the analysis of variance, which in the last few decades has become an important part of statistical methodology.

20.4 Experimental Design

Let us suppose, for the sake of argument, that we were able to show in the problem which we discussed in the previous section that the differences between the four sample means were significant, i.e., that their variation was greater than we could have expected it to be under the null hypothesis that there was no difference between the four kinds of steel. This leads us to the interesting question as to whether we can *really* conclude on the basis of this experiment that there is a difference in the strength of the four kinds of steel. At first though, this question may seem superfluous, since after all, this is precisely what we have just shown. However, if we think about it for a moment, it might occur to us that the differences which we observed between the four samples might be due to other causes. Perhaps the samples were tested at different temperatures; maybe they were measured with different instruments which were not all accurately calibrated; maybe one of the laboratory technicians was bribed by one of the companies to fix the results so that it would get the contract. We could go on indefinitely listing possible *causes* which might conceivably have been the reason for the differences which we observed between the means of the four samples. We are faced, therefore, with a situation which is commonly referred to as the *multiplicity of causes,* and it seems, at this point, as if no statistical methods will be able to help us out of this predicament. It is true that the statistical methods which we have used (or might have used) enabled us to show that a certain relationship exists, e.g., that the differences between the means are significant, but they cannot go further—they cannot tell us *why* such discrepancies occurred. If we therefore want to continue, we shall be forced to use methods which compare to the scientific method as formulated by Bacon and Mill as the *Queen Mary* compares to the *Santa Maria* of Columbus.

There is really only one answer to the problem of the multiplicity of causes. If we want to be able to show that one factor can definitely be singled out as the *cause* of a phenomenon which we have observed (and which we have shown to be significant), *we must make sure that none of the other factors could possibly be held responsible.* In other words, if we hope to show that one particular factor caused certain results, we must make sure that the other factors are *controlled* to such an extent that they could not reasonably have caused the phenomena which we observed. This leads us to the important as well as interesting problem of *experimental control* and *experimental design*.

To demonstrate the important role which statistics plays in the planning as well as in the analysis of scientific experiments, let us consider the following psychological investigation. A problem which is of great interest to psychologists is that of *retroactive inhibition*. It concerns the interference of interpolated activities with the process of learning, or more simply, it refers to the effect which the activities which we undertake soon *after* we have learned something have on our ability to retain that knowledge. Let us suppose, therefore, that to study this phenomenon, a group of scientists has planned to make the following experiment. They will give a list of 100 French words to three different individuals with the instruction to study these words for 30 minutes. After that, one will be exposed for two hours to strenuous physical exercise such as tennis or football, a second will be asked to study mathematics, while the third subject will be asked to relax for two hours by either trying to sleep or by reading comic books. After the two hours have elapsed, each will be given a test to see how much of the knowledge he has been able to retain. (If such an experiment were really conducted, the scientists would, of course, subject several individuals to each of the three treatments, but since we are going to use this only as an illustration, we shall reduce our calculations and simplify the general picture by taking these minute samples.)

It is easy to see that although this experiment may produce results which are, statistically speaking, perfectly significant, the scientists who designed this experiment have also left themselves wide open to all sorts of criticism. Somebody might say, and justifiably so, that the differences which might be observed in this experiment could be due to differences in intelligence of the three people who took the test. Possibly the difference in their performance could also be due to differences in age, differences in their emotional states at the time they took the tests, and dozens of other factors. To eliminate the criticism that the results might be due to causes other than retroactive inhibition, our scientists must thus select individuals who are not only alike in intelligence, age, and emotional stability, but also with respect to all factors which might conceivably affect the outcome of the investigation.

If this could have been done, we would have said that the scientists *isolated* the phenomenon which they had wanted to study. It must be evident, however, that such ideal working conditions can be attained only rarely, and that we must in most cases be satisfied with controlling some of the most relevant factors, keeping our fingers crossed that the others will not affect our results. In the technique which we shall outline very briefly in the next few pages we shall give an example of how we can not only control several factors, but how we can also test *in one experiment and at the same time* whether each factor has a separate effect on the phenomenon which we have decided to study. Let us assume, for instance, that we would like to know whether interpolated activities and (or) a person's intelligence has an effect on his ability to retain French words.

To conduct such an experiment we shall need (at least) 9 persons, among whom 3 are below average intelligence, 3 are of average intelligence, and 3 are of superior intelligence. After we have given all 9 of them 30 minutes to study the list of French words, we shall ask 3 of them (one of each level of intelligence) to rest for two hours; 3 others, again one belonging to each level of intelligence, to study mathematics; and the remaining 3 to play football or tennis for the same period of time. After that they will, as in the previous experiment, be given a test to see how much of the learning they have retained.

Let us suppose that this experiment has actually been conducted and that the scores which the 9 individuals received in the test were:

Interpolated activity	Intelligence	Score
	low	23
Rest	average	40
	high	42
	low	16
Football	average	24
	high	32
	low	18
Mathematics	average	29
	high	31

This table tells us, for instance, that the person with low intelligence who was asked to rest for the two hours remembered 23 of the 100

French words; the one with average intelligence who played football remembered 24; and the very intelligent one who was asked to study mathematics remembered 31.

If we want to use this information to study the effect which the interpolated activities, i.e., rest, physical exercise, and the study of mathematics may have had on the nine persons' ability to retain the vocabulary, we must calculate the means of the three respective groups. This will give us

Interpolated activity		Mean
Rest	$\dfrac{23 + 40 + 42}{3} = 35$	
Football	$\dfrac{16 + 24 + 32}{3} = 24$	
Mathematics	$\dfrac{18 + 29 + 31}{3} = 26$	

and we can now study the differences between these three means, their variation, to see whether the interpolated activities could be held responsible for these results. Whether or not these differences are actually significant is something which must be decided by *analysis of variance* which we have indicated briefly in the previous section. Let us suppose that the variation between the three means is significant and that we have therefore shown that differences in interpolated activities have an effect on the human ability to retain learning.

If now somebody were to come along and challenge the validity of our claims on the grounds that the differences which we observed might well have been due to differences in the intelligence of our subjects, we could point to the fact that the three levels of intelligence were equally represented in each of the three control groups. We, so to speak, *randomized* the intelligence factor by making sure that each level of intelligence was represented equally in the group which we asked to rest, in the group which was asked to play football, and in the group which was asked to study mathematics.

If we randomize a factor, e.g., the intelligence, we are not only making sure that this factor will have no effect on our results, but because of the way our experiment was designed we can even go further. We can now ask whether *intelligence itself* might have an effect on a person's ability to retain knowledge. Taking the means of the scores of our subjects, regrouped according to the three levels of intelligence, we have

Intelligence	Mean
Below average	$\dfrac{23 + 16 + 18}{3} = 19$
Average	$\dfrac{40 + 24 + 29}{3} = 31$
Above average	$\dfrac{42 + 32 + 31}{3} = 35$

and we cannot help but note a considerable variation between this new set of means. If the variation of these three means is significant (which again must be shown by use of the analysis of variance), we could say that a person's intelligence has a definite effect on his ability to retain knowledge. The possible objection that the differences which we observed between 19, 31, and 35 might well have been caused by the interpolated activities can easily be discounted because, as we can see from the design of our experiment, the interpolated activities were also *randomized*. This means that each intelligence group also contained exactly one person who was subjected to each of the three treatments. *Consequently, it could not have been the interpolated activities which caused the variation of this second set of means.*

Our main purpose for giving this illustration was to impress the reader with the importance of careful experimental design. If an experiment or investigation is properly planned, we can not only control factors which we want to eliminate, but we can also test at the same time whether several of these factors have an independent (or joint) effect on the phenomenon which we want to study. Instead of the two factors which we have used in our example we could also have treated three, four, or more, and if the experiment had been properly designed, we could have studied the effect of each factor separately while the others are appropriately randomized.

This discussion has led us far from the scientific method of Bacon and Mill. It has shown that statistical methods are not only needed to tell us whether our results are significant, but that they play an equally important role in designing experiments in such a fashion that we can get meaningful and usable results. In principle, the role played by statistics in scientific experiments is still that of the appraiser of jewelry to whom we have compared it, but it has the additional important task of helping us to design experiments in a manner which will make such an appraisal at all possible. We did not exaggerate, therefore, when we said in the introduction to this book that a sound knowledge of statistics is indispensable for the understanding of modern science.

REFERENCES

W. G. Cochran and G. M. Cox, *Experimental Designs*, Wiley, New York, 1950, Chap. 1.

M. R. Cohen and E. Nagel, *An Introduction to Logic and Scientific Method*, Harcourt, Brace, New York, 1934, Chap. 13.

W. J. Dixon and F. J. Massey, *Introduction to Statistical Analysis*, McGraw-Hill, New York, 1951, Chap. 10.

A. L. Edwards, *Statistical Analysis for Students in Psychology and Education*, Rinehart, New York, 1946, Chaps. 10, 14.

R. A. Fisher, *The Design of Experiments*, 5th ed., Oliver and Boyd, Edinburgh, 1949, Chap. 2.

H. L. Searles, *Logic and Scientific Method*, Ronald Press, New York, 1948, Chap. 12.

STATISTICAL TABLES

I. Normal Curve Areas

II. Critical Values of t

III. 95 Per Cent Confidence Limits for Proportions

IV. Critical Values of χ^2

Va. Critical Values of Total Number of Runs ($u_{.025}$)

Vb. Critical Values of Total Number of Runs ($u_{.975}$)

VI. 95 Per Cent Confidence Limits for the Coefficient of Correlation

VII. Binomial Coefficients

VIII. Squares and Square Roots

TABLE I

Normal Curve Areas*

z	.00	.01	.02	.03	.04	.05	.06	.07	.08	.09
0.0	.0000	.0040	.0080	.0120	.0160	.0199	.0239	.0279	.0319	.0359
0.1	.0398	.0438	.0478	.0517	.0557	.0596	.0636	.0675	.0714	.0753
0.2	.0793	.0832	.0871	.0910	.0948	.0987	.1026	.1064	.1103	.1141
0.3	.1179	.1217	.1255	.1293	.1331	.1368	.1406	.1443	.1480	.1517
0.4	.1554	.1591	.1628	.1664	.1700	.1736	.1772	.1808	.1844	.1879
0.5	.1915	.1950	.1985	.2019	.2054	.2088	.2123	.2157	.2190	.2224
0.6	.2257	.2291	.2324	.2357	.2389	.2422	.2454	.2486	.2517	.2549
0.7	.2580	.2611	.2642	.2673	.2704	.2734	.2764	.2794	.2823	.2852
0.8	.2881	.2910	.2939	.2967	.2995	.3023	.3051	.3078	.3106	.3133
0.9	.3159	.3186	.3212	.3238	.3264	.3289	.3315	.3340	.3365	.3389
1.0	.3413	.3438	.3461	.3485	.3508	.3531	.3554	.3577	.3599	.3621
1.1	.3643	.3665	.3686	.3708	.3729	.3749	.3770	.3790	.3810	.3830
1.2	.3849	.3869	.3888	.3907	.3925	.3944	.3962	.3980	.3997	.4015
1.3	.4032	.4049	.4066	.4082	.4099	.4115	.4131	.4147	.4162	.4177
1.4	.4192	.4207	.4222	.4236	.4251	.4265	.4279	.4292	.4306	.4319
1.5	.4332	.4345	.4357	.4370	.4382	.4394	.4406	.4418	.4429	.4441
1.6	.4452	.4463	.4474	.4484	.4495	.4505	.4515	.4525	.4535	.4545
1.7	.4554	.4564	.4573	.4582	.4591	.4599	.4608	.4616	.4625	.4633
1.8	.4641	.4649	.4656	.4664	.4671	.4678	.4686	.4693	.4699	.4706
1.9	.4713	.4719	.4726	.4732	.4738	.4744	.4750	.4756	.4761	.4767
2.0	.4772	.4778	.4783	.4788	.4793	.4798	.4803	.4808	.4812	.4817
2.1	.4821	.4826	.4830	.4834	.4838	.4842	.4846	.4850	.4854	.4857
2.2	.4861	.4864	.4868	.4871	.4875	.4878	.4881	.4884	.4887	.4890
2.3	.4893	.4896	.4898	.4901	.4904	.4906	.4909	.4911	.4913	.4916
2.4	.4918	.4920	.4922	.4925	.4927	.4929	.4931	.4932	.4934	.4936
2.5	.4938	.4940	.4941	.4943	.4945	.4946	.4948	.4949	.4951	.4952
2.6	.4953	.4955	.4956	.4957	.4959	.4960	.4961	.4962	.4963	.4964
2.7	.4965	.4966	.4967	.4968	.4969	.4970	.4971	.4972	.4973	.4974
2.8	.4974	.4975	.4976	.4977	.4977	.4978	.4979	.4979	.4980	.4981
2.9	.4981	.4982	.4982	.4983	.4984	.4984	.4985	.4985	.4986	.4986
3.0	.4987	.4987	.4987	.4988	.4988	.4989	.4989	.4989	.4990	.4990

* This table is reproduced with the permission of the publishers from J. Neyman, *First Course in Probability and Statistics*, Henry Holt and Company, Inc., New York.

TABLE II

Critical Values of t^*

n	$t_{.100}$	$t_{.050}$	$t_{.025}$	$t_{.010}$	$t_{.005}$	$d.f$
2	3.078	6.314	12.706	31.821	63.657	1
3	1.886	2.920	4.303	6.965	9.925	2
4	1.638	2.353	3.182	4.541	5.841	3
5	1.533	2.132	2.776	3.747	4.604	4
6	1.476	2.015	2.571	3.365	4.032	5
7	1.440	1.943	2.447	3.143	3.707	6
8	1.415	1.895	2.365	2.998	3.499	7
9	1.397	1.860	2.306	2.896	3.355	8
10	1.383	1.833	2.262	2.821	3.250	9
11	1.372	1.812	2.228	2.764	3.169	10
12	1.363	1.796	2.201	2.718	3.106	11
13	1.356	1.782	2.179	2.681	3.055	12
14	1.350	1.771	2.160	2.650	3.012	13
15	1.345	1.761	2.145	2.624	2.977	14
16	1.341	1.753	2.131	2.602	2.947	15
17	1.337	1.746	2.120	2.583	2.921	16
18	1.333	1.740	2.110	2.567	2.898	17
19	1.330	1.734	2.101	2.552	2.878	18
20	1.328	1.729	2.093	2.539	2.861	19
21	1.325	1.725	2.086	2.528	2.845	20
22	1.323	1.721	2.080	2.518	2.831	21
23	1.321	1.717	2.074	2.508	2.819	22
24	1.319	1.714	2.069	2.500	2.807	23
25	1.318	1.711	2.064	2.492	2.797	24
26	1.316	1.708	2.060	2.485	2.787	25
27	1.315	1.706	2.056	2.479	2.779	26
28	1.314	1.703	2.052	2.473	2.771	27
29	1.313	1.701	2.048	2.467	2.763	28
30	1.311	1.699	2.045	2.462	2.756	29
inf.	1.282	1.645	1.960	2.326	2.576	inf.

* This table is abridged from Table IV of R. A. Fisher, *Statistical Methods for Research Workers*, published by Oliver & Boyd Ltd., Edinburgh, by permission of the author and publishers.

TABLE III

95 Per Cent Confidence Limits for Proportions*

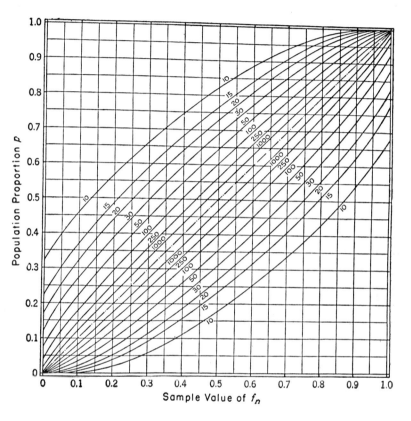

* This table is reproduced from C. J. Clopper and E. S. Pearson, "The use of confidence or fiducial limits illustrated in the case of the binomial," *Biometrika*, Vol. 26 (1934), by permission of Professor E. S. Pearson.

TABLE IV

Critical Values of χ^2

n	$\chi^2_{.99}$	$\chi^2_{.98}$	$\chi^2_{.95}$	$\chi^2_{.05}$	$\chi^2_{.02}$	$\chi^2_{.01}$	d.f.
2	.000157	.000628	.00393	3.841	5.412	6.635	1
3	.0201	.0404	.103	5.991	7.824	9.210	2
4	.115	.185	.352	7.815	9.837	11.341	3
5	.297	.429	.711	9.488	11.668	13.277	4
6	.554	.752	1.145	11.070	13.388	15.086	5
7	.872	1.134	1.635	12.592	15.033	16.812	6
8	1.239	1.564	2.167	14.067	16.622	18.475	7
9	1.646	2.032	2.733	15.507	18.168	20.090	8
10	2.088	2.532	3.325	16.919	19.679	21.666	9
11	2.558	3.059	3.940	18.307	21.161	23.209	10
12	3.053	3.609	4.575	19.675	22.618	24.725	11
13	3.571	4.178	5.226	21.026	24.054	26.217	12
14	4.107	4.765	5.892	22.362	25.472	27.688	13
15	4.660	5.368	6.571	23.685	26.873	29.141	14
16	5.229	5.985	7.261	24.996	28.259	30.578	15
17	5.812	6.614	7.962	26.296	29.633	32.000	16
18	6.408	7.255	8.672	27.587	30.995	33.409	17
19	7.015	7.906	9.390	28.869	32.346	34.805	18
20	7.633	8.567	10.117	30.144	33.687	36.191	19
21	8.260	9.237	10.851	31.410	35.020	37.566	20
22	8.897	9.915	11.591	32.671	36.343	38.932	21
23	9.542	10.600	12.338	33.924	37.659	40.289	22
24	10.196	11.293	13.091	35.172	38.968	41.638	23
25	10.856	11.992	13.848	36.415	40.270	42.980	24
26	11.524	12.697	14.611	37.652	41.566	44.314	25
27	12.198	13.409	15.379	38.885	42.856	45.642	26
28	12.879	14.125	16.151	40.113	44.140	46.963	27
29	13.565	14.847	16.928	41.337	45.419	48.278	28
30	14.256	15.574	17.708	42.557	46.693	49.588	29
31	14.953	16.306	18.493	43.773	47.962	50.892	30

* This table is abridged from Table III of R. A. Fisher, *Statistical Methods for Research Workers*, published by Oliver & Boyd Ltd., Edinburgh, by permission of the author and publishers.

TABLE Va

Critical Values of Total Number of Runs ($u_{.025}$)*

n \ m	2	3	4	5	6	7	8	9	10	11	12	13	14	15	16	17	18	19	20
2											2	2	2	2	2	2	2	2	2
3				2	2	2	2	2	2	2	2	2	2	3	3	3	3	3	3
4				2	2	2	3	3	3	3	3	3	3	3	4	4	4	4	4
5		2	2	3	3	3	3	3	3	4	4	4	4	4	4	4	5	5	5
6		2	2	3	3	3	3	4	4	4	4	5	5	5	5	5	5	6	6
7		2	2	3	3	3	4	4	5	5	5	5	5	6	6	6	6	6	6
8		2	3	3	3	4	4	5	5	5	6	6	6	6	6	7	7	7	7
9		2	3	3	4	4	5	5	5	6	6	6	7	7	7	7	8	8	8
10		2	3	3	4	5	5	5	6	6	7	7	7	7	8	8	8	8	9
11		2	3	4	4	5	5	6	6	7	7	7	8	8	8	9	9	9	9
12	2	2	3	4	4	5	6	6	7	7	7	8	8	8	9	9	9	10	10
13	2	2	3	4	5	5	6	6	7	7	8	8	9	9	9	10	10	10	10
14	2	2	3	4	5	5	6	7	7	8	8	9	9	9	10	10	10	11	11
15	2	3	3	4	5	6	6	7	7	8	8	9	9	10	10	11	11	11	12
16	2	3	4	4	5	6	6	7	8	8	9	9	10	10	11	11	11	12	12
17	2	3	4	4	5	6	7	7	8	9	9	10	10	11	11	11	12	12	13
18	2	3	4	5	5	6	7	8	8	9	9	10	10	11	11	12	12	13	13
19	2	3	4	5	6	6	7	8	8	9	10	10	11	11	12	12	13	13	13
20	2	3	4	5	6	6	7	8	9	9	10	10	11	12	12	13	13	13	14

* This table is adapted from F. S. Swed and C. Eisenhart, "Tables for testing randomness of grouping in a sequence of alternatives," *Annals of Mathematical Statistics*, Vol. 14, p. 66.

TABLE Vb

Critical Values of Total Number of Runs $(u_{.975})^*$

n \ m	2	3	4	5	6	7	8	9	10	11	12	13	14	15	16	17	18	19	20
2																			
3																			
4				9	9														
5			9	10	10	11	11												
6			9	10	11	12	12	13	13	13	13								
7				11	12	13	13	14	14	14	14	15	15	15					
8				11	12	13	14	14	15	15	16	16	16	16	17	17	17	17	17
9					13	14	14	15	16	16	16	17	17	18	18	18	18	18	18
10					13	14	15	16	16	17	17	18	18	18	19	19	19	20	20
11					13	14	15	16	17	17	18	19	19	19	20	20	20	21	21
12					13	14	16	16	17	18	19	19	20	20	21	21	21	22	22
13						15	16	17	18	19	19	20	20	21	21	22	22	23	23
14						15	16	17	18	19	20	20	21	22	22	23	23	23	24
15						15	16	18	18	19	20	21	22	22	23	23	24	24	25
16							17	18	19	20	21	21	22	23	23	24	25	25	25
17							17	18	19	20	21	22	23	23	24	25	25	26	26
18							17	18	19	20	21	22	23	24	25	25	26	26	27
19							17	18	20	21	22	23	23	24	25	26	26	27	27
20							17	18	20	21	22	23	24	25	25	26	27	27	28

* This table is adapted from F. S. Swed and C. Eisenhart, "Tables for testing randomness of grouping in a sequence of alternatives," *Annals of Mathematical Statistics*, Vol. 14, p. 66.

TABLE VI

95 Per Cent Confidence Limits for the
Coefficient of Correlation*

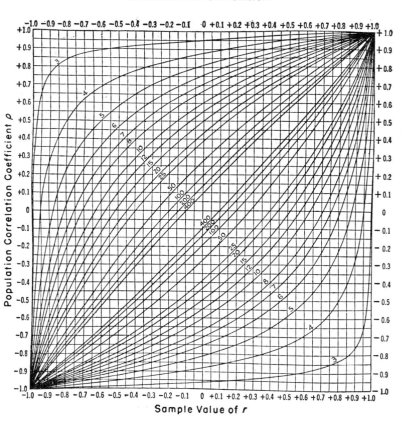

Sample Value of *r*

* This table is reproduced from F. N. David, *Tables of the Ordinates and Probability Integral of the Distribution of the Correlation Coefficient in Small Samples*, The Biometrika Office, London, by permission of Professor E. S. Pearson.

TABLE VII

Binomial Coefficients

n	$\binom{n}{0}$	$\binom{n}{1}$	$\binom{n}{2}$	$\binom{n}{3}$	$\binom{n}{4}$	$\binom{n}{5}$	$\binom{n}{6}$	$\binom{n}{7}$	$\binom{n}{8}$	$\binom{n}{9}$	$\binom{n}{10}$
0	1										
1	1	1									
2	1	2	1								
3	1	3	3	1							
4	1	4	6	4	1						
5	1	5	10	10	5	1					
6	1	6	15	20	15	6	1				
7	1	7	21	35	35	21	7	1			
8	1	8	28	56	70	56	28	8	1		
9	1	9	36	84	126	126	84	36	9	1	
10	1	10	45	120	210	252	210	120	45	10	1
11	1	11	55	165	330	462	462	330	165	55	11
12	1	12	66	220	495	792	924	792	495	220	66
13	1	13	78	286	715	1287	1716	1716	1287	715	286
14	1	14	91	364	1001	2002	3003	3432	3003	2002	1001
15	1	15	105	455	1365	3003	5005	6435	6435	5005	3003
16	1	16	120	560	1820	4368	8008	11440	12870	11440	8008
17	1	17	136	680	2380	6188	12376	19448	24310	24310	19448
18	1	18	153	816	3060	8568	18564	31824	43758	48620	43758
19	1	19	171	969	3876	11628	27132	50388	75582	92378	92378
20	1	20	190	1140	4845	15504	38760	77520	125970	167960	184756

TABLE VIII
Squares and Square Roots*

n	n^2	$\sqrt{n}$	$\sqrt{10n}$	n	n^2	$\sqrt{n}$	$\sqrt{10n}$
1.00	1.0000	1.00000	3.16228	1.50	2.2500	1.22474	3.87298
1.01	1.0201	1.00499	3.17805	1.51	2.2801	1.22882	3.88587
1.02	1.0404	1.00995	3.19374	1.52	2.3104	1.23288	3.89872
1.03	1.0609	1.01489	3.20936	1.53	2.3409	1.23693	3.91152
1.04	1.0816	1.01980	3.22490	1.54	2.3716	1.24097	3.92428
1.05	1.1025	1.02470	3.24037	1.55	2.4025	1.24499	3.93700
1.06	1.1236	1.02956	3.25576	1.56	2.4336	1.24900	3.94968
1.07	1.1449	1.03441	3.27109	1.57	2.4649	1.25300	3.96232
1.08	1.1664	1.03923	3.28634	1.58	2.4964	1.25698	3.97492
1.09	1.1881	1.04403	3.30151	1.59	2.5281	1.26095	3.98748
1.10	1.2100	1.04881	3.31662	1.60	2.5600	1.26491	4.00000
1.11	1.2321	1.05357	3.33167	1.61	2.5921	1.26886	4.01248
1.12	1.2544	1.05830	3.34664	1.62	2.6244	1.27279	4.02492
1.13	1.2769	1.06301	3.36155	1.63	2.6569	1.27671	4.03733
1.14	1.2996	1.06771	3.37639	1.64	2.6896	1.28062	4.04969
1.15	1.3225	1.07238	3.39116	1.65	2.7225	1.28452	4.06202
1.16	1.3456	1.07703	3.40588	1.66	2.7556	1.28841	4.07431
1.17	1.3689	1.08167	3.42053	1.67	2.7889	1.29228	4.08656
1.18	1.3924	1.08628	3.43511	1.68	2.8224	1.29615	4.09878
1.19	1.4161	1.09087	3.44964	1.69	2.8561	1.30000	4.11096
1.20	1.4400	1.09545	3.46410	1.70	2.8900	1.30384	4.12311
1.21	1.4641	1.10000	3.47851	1.71	2.9241	1.30767	4.13521
1.22	1.4884	1.10454	3.49285	1.72	2.9584	1.31149	4.14729
1.23	1.5129	1.10905	3.50714	1.73	2.9929	1.31529	4.15933
1.24	1.5376	1.11355	3.52136	1.74	3.0276	1.31909	4.17133
1.25	1.5625	1.11803	3.53553	1.75	3.0625	1.32288	4.18330
1.26	1.5876	1.12250	3.54965	1.76	3.0976	1.32665	4.19524
1.27	1.6129	1.12694	3.56371	1.77	3.1329	1.33041	4.20714
1.28	1.6384	1.13137	3.57771	1.78	3.1684	1.33417	4.21900
1.29	1.6641	1.13578	3.59166	1.79	3.2041	1.33791	4.23084
1.30	1.6900	1.14018	3.60555	1.80	3.2400	1.34164	4.24264
1.31	1.7161	1.14455	3.61939	1.81	3.2761	1.34536	4.25441
1.32	1.7424	1.14891	3.63318	1.82	3.3124	1.34907	4.26615
1.33	1.7689	1.15326	3.64692	1.83	3.3489	1.35277	4.27785
1.34	1.7956	1.15758	3.66060	1.84	3.3856	1.35647	4.28952
1.35	1.8225	1.16190	3.67423	1.85	3.4225	1.36015	4.30116
1.36	1.8496	1.16619	3.68782	1.86	3.4596	1.36382	4.31277
1.37	1.8769	1.17047	3.70135	1.87	3.4969	1.36748	4.32435
1.38	1.9044	1.17473	3.71484	1.88	3.5344	1.37113	4.33590
1.39	1.9321	1.17898	3.72827	1.89	3.5721	1.37477	4.34741
1.40	1.9600	1.18322	3.74166	1.90	3.6100	1.37840	4.35890
1.41	1.9881	1.18743	3.75500	1.91	3.6481	1.38203	4.37035
1.42	2.0164	1.19164	3.76829	1.92	3.6864	1.38564	4.38178
1.43	2.0449	1.19583	3.78153	1.93	3.7249	1.38924	4.39318
1.44	2.0736	1.20000	3.79473	1.94	3.7636	1.39284	4.40454
1.45	2.1025	1.20416	3.80789	1.95	3.8025	1.39642	4.41588
1.46	2.1316	1.20830	3.82099	1.96	3.8416	1.40000	4.42719
1.47	2.1609	1.21244	3.83406	1.97	3.8809	1.40357	4.43847
1.48	2.1904	1.21655	3.84708	1.98	3.9204	1.40712	4.44972
1.49	2.2201	1.22066	3.86005	1.99	3.9601	1.41067	4.46094

* This Table is reproduced, by permission, from the *Macmillan Tables*, The Macmillan Company, New York.

TABLE VIII (*Cont'd*)
Squares and Square Roots

n	n^2	$\sqrt{n}$	$\sqrt{10n}$	n	n^2	$\sqrt{n}$	$\sqrt{10n}$
2.00	4.0000	1.41421	4.47214	**2.50**	6.2500	1.58114	5.00000
2.01	4.0401	1.41774	4.48330	2.51	6.3001	1.58430	5.00999
2.02	4.0804	1.42127	4.49444	2.52	6.3504	1.58745	5.01996
2.03	4.1209	1.42478	4.50555	2.53	6.4009	1.59060	5.02991
2.04	4.1616	1.42829	4.51664	2.54	6.4516	1.59374	5.03984
2.05	4.2025	1.43178	4.52769	2.55	6.5025	1.59687	5.04975
2.06	4.2436	1.43527	4.53872	2.56	6.5536	1.60000	5.05964
2.07	4.2849	1.43875	4.54973	2.57	6.6049	1.60312	5.06952
2.08	4.3264	1.44222	4.56070	2.58	6.6564	1.60624	5.07937
2.09	4.3681	1.44568	4.57165	2.59	6.7081	1.60935	5.08920
2.10	4.4100	1.44914	4.58258	**2.60**	6.7600	1.61245	5.09902
2.11	4.4521	1.45258	4.59347	2.61	6.8121	1.61555	5.10882
2.12	4.4944	1.45602	4.60435	2.62	6.8644	1.61864	5.11859
2.13	4.5369	1.45945	4.61519	2.63	6.9169	1.62173	5.12835
2.14	4.5796	1.46287	4.62601	2.64	6.9696	1.62481	5.13809
2.15	4.6225	1.46629	4.63681	2.65	7.0225	1.62788	5.14782
2.16	4.6656	1.46969	4.64758	2.66	7.0756	1.63095	5.15752
2.17	4.7089	1.47309	4.65833	2.67	7.1289	1.63401	5.16720
2.18	4.7524	1.47648	4.66905	2.68	7.1824	1.63707	5.17687
2.19	4.7961	1.47986	4.67974	2.69	7.2361	1.64012	5.18652
2.20	4.8400	1.48324	4.69042	**2.70**	7.2900	1.64317	5.19615
2.21	4.8841	1.48661	4.70106	2.71	7.3441	1.64621	5.20577
2.22	4.9284	1.48997	4.71169	2.72	7.3984	1.64924	5.21536
2.23	4.9729	1.49332	4.72229	2.73	7.4529	1.65227	5.22494
2.24	5.0176	1.49666	4.73286	2.74	7.5076	1.65529	5.23450
2.25	5.0625	1.50000	4.74342	2.75	7.5625	1.65831	5.24404
2.26	5.1076	1.50333	4.75395	2.76	7.6176	1.66132	5.25357
2.27	5.1529	1.50665	4.76445	2.77	7.6729	1.66433	5.26308
2.28	5.1984	1.50997	4.77493	2.78	7.7284	1.66733	5.27257
2.29	5.2441	1.51327	4.78539	2.79	7.7841	1.67033	5.28205
2.30	5.2900	1.51658	4.79583	**2.80**	7.8400	1.67332	5.29150
2.31	5.3361	1.51987	4.80625	2.81	7.8961	1.67631	5.30094
2.32	5.3824	1.52315	4.81664	2.82	7.9524	1.67929	5.31037
2.33	5.4289	1.52643	4.82701	2.83	8.0089	1.68226	5.31977
2.34	5.4756	1.52971	4.83735	2.84	8.0656	1.68523	5.32917
2.35	5.5225	1.53297	4.84768	2.85	8.1225	1.68819	5.33854
2.36	5.5696	1.53623	4.85798	2.86	8.1796	1.69115	5.34790
2.37	5.6169	1.53948	4.86826	2.87	8.2369	1.69411	5.35724
2.38	5.6644	1.54272	4.87852	2.88	8.2944	1.69706	5.36656
2.39	5.7121	1.54596	4.88876	2.89	8.3521	1.70000	5.37587
2.40	5.7600	1.54919	4.89898	**2.90**	8.4100	1.70294	5.38516
2.41	5.8081	1.55242	4.90918	2.91	8.4681	1.70587	5.39444
2.42	5.8564	1.55563	4.91935	2.92	8.5264	1.70880	5.40370
2.43	5.9049	1.55885	4.92950	2.93	8.5849	1.71172	5.41295
2.44	5.9536	1.56205	4.93964	2.94	8.6436	1.71464	5.42218
2.45	6.0025	1.56525	4.94975	2.95	8.7025	1.71756	5.43139
2.46	6.0516	1.56844	4.95984	2.96	8.7616	1.72047	5.44059
2.47	6.1009	1.57162	4.96991	2.97	8.8209	1.72337	5.44977
2.48	6.1504	1.57480	4.97996	2.98	8.8804	1.72627	5.45894
2.49	6.2001	1.57797	4.98999	2.99	8.9401	1.72916	5.46809

TABLE VIII (*Cont'd*)
Squares and Square Roots

n	n^2	$\sqrt{n}$	$\sqrt{10n}$	n	n^2	$\sqrt{n}$	$\sqrt{10n}$
3.00	9.0000	1.73205	5.47723	**3.50**	12.2500	1.87083	5.91608
3.01	9.0601	1.73494	5.48635	3.51	12.3201	1.87350	5.92453
3.02	9.1204	1.73781	5.49545	3.52	12.3904	1.87617	5.93296
3.03	9.1809	1.74069	5.50454	3.53	12.4609	1.87883	5.94138
3.04	9.2416	1.74356	5.51362	3.54	12.5316	1.88149	5.94979
3.05	9.3025	1.74642	5.52268	3.55	12.6025	1.88414	5.95819
3.06	9.3636	1.74929	5.53173	3.56	12.6736	1.88680	5.96657
3.07	9.4249	1.75214	5.54076	3.57	12.7449	1.88944	5.97495
3.08	9.4864	1.75499	5.54977	3.58	12.8164	1.89209	5.98331
3.09	9.5481	1.75784	5.55878	3.59	12.8881	1.89473	5.99166
3.10	9.6100	1.76068	5.56776	**3.60**	12.9600	1.89737	6.00000
3.11	9.6721	1.76352	5.57674	3.61	13.0321	1.90000	6.00833
3.12	9.7344	1.76635	5.58570	3.62	13.1044	1.90263	6.01664
3.13	9.7969	1.76918	5.59464	3.63	13.1769	1.90526	6.02495
3.14	9.8596	1.77200	5.60357	3.64	13.2496	1.90788	6.03324
3.15	9.9225	1.77482	5.61249	3.65	13.3225	1.91050	6.04152
3.16	9.9856	1.77764	5.62139	3.66	13.3956	1.91311	6.04979
3.17	10.0489	1.78045	5.63028	3.67	13.4689	1.91572	6.05805
3.18	10.1124	1.78326	5.63915	3.68	13.5424	1.91833	6.06630
3.19	10.1761	1.78606	5.64801	3.69	13.6161	1.92094	6.07454
3.20	10.2400	1.78885	5.65685	**3.70**	13.6900	1.92354	6.08276
3 21	10.3041	1.79165	5.66569	3.71	13.7641	1.92614	6.09098
3 22	10.3684	1.79444	5.67450	3.72	13.8384	1.92873	6.09918
3.23	10.4329	1.79722	5.68331	3.73	13.9129	1.93132	6.10737
3.24	10.4976	1.80000	5.69210	3.74	13.9876	1.93391	6.11555
3.25	10.5625	1.80278	5.70088	3.75	14.0625	1.93649	6.12372
3 26	10.6276	1.80555	5.70964	3.76	14.1376	1.93907	6.13188
3.27	10.6929	1.80831	5.71839	3.77	14.2129	1.94165	6.14003
3.28	10.7584	1.81108	5.72713	3.78	14.2884	1.94422	6.14817
3 29	10.8241	1.81384	5.73585	3.79	14.3641	1.94679	6.15630
3.30	10.8900	1.81659	5.74456	**3.80**	14.4400	1.94936	6.16441
3.31	10.9561	1.81934	5.75326	3.81	14.5161	1.95192	6.17252
3.32	11.0224	1.82209	5.76194	3.82	14.5924	1.95448	6.18061
3.33	11.0889	1.82483	5.77062	3.83	14.6689	1.95704	6.18870
3.34	11.1556	1.82757	5.77927	3.84	14.7456	1.95959	6.19677
3.35	11.2225	1.83030	5.78792	3.85	14.8225	1.96214	6.20484
3.36	11.2896	1.83303	5.79655	3.86	14.8996	1.96469	6.21289
3.37	11.3569	1.83576	5.80517	3.87	14.9769	1.96723	6.22093
3.38	11.4244	1.83848	5.81378	3.88	15.0544	1.96977	6.22896
3.39	11.4921	1.84120	5.82237	3.89	15.1321	1.97231	6.23699
3.40	11.5600	1.84391	5.83095	**3.90**	15.2100	1.97484	6.24500
3.41	11.6281	1.84662	5.83952	3.91	15.2881	1.97737	6.25300
3 42	11.6964	1.84932	5.84808	3.92	15.3664	1.97990	6.26099
3.43	11.7649	1.85203	5.85662	3.93	15.4449	1.98242	6.26897
3.44	11.8336	1.85472	5.86515	3.94	15.5236	1.98494	6.27694
3.45	11.9025	1.85742	5.87367	3.95	15.6025	1.98746	6.28490
3.46	11.9716	1.86011	5.88218	3.96	15.6816	1.98997	6.29285
3.47	12.0409	1.86279	5.89067	3.97	15.7609	1.99249	6.30079
3.48	12.1104	1.86548	5.89915	3.98	15.8404	1.99499	6.30872
3 49	12.1801	1.86815	5.90762	3 99	15.9201	1.99750	6.31664

TABLE VIII (Cont'd)
Squares and Square Roots

n	n^2	$\sqrt{n}$	$\sqrt{10n}$	n	n^2	$\sqrt{n}$	$\sqrt{10n}$
4.00	16.0000	2.00000	6.32456	4.50	20.2500	2.12132	6.70820
4.01	16.0801	2.00250	6.33246	4.51	20.3401	2.12368	6.71565
4.02	16.1604	2.00499	6.34035	4.52	20.4304	2.12603	6.72309
4.03	16.2409	2.00749	6.34823	4.53	20.5209	2.12838	6.73053
4.04	16.3216	2.00998	6.35610	4.54	20.6116	2.13073	6.73795
4.05	16.4025	2.01246	6.36396	4.55	20.7025	2.13307	6.74537
4.06	16.4836	2.01494	6.37181	4.56	20.7936	2.13542	6.75278
4.07	16.5649	2.01742	6.37966	4.57	20.8849	2.13776	6.76018
4.08	16.6464	2.01990	6.38749	4.58	20.9764	2.14009	6.76757
4.09	16.7281	2.02237	6.39531	4.59	21.0681	2.14243	6.77495
4.10	16.8100	2.02485	6.40312	4.60	21.1600	2.14476	6.78233
4.11	16.8921	2.02731	6.41093	4.61	21.2521	2.14709	6.78970
4.12	16.9744	2.02978	6.41872	4.62	21.3444	2.14942	6.79706
4.13	17.0569	2.03224	6.42651	4.63	21.4369	2.15174	6.80441
4.14	17.1396	2.03470	6.43428	4.64	21.5296	2.15407	6.81175
4.15	17.2225	2.03715	6.44205	4.65	21.6225	2.15639	6.81909
4.16	17.3056	2.03961	6.44981	4.66	21.7156	2.15870	6.82642
4.17	17.3889	2.04206	6.45755	4.67	21.8089	2.16102	6.83374
4.18	17.4724	2.04450	6.46529	4.68	21.9024	2.16333	6.84105
4.19	17.5561	2.04695	6.47302	4.69	21.9961	2.16564	6.84836
4.20	17.6400	2.04939	6.48074	4.70	22.0900	2.16795	6.85565
4.21	17.7241	2.05183	6.48845	4.71	22.1841	2.17025	6.86294
4.22	17.8084	2.05426	6.49615	4.72	22.2784	2.17256	6.87023
4.23	17.8929	2.05670	6.50384	4.73	22.3729	2.17486	6.87750
4.24	17.9776	2.05913	6.51153	4.74	22.4676	2.17715	6.88477
4.25	18.0625	2.06155	6.51920	4.75	22.5625	2.17945	6.89202
4.26	18.1476	2.06398	6.52687	4.76	22.6576	2.18174	6.89928
4.27	18.2329	2.06640	6.53452	4.77	22.7529	2.18403	6.90652
4.28	18.3184	2.06882	6.54217	4.78	22.8484	2.18632	6.91375
4.29	18.4041	2.07123	6.54981	4.79	22.9441	2.18861	6.92098
4.30	18.4900	2.07364	6.55744	4.80	23.0400	2.19089	6.92820
4.31	18.5761	2.07605	6.56506	4.81	23.1361	2.19317	6.93542
4.32	18.6624	2.07846	6.57267	4.82	23.2324	2.19545	6.94262
4.33	18.7489	2.08087	6.58027	4.83	23.3289	2.19773	6.94982
4.34	18.8356	2.08327	6.58787	4.84	23.4256	2.20000	6.95701
4.35	18.9225	2.08567	6.59545	4.85	23.5225	2.20227	6.96419
4.36	19.0096	2.08806	6.60303	4.86	23.6196	2.20454	6.97137
4.37	19.0969	2.09045	6.61060	4.87	23.7169	2.20681	6.97854
4.38	19.1844	2.09284	6.61816	4.88	23.8144	2.20907	6.98570
4.39	19.2721	2.09523	6.62571	4.89	23.9121	2.21133	6.99285
4.40	19.3600	2.09762	6.63325	4.90	24.0100	2.21359	7.00000
4.41	19.4481	2.10000	6.64078	4.91	24.1081	2.21585	7.00714
4.42	19.5364	2.10238	6.64831	4.92	24.2064	2.21811	7.01427
4.43	19.6249	2.10476	6.65582	4.93	24.3049	2.22036	7.02140
4.44	19.7136	2.10713	6.66333	4.94	24.4036	2.22261	7.02851
4.45	19.8025	2.10950	6.67083	4.95	24.5025	2.22486	7.03562
4.46	19.8916	2.11187	6.67832	4.96	24.6016	2.22711	7.04273
4.47	19.9809	2.11424	6.68581	4.97	24.7009	2.22935	7.04982
4.48	20.0704	2.11660	6.69328	4.98	24.8004	2.23159	7.05691
4.49	20.1601	2.11896	6.70075	4.99	24.9001	2.23383	7.06399

TABLE VIII (Cont'd)
Squares and Square Roots

n	n^2	$\sqrt{n}$	$\sqrt{10n}$	n	n^2	$\sqrt{n}$	$\sqrt{10n}$
5.00	25.0000	2.23607	7.07107	5.50	30.2500	2.34521	7.41620
5.01	25.1001	2.23830	7.07814	5.51	30.3601	2.34734	7.42294
5.02	25.2004	2.24054	7.08520	5.52	30.4704	2.34947	7.42967
5.03	25.3009	2.24277	7.09225	5.53	30.5809	2.35160	7.43640
5.04	25.4016	2.24499	7.09930	5.54	30.6916	2.35372	7.44312
5.05	25.5025	2.24722	7.10634	5.55	30.8025	2.35584	7.44983
5.06	25.6036	2.24944	7.11337	5.56	30.9136	2.35797	7.45654
5.07	25.7049	2.25167	7.12039	5.57	31.0249	2.36008	7.46324
5.08	25.8064	2.25389	7.12741	5.58	31.1364	2.36220	7.46994
5.09	25.9081	2.25610	7.13442	5.59	31.2481	2.36432	7.47663
5.10	26.0100	2.25832	7.14143	5.60	31.3600	2.36643	7.48331
5.11	26.1121	2.26053	7.14843	5.61	31.4721	2.36854	7.48999
5.12	26.2144	2.26274	7.15542	5.62	31.5844	2.37065	7.49667
5.13	26.3169	2.26495	7.16240	5.63	31.6969	2.37276	7.50333
5.14	26.4196	2.26716	7.16938	5.64	31.8096	2.37487	7.50999
5.15	26.5225	2.26936	7.17635	5.65	31.9225	2.37697	7.51665
5.16	26.6256	2.27156	7.18331	5.66	32.0356	2.37908	7.52330
5.17	26.7289	2.27376	7.19027	5.67	32.1489	2.38118	7.52994
5.18	26.8324	2.27596	7.19722	5.68	32.2624	2.38238	7.53658
5.19	26.9361	2.27816	7.20417	5.69	32.3761	2.38537	7.54321
5.20	27.0400	2.28035	7.21110	5.70	32.4900	2.38747	7.54983
5.21	27.1441	2.28254	7.21803	5.71	32.6041	2.38956	7.55645
5.22	27.2484	2.28473	7.22496	5.72	32.7184	2.39165	7.56307
5.23	27.3529	2.28692	7.23187	5.73	32.8329	2.39374	7.56968
5.24	27.4576	2.28910	7.23878	5.74	32.9476	2.39583	7.57628
5.25	27.5625	2.29129	7.24569	5.75	33.0625	2.39792	7.58288
5.26	27.6676	2.29347	7.25259	5.76	33.1776	2.40000	7.58947
5.27	27.7729	2.29565	7.25948	5.77	33.2929	2.40208	7.59605
5.28	27.8784	2.29783	7.26636	5.78	33.4084	2.40416	7.60263
5.29	27.9841	2.30000	7.27324	5.79	33.5241	2.40624	7.60920
5.30	28.0900	2.30217	7.28011	5.80	33.6400	2.40832	7.61577
5.31	28.1961	2.30434	7.28697	5.81	33.7561	2.41039	7.62234
5.32	28.3024	2.30651	7.29383	5.82	33.8724	2.41247	7.62889
5.33	28.4089	2.30868	7.30068	5.83	33.9889	2.41454	7.63544
5.34	28.5156	2.31084	7.30753	5.84	34.1056	2.41661	7.64199
5.35	28.6225	2.31301	7.31437	5.85	34.2225	2.41868	7.64853
5.36	28.7296	2.31517	7.32120	5.86	34.3396	2.42074	7.65506
5.37	28.8369	2.31733	7.32803	5.87	34.4569	2.42281	7.66159
5.38	28.9444	2.31948	7.33485	5.88	34.5744	2.42487	7.66812
5.39	29.0521	2.32164	7.34166	5.89	34.6921	2.42693	7.67463
5.40	29.1600	2.32379	7.34847	5.90	34.8100	2.42899	7.68115
5.41	29.2681	2.32594	7.35527	5.91	34.9281	2.43105	7.68765
5.42	29.3764	2.32809	7.36206	5.92	35.0464	2.43311	7.69415
5.43	29.4849	2.33024	7.36885	5.93	35.1649	2.43516	7.70065
5.44	29.5936	2.33238	7.37564	5.94	35.2836	2.43721	7.70714
5.45	29.7025	2.33452	7.38241	5.95	35.4025	2.43926	7.71362
5.46	29.8116	2.33666	7.38918	5.96	35.5216	2.44131	7.72010
5.47	29.9209	2.33880	7.39594	5.97	35.6409	2.44336	7.72658
5.48	30.0304	2.34094	7.40270	5.98	35.7604	2.44540	7.73305
5.49	30.1401	2.34307	7.40945	5.99	35.8801	2.44745	7.73951

TABLE VIII (Cont'd)
Squares and Square Roots

n	n^2	$\sqrt{n}$	$\sqrt{10n}$	n	n^2	$\sqrt{n}$	$\sqrt{10n}$
6.00	36.0000	2.44949	7.74597	**6.50**	42.2500	2.54951	8.06226
6.01	36.1201	2.45153	7.75242	6.51	42.3801	2.55147	8.06846
6.02	36.2404	2.45357	7.75887	6.52	42.5104	2.55343	8.07465
6.03	36.3609	2.45561	7.76531	6.53	42.6409	2.55539	8.08084
6.04	36.4816	2.45764	7.77174	6.54	42.7716	2.55734	8.08703
6.05	36.6025	2.45967	7.77817	6.55	42.9025	2.55930	8.09321
6.06	36.7236	2.46171	7.78460	6.56	43.0336	2.56125	8.09938
6.07	36.8449	2.46374	7.79102	6.57	43.1649	2.56320	8.10555
6.08	36.9664	2.46577	7.79744	6.58	43.2964	2.56515	8.11172
6.09	37.0881	2.46779	7.80385	6.59	43.4281	2.56710	8.11788
6.10	37.2100	2.46982	7.81025	**6.60**	43.5600	2.56905	8.12404
6.11	37.3321	2.47184	7.81665	6.61	43.6921	2.57099	8.13019
6.12	37.4544	2.47386	7.82304	6.62	43.8244	2.57294	8.13634
6.13	37.5769	2.47588	7.82943	6.63	43.9569	2.57488	8.14248
6.14	37.6996	2.47790	7.83582	6.64	44.0896	2.57682	8.14862
6.15	37.8225	2.47992	7.84219	6.65	44.2225	2.57876	8.15475
6.16	37.9456	2.48193	7.84857	6.66	44.3556	2.58070	8.16088
6.17	38.0689	2.48395	7.85493	6.67	44.4889	2.58263	8.16701
6.18	38.1924	2.48596	7.86130	6.68	44.6224	2.58457	8.17313
6.19	38.3161	2.48797	7.86766	6.69	44.7561	2.58650	8.17924
6.20	38.4400	2.48998	7.87401	**6.70**	44.8900	2.58844	8.18535
6.21	38.5641	2.49199	7.88036	6.71	45.0241	2.59037	8.19146
6.22	38.6884	2.49399	7.88670	6.72	45.1584	2.59230	8.19756
6.23	38.8129	2.49600	7.89303	6.73	45.2929	2.59422	8.20366
6.24	38.9376	2.49800	7.89937	6.74	45.4276	2.59615	8.20975
6.25	39.0625	2.50000	7.90569	6.75	45.5625	2.59808	8.21584
6.26	39.1876	2.50200	7.91202	6.76	45.6976	2.60000	8.22192
6.27	39.3129	2.50400	7.91833	6.77	45.8329	2.60192	8.22800
6.28	39.4384	2.50599	7.92465	6.78	45.9684	2.60384	8.23408
6.29	39.5641	2.50799	7.93095	6.79	46.1041	2.60576	8.24015
6.30	39.6900	2.50998	7.93725	**6.80**	46.2400	2.60768	8.24621
6.31	39.8161	2.51197	7.94355	6.81	46.3761	2.60960	8.25227
6.32	39.9424	2.51396	7.94984	6.82	46.5124	2.61151	8.25833
6.33	40.0689	2.51595	7.95613	6.83	46.6489	2.61343	8.26438
6.34	40.1956	2.51794	7.96241	6.84	46.7856	2.61534	8.27043
6.35	40.3225	2.51992	7.96869	6.85	46.9225	2.61725	8.27647
6.36	40.4496	2.52190	7.97496	6.86	47.0596	2.61916	8.28251
6.37	40.5769	2.52389	7.98123	6.87	47.1969	2.62107	8.28855
6.38	40.7044	2.52587	7.98749	6.88	47.3344	2.62298	8.29458
6.39	40.8321	2.52784	7.99375	6.89	47.4721	2.62488	8.30060
6.40	40.9600	2.52982	8.00000	**6.90**	47.6100	2.62679	8.30662
6.41	41.0881	2.53180	8.00625	6.91	47.7481	2.62869	8.31264
6.42	41.2164	2.53377	8.01249	6.92	47.8864	2.63059	8.31865
6.43	41.3449	2.53574	8.01873	6.93	48.0249	2.63249	8.32466
6.44	41.4736	2.53772	8.02496	6.94	48.1636	2.63439	8.33067
6.45	41.6025	2.53969	8.03119	6.95	48.3025	2.63629	8.33667
6.46	41.7316	2.54165	8.03741	6.96	48.4416	2.63818	8.34266
6.47	41.8609	2.54362	8.04363	6.97	48.5809	2.64008	8.34865
6.48	41.9904	2.54558	8.04984	6.98	48.7204	2.64197	8.35464
6.49	42.1201	2.54755	8.05605	6.99	48.8601	2.64386	8.36062

TABLE VIII (Cont'd)
Squares and Square Roots

n	n²	√n	√10n	n	n²	√n	√10n
7.00	49.0000	2.64575	8.36660	7.50	56.2500	2.73861	8.66025
7.01	49.1401	2.64764	8.37257	7.51	56.4001	2.74044	8.66603
7.02	49.2804	2.64953	8.37854	7.52	56.5504	2.74226	8.67179
7.03	49.4209	2.65141	8.38451	7.53	56.7009	2.74408	8.67756
7.04	49.5616	2.65330	8.39047	7.54	56.8516	2.74591	8.68332
7.05	49.7025	2.65518	8.39643	7.55	57.0025	2.74773	8.68907
7.06	49.8436	2.65707	8.40238	7.56	57.1536	2.74955	8.69483
7.07	49.9849	2.65895	8.40833	7.57	57.3049	2.75136	8.70057
7.08	50.1264	2.66083	8.41427	7.58	57.4564	2.75318	8.70632
7.09	50.2681	2.66271	8.42021	7.59	57.6081	2.75500	8.71206
7.10	50.4100	2.66458	8.42615	7.60	57.7600	2.75681	8.71780
7.11	50.5521	2.66646	8.43208	7.61	57.9121	2.75862	8.72353
7.12	50.6944	2.66833	8.43801	7.62	58.0644	2.76043	8.72926
7.13	50.8369	2.67021	8.44393	7.63	58.2169	2.76225	8.73499
7.14	50.9796	2.67208	8.44985	7.64	58.3696	2.76405	8.74071
7.15	51.1225	2.67395	8.45577	7.65	58.5225	2.76586	8.74643
7.16	51.2656	2.67582	8.46168	7.66	58.6756	2.76767	8.75214
7.17	51.4089	2.67769	8.46759	7.67	58.8289	2.76948	8,75785
7.18	51.5524	2.67955	8.47349	7.68	58.9824	2.77128	8.76356
7.19	51.6961	2.68142	8.47939	7.69	59.1361	2.77308	8.76926
7.20	51.8400	2.68328	8.48528	7.70	59.2900	2.77489	8.77496
7.21	51.9841	2.68514	8.49117	7.71	59.4441	2.77669	8.78066
7.22	52.1284	2.68701	8.49706	7.72	59.5984	2.77849	8.78635
7.23	52.2729	2.68887	8.50294	7.73	59.7529	2.78029	8.79204
7.24	52.4176	2.69072	8.50882	7.74	59.9076	2.78209	8.79773
7.25	52.5625	2.69258	8.51469	7.75	60.0625	2.78388	8.80341
7.26	52.7076	2.69444	8.52056	7.76	60.2176	2.78568	8.80909
7.27	52.8529	2.69629	8.52643	7.77	60.3729	2.78747	8.81476
7.28	52.9984	2.69815	8.53229	7.78	60.5284	2.78927	8.82043
7.29	53.1441	2.70000	8.53815	7.79	60.6841	2.79106	8.82610
7.30	53.2900	2.70185	8.54400	7.80	60.8400	2.79285	8.83176
7.31	53.4361	2.70370	8.54985	7.81	60.9961	2.79464	8.83742
7.32	53.5824	2.70555	8.55570	7.82	61.1524	2.79643	8.84308
7.33	53.7289	2.70740	8.56154	7.83	61.3089	2.79821	8.84873
7.34	53.8756	2.70924	8.56738	7.84	61.4656	2.80000	8.85438
7.35	54.0225	2.71109	8.57321	7.85	61.6225	2.80179	8.86002
7.36	54.1696	2.71293	8.57904	7.86	61.7796	2.80357	8.86566
7.37	54.3169	2.71477	8.58487	7.87	61.9369	2.80535	8.87130
7.38	54.4644	2.71662	8.59069	7.88	62.0944	2.80713	8.87694
7.39	54.6121	2.71846	8.59651	7.89	62.2521	2.80891	8.88257
7.40	54.7600	2.72029	8.60233	7.90	62.4100	2.81069	8.88819
7.41	54.9081	2.72213	8.60814	7.91	62.5681	2.81247	8.89382
7.42	55.0564	2.72397	8.61394	7.92	62.7264	2.81425	8.89944
7.43	55.2049	2.72580	8.61974	7.93	62.8849	2.81603	8.90505
7.44	55.3536	2.72764	8.62554	7.94	63.0436	2.81780	8.91067
7.45	55.5025	2.72947	8.63134	7.95	63.2025	2.81957	8.91628
7.46	55.6516	2.73130	8.63713	7.96	63.3616	2.82135	8.92188
7.47	55.8009	2.73313	8.64292	7.97	63.5209	2.82312	8.92749
7.48	55.9504	2.73496	8.64870	7.98	63.6804	2.82489	8.93308
7.49	56.1001	2.73679	8.65448	7.99	63.8401	2.82666	8.93868

TABLE VIII *(Cont'd)*
Squares and Square Roots

n	n^2	$\sqrt{n}$	$\sqrt{10n}$	n	n^2	$\sqrt{n}$	$\sqrt{10n}$
8.00	64.0000	2.82843	8.94427	**8.50**	72.2500	2.91548	9.21954
8.01	64.1601	2.83019	8.94986	8.51	72.4201	2.91719	9.22497
8.02	64.3204	2.83196	8.95545	8.52	72.5904	2.91890	9.23038
8.03	64.4809	2.83373	8.96103	8.53	72.7609	2.92062	9.23580
8.04	64.6416	2.83549	8.96660	8.54	72.9316	2.92233	9.24121
8.05	64.8025	2.83725	8.97218	8.55	73.1025	2.92404	9.24662
8.06	64.9636	2.83901	8.97775	8.56	73.2736	2.92575	9.25203
8.07	65.1249	2.84077	8.98332	8.57	73.4449	2.92746	9.25743
8.08	65.2864	2.84253	8.98888	8.58	73.6164	2.92916	9.26283
8.09	65.4481	2.84429	8.99444	8.59	73.7881	2.93087	9.26823
8.10	65.6100	2.84605	9.00000	**8.60**	73.9600	2.93258	9.27362
8.11	65.7721	2.84781	9.00555	8.61	74.1321	2.93428	9.27901
8.12	65.9344	2.84956	9.01110	8.62	74.3044	2.93598	9.28440
8.13	66.0969	2.85132	9.01665	8.63	74.4769	2.93769	9.28978
8.14	66.2596	2.85307	9.02219	8.64	74.6496	2.93939	9.29516
8.15	66.4225	2.85482	9.02774	8.65	74.8225	2.94109	9.30054
8.16	66.5856	2.85657	9.03327	8.66	74.9956	2.94279	9.30591
8.17	66.7489	2.85832	9.03881	8.67	75.1689	2.94449	9.31128
8.18	66.9124	2.86007	9.04434	8.68	75.3424	2.94618	9.31665
8.19	67.0761	2.86182	9.04986	8.69	75.5161	2.94788	9.32202
8.20	67.2400	2.86356	9.05539	**8.70**	75.6900	2.94958	9.32738
8.21	67.4041	2.86531	9.06091	8.71	75.8641	2.95127	9.33274
8.22	67.5684	2.86705	9.06642	8.72	76.0384	2.95296	9.33809
8.23	67.7329	2.86880	9.07193	8.73	76.2129	2.95466	9.34345
8.24	67.8976	2.87054	9.07744	8.74	76.3876	2.95635	9.34880
8.25	68.0625	2.87228	9.08295	8.75	76.5625	2.95804	9.35414
8.26	68.2276	2.87402	9.08845	8.76	76.7376	2.95973	9.35949
8.27	68.3929	2.87576	9.09395	8.77	76.9129	2.96142	9.36483
8.28	68.5584	2.87750	9.09945	8.78	77.0884	2.96311	9.37017
8.29	68.7241	2.87924	9.10494	8.79	77.2641	2.96479	9.37550
8.30	68.8900	2.88097	9.11043	**8.80**	77.4400	2.96648	9.38083
8.31	69.0561	2.88271	9.11592	8.81	77.6161	2.96816	9.38616
8.32	69.2224	2.88444	9.12140	8.82	77.7924	2.96985	9.39149
8.33	69.3889	2.88617	9.12688	8.83	77.9689	2.97153	9.39681
8.34	69.5556	2.88791	9.13236	8.84	78.1456	2.97321	9.40213
8.35	69.7225	2.88964	9.13783	8.85	78.3225	2.97489	9.40744
8.36	69.8896	2.89137	9.14330	8.86	78.4996	2.97658	9.41276
8.37	70.0569	2.89310	9.14877	8.87	78.6769	2.97825	9.41807
8.38	70.2244	2.89482	9.15423	8.88	78.8544	2.97993	9.42338
8.39	70.3921	2.89655	9.15969	8.89	79.0321	2.98161	9.42868
8.40	70.5600	2.89828	9.16515	**8.90**	79.2100	2.98329	9.43398
8.41	70.7281	2.90000	9.17061	8.91	79.3881	2.98496	9.43928
8.42	70.8964	2.90172	9.17606	8.92	79.5664	2.98664	9.44458
8.43	71.0649	2.90345	9.18150	8.93	79.7449	2.98831	9.44987
8.44	71.2336	2.90517	9.18695	8.94	79.9236	2.98998	9.45516
8.45	71.4025	2.90689	9.19239	8.95	80.1025	2.99166	9.46044
8.46	71.5716	2.90861	9.19783	8.96	80.2816	2.99333	9.46573
8.47	71.7409	2.91033	9.20326	8.97	80.4609	2.99500	9.47101
8.48	71.9104	2.91204	9.20869	8.98	80.6404	2.99666	9.47629
8.49	72.0801	2.91376	9.21412	8.99	80.8201	2.99833	9.48156

TABLE VIII (*Cont'd*)
Squares and Square Roots

n	n^2	$\sqrt{n}$	$\sqrt{10n}$	n	n^2	$\sqrt{n}$	$\sqrt{10n}$
9.00	81.0000	3.00000	9.48683	**9.50**	90.2500	3.08221	9.74679
9.01	81.1801	3.00167	9.49210	9.51	90.4401	3.08383	9.75192
9.02	81.3604	3.00333	9.49737	9.52	90.6304	3.08545	9.75705
9.03	81.5409	3.00500	9.50263	9.53	90.8209	3.08707	9.76217
9.04	81.7216	3.00666	9.50789	9.54	91.0116	3.08869	9.76729
9.05	81.9025	3.00832	9.51315	9.55	91.2025	3.09031	9.77241
9.06	82.0836	3.00998	9.51840	9.56	91.3936	3.09192	9.77753
9.07	82.2649	3.01164	9.52365	9.57	91.5849	3.09354	9.78264
9.08	82.4464	3.01330	9.52890	9.58	91.7764	3.09516	9.78775
9.09	82.6281	3.01496	9.53415	9.59	91.9681	3.09677	9.79285
9.10	82.8100	3.01662	9.53939	**9.60**	92.1600	3.09839	9.79796
9.11	82.9921	3.01828	9.54463	9.61	92.3521	3.10000	9.80306
9.12	83.1744	3.01993	9.54987	9.62	92.5444	3.10161	9.80816
9.13	83.3569	3.02159	9.55510	9.63	92.7369	3.10322	9.81326
9.14	83.5396	3.02324	9.56033	9.64	92.9296	3.10483	9.81835
9.15	83.7225	3.02490	9.56556	9.65	93.1225	3.10644	9.82344
9.16	83.9056	3.02655	9.57079	9.66	93.3156	3.10805	9.82853
9.17	84.0889	3.02820	9.57601	9.67	93.5089	3.10966	9.83362
9.18	84.2724	3.02985	9.58123	9.68	93.7024	3.11127	9.83870
9.19	84.4561	3.03150	9.58645	9.69	93.8961	3.11288	9.84378
9.20	84.6400	3.03315	9.59166	**9.70**	94.0900	3.11448	9.84886
9.21	84.8241	3.03480	9.59687	9.71	94.2841	3.11609	9.85393
9.22	85.0084	3.03645	9.60208	9.72	94.4784	3.11769	9.85901
9.23	85.1929	3.03809	9.60729	9.73	94.6729	3.11929	9.86408
9.24	85.3776	3.03974	9.61249	9.74	94.8676	3.12090	9.86914
9.25	85.5625	3.04138	9.61769	9.75	95.0625	3.12250	9.87421
9.26	85.7476	3.04302	9.62289	9.76	95.2576	3.12410	9.87927
9.27	85.9329	3.04467	9.62808	9.77	95.4529	3.12570	9.88433
9.28	86.1184	3.04631	9.63328	9.78	95.6484	3.12730	9.88939
9.29	86.3041	3.04795	9.63846	9.79	95.8441	3.12890	9.89444
9.30	86.4900	3.04959	9.64365	**9.80**	96.0400	3.13050	9.89949
9.31	86.6761	3.05123	9.64883	9.81	96.2361	3.13209	9.90454
9.32	86.8624	3.05287	9.65401	9.82	96.4324	3.13369	9.90959
9.33	87.0489	3.05450	9.65919	9.83	96.6289	3.13528	9.91464
9.34	87.2356	3.05614	9.66437	9.84	96.8256	3.13688	9.91968
9.35	87.4225	3.05778	9.66954	9.85	97.0225	3.13847	9.92472
9.36	87.6096	3.05941	9.67471	9.86	97.2196	3.14006	9.92975
9.37	87.7969	3.06105	9.67988	9.87	97.4169	3.14166	9.93479
9.38	87.9844	3.06268	9.68504	9.88	97.6144	3.14325	9.93982
9.39	88.1721	3.06431	9.69020	9.89	97.8121	3.14484	9.94485
9.40	88.3600	3.06594	9.69536	**9.90**	98.0100	3.14643	9.94987
9.41	88.5481	3.06757	9.70052	9.91	98.2081	3.14802	9.95490
9.42	88.7364	3.06920	9.70567	9.92	98.4064	3.14960	9.95992
9.43	88.9249	3.07083	9.71082	9.93	98.6049	3.15119	9.96494
9.44	89.1136	3.07246	9.71597	9.94	98.8036	3.15278	9.96995
9.45	89.3025	3.07409	9.72111	9.95	99.0025	3.15436	9.97497
9.46	89.4916	3.07571	9.72625	9.96	99.2016	3.15595	9.97998
9.47	89.6809	3.07734	9.73139	9.97	99.4009	3.15753	9.98499
9.48	89.8704	3.07896	9.73653	9.98	99.6004	3.15911	9.98999
9.49	90.0601	3.08058	9.74166	9.99	99.8001	3.16070	9.99500

ANSWERS TO EXERCISES

PAGE 9

3. (a) $\sum_{i=1}^{21} z_i;$ (b) $\sum_{i=1}^{9} x_i y_i;$ (c) $\sum_{i=1}^{n} (x_i - y_i);$ (d) $\sum_{i=1}^{8} x_{ij}^3 f_i.$

5. No.

PAGE 19

1. (a) 6;   (b) 9;   (c) 12.   5. $10 - 16,\ 17 - 23,\ 24 - 30,\ 31 - 37,$
$38 - 44.$

PAGE 45

3. (a) discrete;   (b) continuous;   (c) discrete;   (d) continuous;
   (e) discrete;   (f) discrete;   (g) discrete;   (h) continuous.
7. (a) 3.125 per cent;   (b) 31.25 per cent;   (c) 15.625 per cent.
9. 1.7 per cent of the time.

PAGE 51

1. 31.8 cents.   3. 129.5.   5. 4.375.
7. $11,873.   9. $42.99.

PAGE 58

1. 65.68.   3. .80.   5. 5.05 heads.

PAGE 70

1. 80.5, 78, 77.   3. 8.5.
5. (a) 7;   (b) no mode;   (c) 13;   (d) 5 and 8.
7. mode = 1.50;   median = 1.50.   11. median = 39.23;   mode = 41.87.

PAGE 75

1. geometric mean = 100;   harmonic mean = 72.
3. 2.25.   5. .330.

407

PAGE 78

1. $Q_1 = 53.8$; $Q_3 = 77.5$.
5. 43.0, 51.1, 56.5, 61.5, 65.5, 70.1, 75.0, 80.0, 88.5.
7. $P_{70} = 75.0$; $P_{75} = 77.5$; $P_{95} = 94.9$.

PAGE 87

1. 1.83.   *3.* 44, 37, 37.   *5.* 1.875.

PAGE 95

1. 3.24.   *3.* 10.6.   *5.* .02.   *7.* 17.2.   *9.* .63.

PAGE 98

1. 11.85, 18.   *5.* 13.4.

PAGE 102

1. 0, −.02.   *3.* −.04.

PAGE 110

1. (a) 1.83;   (b) 1.00;   (c) −3.25;   (d) −.17;   (e) 2.42;   (f) −.50.
3. (a) .0418;   (b) .3450;   (c) .8925;   (d) .1977;
     (e) .0871;   (f) .0482;   (g) .0614;   (h) .3729.

PAGE 119

1. 77.3 per cent.   *3.* 1.95.   *5.* $Q_1 = 11.65$, $Q_3 = 13.95$.
11. Expected normal curve frequencies are:
         4,   16,   52,   117,   193,   228,   195,   120,   53,   17,   4.

PAGE 135

1. (a) $1 - P(A)$;   (b) $P_A(B)$;   (c) $P(A \text{ and } B)$;   (d) $P_B(A)$.
3. Yes. The probability that a man is fat and has a weak heart.
5. (a) 1/13;   (b) 2/13;   (c) 0;   (d) 12/13.
7. .72. The two events are assumed to be independent.

PAGE 141

1. .205 and .203.   *3.* .166.   *5.* .0427.   *7.* .1768.

PAGE 157

1. Yes. All possible measurements of the length of the table.
3. It is divided by 2.

PAGE 171

1. (a) $64.77 - 66.03$; (b) $38.45 - 38.75$;
  (c) $48.38 - 55.82$; (d) $12.78 - 14.42$.
3. (a) $64.57 - 66.23$; (b) $38.41 - 38.79$;
  (c) $46.85 - 57.35$; (d) $12.47 - 14.73$.
5. $32.34 - 32.66$. *9.* $.96^+$. *11.* (a) $n = 125$; (b) $n = 154$.

PAGE 178

1. $.12 - .28$. *3.* $.03 - .10$. *5.* At least 862.
7. $n = 9604$. *9.* $n = 385$.

PAGE 183

1. $29.3 - 37.5$. *3.* $12.2 - 15.8$. *5.* $.014 - .040$.

PAGE 211

1. Reject hypothesis if there are less than 181 or more than 219 heads.
3. Reject hypothesis if there are less than 74 cures.
5. Reject. *7.* Cannot reject.
9. The level of significance is .06. *11.* No significant difference.

PAGE 218

1. Reject. *3.* Reject. *5.* Reject.
7. Difference is significant. *9.* Difference is significant.

PAGE 230

1. Significant deviation from randomness. *3.* Not significant.
5. Significant deviation from randomness. *7.* Not significant.
9. Significant.

PAGE 244

1. 139.4. *3.* (a) 17; (b) 18; (c) 21; (d) 23.

PAGE 256

1. $y = .8x + .4$.
3. Predicted values of y are: 2.0, 1.2, 2.8, 3.6, 4.4 and $s_e = .69$.
5. $y = 2068x + 1682$; 6,025. *7.* $y = .766x + 20.5$. *9.* 63.2.

PAGE 268

1. .85. *3.* .94. *5.* No.

PAGE 277

1. .73. *3.* Depends on grouping.

PAGE 285

1. (a) .42 − .85;   (b) (−.28) − .10;   (c) .33 − .94;   (d) .59 − .70;
  (e) (−.60) − (−.13); (f) .45 − .89; (g) (−.35) − (−.10); (h) 0 − .33.
3. .73 − .97.
7. (a) Not significant;   (b) significant;   (c) not significant;
  (d) not significant;   (e) not significant; (f) not significant.
9. Significant.

PAGE 288

1. .81.   *3.* .77.   *5.* .05.

PAGE 304

1. Significant correlation.
3. There is a significant difference between the three materials.

PAGE 312

3. Good fit.

PAGE 315

1. Reject hypothesis that the die is balanced.   *3.* No.
5. Reject the claim.

PAGE 342

1. (a) 196; (b) 123; (c) 196; (d) 121; (e) 67, 66.5.
3. 122.   *5.* 138.

PAGE 346

1. 121.   *3.* 121.   *5.* (a) 125; (b) 80; $1.25 \times .80 = 1$.

PAGE 360

1.

Year	Trend Value
1934	127.5
1939	116.9

3

Year	Trend Value
1934	126.4
1942	135.0

5. Annual trend increment of annual totals = 2.37

Year	Trend Value
1940	4.3
1941	6.7
1942	9.1
1943	11.4
1944	13.8
1945	16.2
1946	18.5
1947	20.9
1948	23.3
1949	25.6

PAGE 364

1.

Day	Index
Monday	128.3
Tuesday	125.7
Wednesday	125.9
Thursday	126.2
Friday	128.6
Saturday	54.8
Sunday	10.5

3.

Month	Index
January	51.9
February	38.1
March	36.7
April	56.1
May	88.3
June	124.7
July	155.9
August	167.5
September	159.2
October	138.5
November	107.4
December	75.7

PAGE 371

3.

Year	Moving Average
1928	1498
1929	1549
1930	1562
1931	1588
1932	1597
1933	1628
1934	1628
1935	1668
1936	1747
1937	1845
1938	1906
1939	2008
1940	2011
1941	2053
1942	2170
1943	2301

5.

Year	Moving Average
1933	10.1
1934	10.8
1935	11.6
1936	12.8
1937	14.5
1938	16.0
1939	17.1
1940	18.0
1941	18.6
1942	18.7
1943	18.4
1944	17.9
1945	18.4
1946	18.5

INDEX

A

Absolute value, 85, 240
Alpha four, α_4, 101
Alpha three, α_3, 100–101
Analysis of variance, 378–381
Approximate numbers, arithmetic of, 79–81
Area under frequency curve, 31–33
Arithmetic mean (*see* Mean)
Average (*see* Mean)
Average deviation, 86–87

B

Bacon, F., 374
Bailey, A. L., 187
Bar chart, 35, 337
Base year, 338–339
Binomial coefficient, 39
Binomial distribution, 37–42, 136, 141, 173, 192
  and the normal curve, 42, 138
  formula of, 39, 136
  goodness of fit of, 310
  mean of, 138, 173, 205
  standard deviation of, 138, 173, 205
Biometrika, 176
Business cycle, 354, 367

C

Calculated risk, 124
Categorical classification, 11
Causality, 374
Causation and correlation, 289–290, 322
Cell frequencies, calculation of, 293–295, 297
Central limit theorem, 156
Central tendencies, 48
Change of scale, 55–57, 92, 106
Chi-square, χ^2, 299, 307
Chi-square criterion:
  correlation, 299–302
  fitting of binomial distribution, 310
  fitting of normal curve, 307–309
  multinomial case, 313–315
Chi-square distribution, 181, 299–300, 392
Circularity test, 347
Class:
  boundary, 15
  frequency, 14
  interval, 15
  limit, 15
  mark, 15
Classification:
  categorical, 11
  numerical, 11
Clopper, C. J., 391
Coefficient of correlation (*see also* Correlation), 258–299
Coefficient of multiple correlation, 318, 320
Coefficient of partial correlation, 323
Coefficient of quartile variation, 97
Coefficient of rank correlation, 287
Coefficient of variation, 97
Conditional probability, 133
Confidence interval, 162–163, 183
  for coefficient of correlation, 281–283, 395
  for mean of population, 163–172
  for proportion, 172–179
  for standard deviation, 179–183
Confidence limits (*see* Confidence interval)
Consumer's risk, 199
Contingency coefficient, 303

Contingency table, 295
Continuous variable, 14, 35
Correlation:
  and causation, 289–290, 322
  by ranks, 286–288
  coefficient of, 258–285
  index, 325
  linearity of, 263, 271, 328
  multiple, 290, 317–321
  negative, 266
  nonlinear, 324–329
  partial, 290, 322–324
  positive, 266
  ratio, 290, 328
  strength of, 280, 303
  table, 275
Correlation, coefficient of:
  computation of, 264–277
  confidence interval for, 281–283
  definition of, 263
  formulas for, 265, 274
  interpretation of, 278–280
  meaning of, 263, 266
  significance of, 264, 283–284
  standard error of, 284
Cumulative distributions, 17, 18
Curve of means, 327

D

David, F. N., 395
Deciles, 77
Degress of freedom, 300–301, 308–309
  contingency table, 301
  fitting of binomial distribution, 311
  fitting of normal curve, 308–309
de Moivre, A., 42
Descriptive statistics, 5–6, 123, 333–334, 336
Destructive sampling, 145
Deviation from mean, 85
Discrete distribution, 139
Discrete variable, 35
Distribution (*see also* frequency, theoretical, and sampling distributions):
  binomial, 37–42, 136–141
  discrete, 139
  multimodal, 66, 69
  normal, 42–45, 106–119, 306–309
  population, 146, 149
  probability, 103
  sampling, 149–158

E

Eisenhart, C., 393, 394
Equation:
  exponential, 242, 352
  linear, 246, 318
Erratic variation, time series, 350–351
Error, grouping, 69, 80, 94
Error variance, 240, 249–250, 320
  about regression line, 251, 258–259
  about regression plane, 320
Eta, η, 328
Exhaustive sampling, 145
Expected cell frequencies, calculation of, 293–295
Expected frequency distribution, 33
Experimental design, 381–386
Exponential equation, 242, 352

F

Factorials, 39
Factor reversal test, 347
Finite population, 145–146
  sampling from, 185–187
Fisher, I., 345
Fisher, R. A., 390, 392
Frequency:
  class, 14
  cumulative, 17
  relative, 127, 172
Frequency distribution (*see also* distribution), 10–46
  and ambiguities in grouping, 13, 15
  bell-shaped, 25
  class boundaries of, 15
  class frequencies of, 14
  class intervals of, 15
  class limits of, 15
  class marks of, 15
  continuous, 29–33
  cumulative, 17–19
  expected, 33
  graphical presentation of, 21–28
  J-shaped, 26
  number of classes of, 12–13
  open class intervals of, 15–16, 58
  percentage, 18–19
  skewed, 26
  symmetrical, 26
  theoretical, 29–46
  two-dimensional, 270
  unequal intervals, 13, 22
  U-shaped, 26

Frequency polygon, 24–25
Function:
  exponential, 242, 352
  linear, 246, 318

G

Gauss, C., 42
Geometric mean, 71–72, 342
Goodness of fit:
  binomial distribution, 310
  criteria for, 246
  normal curve, 306–309
  theoretical distributions, 309–312
Goodness of predictions, 237–241, 247–249 253–255, 259–263
Gosset, W. S., 169
Graphical presentations, 21–28, 337
Grouping error, 69, 80, 94

H

Harmonic mean, 72–73
Histogram, 22–24
  three-dimensional, 273
Hume, D., 374
Hypothesis testing (*see also* Tests of significance), 148, 189–219

I

Ideal index, 345
Independence, 132–134, 294, 299
Index:
  Fisher's, 345
  ideal, 345
  simple aggregate, 340
  unweighted, 340–342
  weighted, 339–340, 343–348
  weighted aggregate, 343–344
Index Numbers, 337–348
  properties of, 342, 346–348
Index of correlation, 325
Index of seasonal variation, 354, 361–364
Inductive statistics, 5–6, 123, 147–149
Infinite population, 145–146, 185
Interquartile range, 96
Interval estimate, 162

J

J-shaped distribution, 26

K

Kinsey report, 222
Kurtosis, 101–102

L

Laplace, P., 42
Law of average, 141–142
Law of large numbers, **141–142**
Least squares, method of, 255, 319, 355
Leptokurtic distribution, 101
Level of significance, 203
Linear equation, 246, 318
Linear relationship, 246–257, 263
Link relatives, 361, 363
Literary Digest, 221
Long-term trend, 351–352, 355–360

M

Mean:
  arithmetic, 49
  assumptions for grouped data, 53, 80
  combined, 50–51
  confidence interval for, 163–172
  distribution of, 152–156
  distribution of difference of, 216–218
  grouped data, 52–59
  of binomial distribution, 138, 173, 205
  of distribution of proportions, 173
  of theoretical distributions, 105
  probable error of, 184
  properties of, 49
  reliability of, 51, 62
  short formula for, 57
  standard error of, 154–155
  test of significance for, 212–215
Mean deviation, 86–87
Median:
  assumptions for grouped data, 63, 80
  definition for grouped data, 63
  definition for ungrouped data, 59–60
  distribution of, 155–156
  properties of, 61–62
  reliability of, 62
  standard error of, 156
Mendel, G., 314
Method of decision, 189–190
Method of least squares, 255, 319, 355
Method of semiaverages, 356–360
Mill, J. S., 375
Modal class, 67

Mode, 65–71
  definition for grouped data, 68
  grouping errors of, 69, 80
  properties of, 66
  relation to mean and median, 70
Moments of a distribution, 100
Moving average, 368–372
Multimodal data, 66, 69
Multinomial case, 312–315
Multiple correlation, 290, **317–321**
Multiplicity of causes, 381
Mutually exclusive events, 131–132

N

Negative correlation, 266
Newton's formula, 39
Neyman, J., 389
Nonlinear correlation, 324–329
Normal curve, 42–46, 105–119, 306–309
  and binomial distribution, 42–44
  fitting of, 117–119
  goodness of fit of, 306–309
  graph paper, 114–117
  "machine," 42–44
  shape of, 105
  use of areas of, 105–119
Normal, of a time series, 365–368
Null hypothesis, 202–205
Numerical classification, 11

O

Ogive, 24–25
Open class interval, 15–16, 58

P

Parameter, 147
Partial correlation, 290, 322–324
Peakedness, 48, 101–102
Pearson, E. S., 391
Pearsonian coefficient of skewness, 98–99
Pearson-product-moment coefficient of
  correlation, 263
Percentage distribution, 18–19
Percentiles, 78
Pictograph, 337
Pie chart, 337
Platykurtic distribution, 101–102
Point estimate, 161–162
Poisson Distribution, 40–42

Population, 145
  composition of, 146
  distribution of, 146–147, 149
  finite, 145–146
  infinite, 145–146
  mean, 147, 149
  parameter, 147
  standard deviation, 147, 149
Positive correlation, 266
Predictions:
  criteria for, 239
  errors of, 248
  goodness of, 237–241, 247–249, 253–255, 259–263
  nature of, 235–236
Price relatives, 341
Probability:
  and certainty, 128
  and statistical methods, 129–130, 161, 167
  conditional, 133
  definition of, 38, 124–125, 127
  distribution, 103
  equally likely, 125–126
  graph paper, 114–117
  independent, 132–134
  meaning of, 124–130
  rules of, 130–136
Probable error, 183–185
Producer's risk, 199
Proportions:
  confidence interval for, 172–179
  difference between, 208–212
  distribution of, 173
  probable error of, 184
  standard deviation of, 173, 176
  standard error of, 173, 176
  test of significance for, 205–208

Q

Qualitative variable, 291
Quantity index, 347
Quartile deviation, 95–96
Quartiles, 75–77

R

r (*see* coefficient of correlation)
Randomization, 384, 385
Randomness, 148–149, 220–221
  tests of, 220–231
Range, 83–84
Rank correlation, 286–288

Raw data, 12
Regression coefficient, 251, 254–255
Regression line, 250, 258
Regression plane, 319–320
Relationship, linear, 246–257, 263
Relative frequency (*see also* Proportions), 127, 172
Relative variation, 96–98
Reliability, of objective test, 272
Rho, ρ, 281
Runs, 223–231
    above and below median, 228–231
    definition of, 225
    distribution of, 225, 227
    mean of, 227
    standard error of, 227
    table of, 393, 394
    test of significance for, 225–231

S

s (*see* Standard deviation)
Sample, 144–145
Sampling, 144–158
    destructive, 145
    exhaustive, 145
    random, 148–149, 220–221
    stratified, 222–223
Sampling distribution, 144, 149–158
    experimental, 152
    of coefficient of correlation, 281, 284, 285
    of difference of means, 216
    of difference of proportions, 208 209
    of mean, 152–155, 156
    of median, 155–156
    of number of runs, 225, 227
    of proportions, 173, 205
Scattergram, 270
Scientific method, 375–378
Seasonal variation, 352–354, 361–364
Secular trend, 351–352, 355–360
Semiaverages, method of, 356
Semi-interquartile range, 96
Sheppard's correction, 94
Sigma, σ, (*see also* Standard deviation), 105
Sigma, Σ, 7
Significance test (*see also* Test of significance), 201–205
Significant digits, 79
Simple aggregate index, 340
Smoothing of time series, 368–371
Square roots, table of, 397–405

Squares, table of, 397–405
Standard deviation:
    applications of, 91–92
    confidence interval for, 179–183
    definition of, 88, 92
    of binomial distribution, 138
    of proportions, 173, 205
    of theoretical distribution, 105
    sampling distribution of, 179, 181
    short formula for, 89, 93
Standard error, 154
    and reliability, 155
    of coefficient of correlation, 284
    of difference of means, 216–217
    of difference of proportions, 208
    of estimate, 254
    of mean, 154–155
    of median, 156
    of number of runs, 227
    of proportion, 173, 176
    of standard deviation, 179–180
Standard form of distribution, 105–106
Standard units, 91, 106
Statistic, 5
Statistics:
    definition of, 4–5
    role of, 378, 385–386
Stratified sampling, 222–223
"Student," 169
Student-t distribution, 169, 214–215, 218, 390
Sturges' rule, 12–13
Subscripts, 7
Success-ratio, 130, 167, 190
Summation, 7–9
Superman, 149
Swed, F. S., 393, 394
Symmetry, 48, 98–101

T

t distribution, 169, 214–215, 218, 390
Test of significance, 201–205, 219
    for correlation, 283–284, 302
    for difference of means, 216–218
    for difference of proportions, 208–212
    for means, 212–215
    for proportions, 205–208
    for runs, 225–231
Tests of hypotheses, 148, 189–219
Theoretical distribution (*see also* binomial, normal, Poisson, t, and χ^2 distributions), 29–46
    area under, 30–32, 104
    description of, 103

Ties in ranking, 288
Time reversal test, 347
Time series, 349–372
  definition of, 349
  fluctuations of, 350–355
  smoothing of, 368–372
Trend:
  elimination of, 358–360
  increment, 357, 358
  linear, 351–352
  secular, 351–352, 355–360
Two-by-two table, 292
Type I error, 193, 199, 201
Type II error, 193, 199, 201–202

U

ı (*see* Runs)
Universe, 145
u scale, 55–57

V

Variance, 89
Variation, 48, 82–84
Variation, seasonal, 352–354, 361–364
Value Index, 347

W

Weighted mean, 73–75
Weighted index number, 339–340, 343–348

Z

z scale, 106
z-transformation, 282